SolidWorks 2010
Part II - Advanced Techniques

Advanced Level Tutorials
**Parts, Surfaces, Sheet Metal, SimulationXpress,
Top-Down Assemblies, Core / Cavity Molds & Repair Errors**

Written by: Sr. Certified SolidWorks Instructor
Paul Tran, CSWP, CSWI

Schroff Development Corporation

P.O. Box 1334

Mission KS 66222

(913) 262-2664

www.SDCPublications.com

Publisher: Stephen Schroff

ISBN: 978-1-58503-578-6

Printed and bound in the United States of America.

Foreword

I first met Paul Tran when I was busy creating another challenge in my life. I needed to take a vision from one man's mind, understand what the vision looked like, how it was going to work and comprehend the scale of his idea. My challenge was I was missing one very important ingredient, a tool that would create a picture with all the moving parts.

A vision born in the mind of man, only becomes a reality when seen through that man's eyes, and that man was blind. Over time and many conversations, mostly with him talking and me asking endless questions, I came to understand his idea and adopt his vision. The challenge now became, how do I make it real, *how do help a blind man build his dream?*

Research led me to discover a great tool, SolidWorks. It claimed to allow one to make 3D components, in picture quality, on a computer, add in all moving parts, assemble it and make it run, all before money was spent on bending steel and buying parts that may not fit together. I needed to design and build a product with thousands of parts, make them all fit and work in harmony with millimeters tolerance. The possible cost implications of failed experimentation were daunting.

To my good fortune, one company's marketing strategy of selling a product without an instruction manual and requiring one to attend an instructional class to get it, led me to meet a communicator who made it all seem so simple.

Paul Tran has worked with and taught SolidWorks as his vocation for more than 20 years. Paul knows the SolidWorks product and manipulates it like a fine musical instrument. I watched Paul explain the unexplainable to baffled students with great skill and clarity. He taught me how to navigate the intricacies of the product so that I could use it as a communication tool with skilled engineers. *He teaches the teachers.*

I employed Paul as a consultant and designer to create the thousands of parts for my company's product. Paul Tran's knowledge and teaching skill has added immeasurable value to my company.

When I read through the pages of these manuals, I now have an "instant replay" of his communication skill with the clarity of having him looking over my shoulder - *continuously*. We can now design, prove and build our product and know it will always work and not fail.

Most important of all, Paul Tran helped me turn a blind man's vision into reality and a monument to his dream. Thanks Paul.

These books will make dreams come true and help visionaries change the world.

Peter J. Douglas – CEO, Cake Energy, LLC

Author's Note

SolidWorks 2010 Basic Tools and Advanced Techniques are comprised of lessons and exercises based on the author's extensive knowledge on this software. Paul has nearly 25 years of experience in the fields of mechanical and manufacturing engineering, 14 of which were in teaching and supporting the SolidWorks software and its add-ins. As an active Sr. SolidWorks instructor and design engineer, Paul has worked and consulted with hundreds of reputable companies including; IBM, Intel, NASA, US- Navy, Boeing, Disneyland, Medtronic, Guidant, Terumo, Kingston and many more. Today, he has trained over 5000 engineering professionals, and given guidance to nearly ½ of the number of Certified SolidWorks Professionals (CSWP) in the state of California.

Every lesson and exercise in this book was created based on real world projects. Each of these projects have been broken down and developed into easy and comprehendible steps for the reader. Furthermore, at the end of every chapter, there are self test questionnaires to ensure that the reader has gained sufficient knowledge from each section before moving on to more advanced lessons.

Paul believes that the most effective way to learn the "world's most sophisticated software" is to learn it inside and out, create everything from the beginning, and take it step by step. This is what the **SolidWorks 2010 Basic Tools & Advanced Techniques** manuals are all about.

Who this book is for

This book is for the advanced user, who has already completed the Part-1 Basic Tools textbook, or someone who is very familiar with the SolidWorks program and its add-ins. It also for the more CAD literate individuals who wants to expand their knowledge of the different advanced features that SolidWorks 2010 has to offer.

The organization of the book

The chapters in this book are organized in the logical order in which you would learn the SolidWorks 2010 program. Each chapter will guide you through some different tasks, from navigating through the user interface, to exploring the toolbars, from some simple 3D modeling and move on to more complex tasks that are common to all SolidWorks releases. There is also a self-test questionnaire at the end of each chapter to ensure that you have gained sufficient knowledge before moving on to the next chapter.

The conventions in this book

This book uses the following conventions to describe the actions you perform when using the keyboard and mouse to work in SolidWorks 2010:

Click: means to press and release the mouse button. A click of a mouse button is used to select a command or an item on the screen.

Double Click: means to quickly press and release the left mouse button twice. A double mouse click is used to open a program, or showing the dimensions of a feature.

Right Click: means to press and release the right mouse button. A right mouse click is used to display a list of commands, a list of shortcuts that is related to the selected item.

Click and Drag: means to position the mouse cursor over an item on the screen and then press and hold down the left mouse button; still holding down the left button, move the mouse to the new destination and release the mouse button. Drag and drop makes it easy to move things around within a SolidWorks document.

Bolded words: indicated the action items that you need to perform.

Italic words: Side notes and tips that give you additional information, or to explain special conditions that may occur during the course of the task.

Numbered Steps: indicates that you should follow these steps in order to successfully perform the task.

Icons: indicates the buttons or commands that you need to press.

SolidWorks 2010

SolidWorks 2010 is program suite, or a collection of engineering programs that can help you design better products faster. SolidWorks 2010 contains different combinations of programs; some of the programs used in this book may not be available in your suites.

Start and exit SolidWorks

SolidWorks allows you to start its program in several ways. You can either double click on its shortcut icon on the desktop, or go to the Start menu and select the following: All Program / SolidWorks 2010 / SolidWorks, or drag a SolidWorks document and drop it on the SolidWorks shortcut icon.

Before exiting SolidWorks, be sure to save any open documents, and then click File / Exit, or you can also click the X button on the top right of your screen.

Using the Toolbars

You can use toolbars to select commands in SolidWorks rather than using the drop down menus. Using the toolbars is normally faster. The toolbars come with commonly used commands in SolidWorks, but they can be customized to help you work more efficiently.

To access the toolbars, either right click in an empty spot on the top right of your screen or select View / Toolbars.

To customize the toolbars, select Tools / Customize. When the dialog pops up, click on the Commands tab, select a Category, and then drag an icon out of the dialog box and drop it on a toolbar that you want to customize. To remove an icon from a toolbar, drag an icon out of the toolbar and drop it into the dialog box.

Using the task pane

The task pane is normally kept on the right side of your screen. It display various options like SolidWorks resources, Design library, File explorer, Search, View palette, Appearances and Scenes, Custom properties, Built-in libraries, Technical alerts and news, etc,.

The task pane provides quick access to any of the mentioned items by offering the drag and drop function to all of its contents. You can see a large preview of a SolidWorks document before opening it. New documents can be saved in the task pane at anytime, and existing documents can also be edited and re-saved. The task pane can be resized, close or move to different location on your screen if needed.

Table of Contents

Advanced Modeling Topics

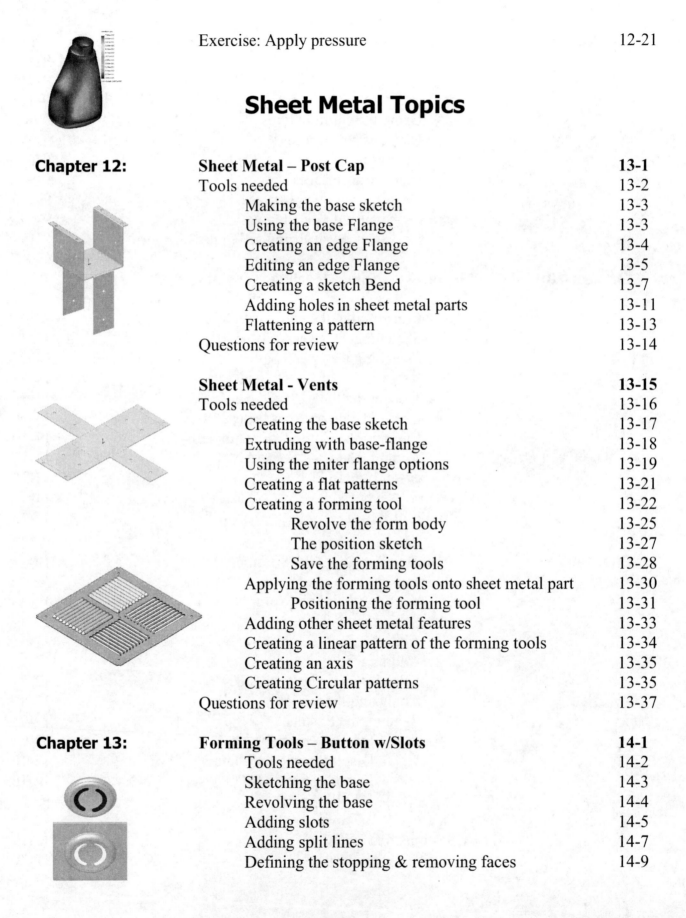

Top-Down Assembly Topics

CSWP Core Preparation Practice

Student Testimonials:

Some of the actual student testimonials after completing the training courses from the Author. All documents are filed at local SolidWorks resellers.

SolidWorks 2010 Quick-Guides:

Quick Reference Guide to SolidWorks 2010 Command Icons and Toolbars.

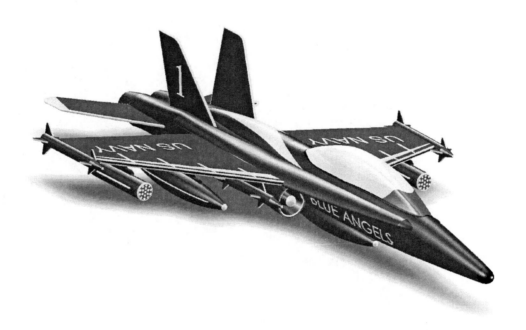

Introduction

SolidWorks User Interface

The SolidWorks 2010 User Interface

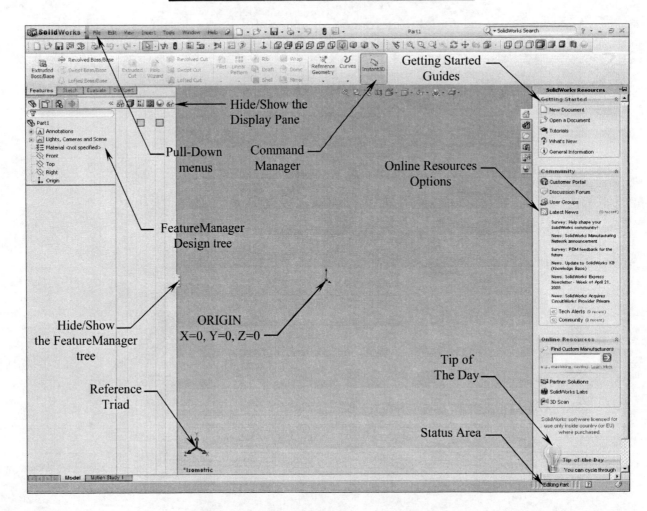

The 3 reference planes:

- The Front, Top and the Right plane are 90°apart. They share the same center point called the Origin.

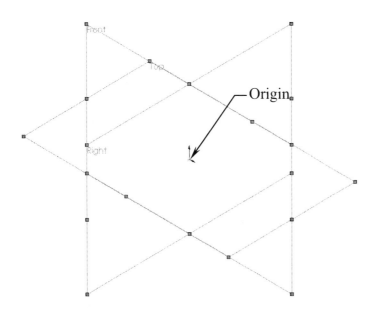

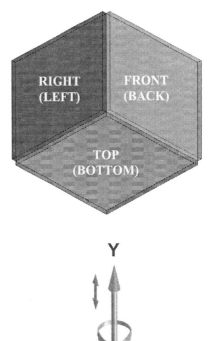

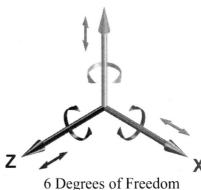

6 Degrees of Freedom

The Toolbars:

- Toolbars can be moved, docked or left floating in the graphics area.

- They can also be "shaped" from horizontal to vertical, or from a single to double rows when dragging on their corners.

- The CommandManager is recommended for the newer releases of SolidWorks.

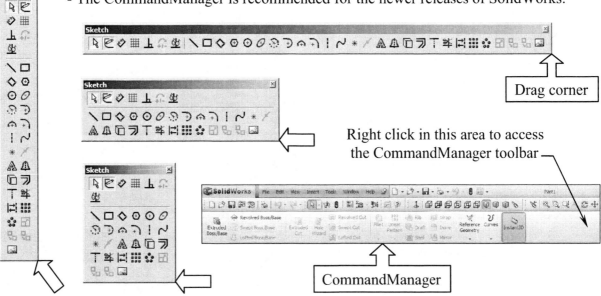

Drag corner

Right click in this area to access the CommandManager toolbar

CommandManager

- To change the colors view port background go to: **Tools / Options / Colors**.

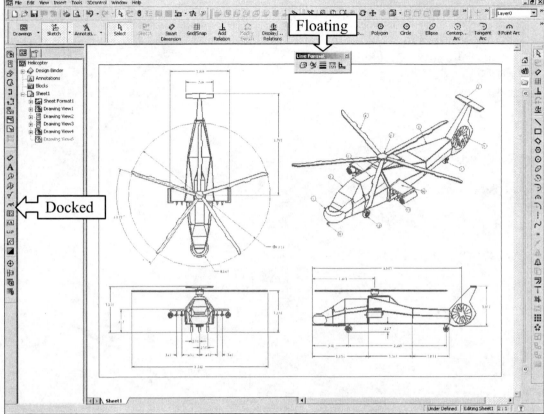

- Toolbars can be toggled Off or On by activating or de-activating their check boxes:

- Select **Tools / Customize / Toolbars** tab.

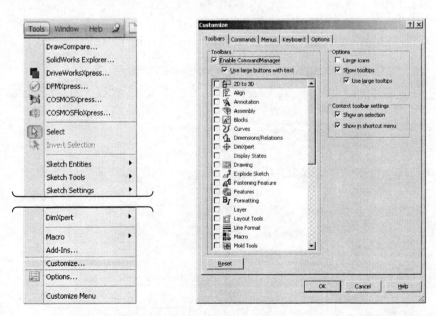

- The icons in the toolbars can be enlarged when its check box is selected.

The View ports: You can view or work with SolidWorks model or an assembly using one, two or four view ports.

View Orientation

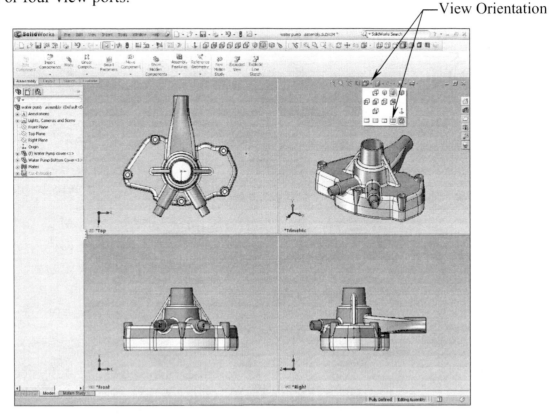

- Some of the **System Feedback symbols** (Inference pointers):

Snap to Vertex (endpoint)   Snap to Intersection

Snap to Edge (curve)   Horizontal Line

Snap to Mid-point   Vertical Line

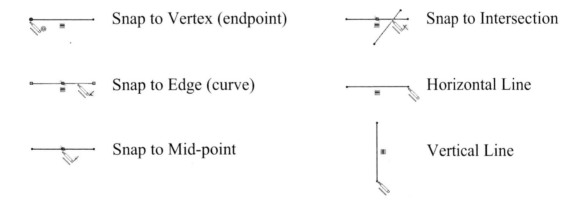

The Status Bar: (View / Status Bar)

Displays the status of the sketch entity using different colors to indicate:

Green = Selected   **Blue** = Under defined
Black = Fully defined   **Red** = Over defined

<u>2D Sketch examples:</u>

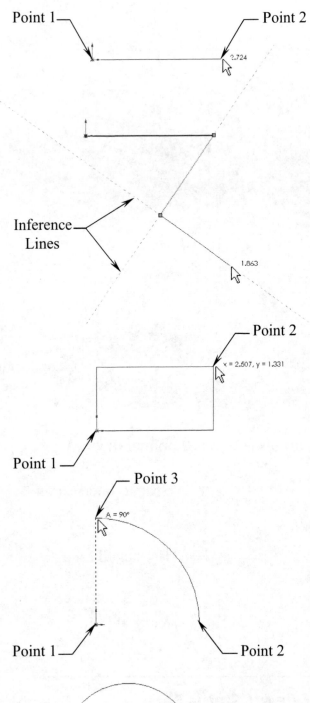

Point 1   Point 2

2.724

Click-Drag-Release: Single entity.

(Click point 1, hold the mouse button, drag to point 2 and release).

Inference Lines

1.863

Click-Release: Continuous multiple entities.

(The Inference Lines appear when the sketch entities are Parallel, Perpendicular or Tangent with each other).

Point 2

x = 2.507, y = 1.331

Click-Drag-Release: Single Rectangle

(Click point 1, hold the mouse button, drag to point 2 and release).

Point 1

Point 3

A = 90°

Click-Drag-Release: Single Centerpoint Arc

(Click point 1, hold the mouse button and drag to point 2, release; then drag to point 3 and release).

Point 1   Point 2

Point 2

R = 1.434

Click-Drag-Release: Single Circle

(Click point 1 [center of circle], hold the mouse button, drag to point 2 [Radius] and release).

Point 1

3D Feature examples:

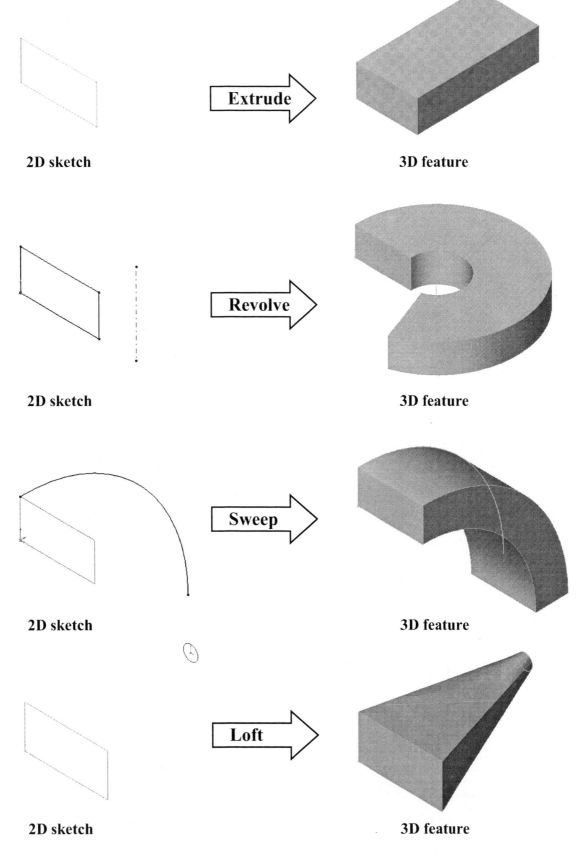

2D sketch   **Extrude**   3D feature

2D sketch   **Revolve**   3D feature

2D sketch   **Sweep**   3D feature

2D sketch   **Loft**   3D feature

<u>Box-Select:</u> Use the Select Pointer 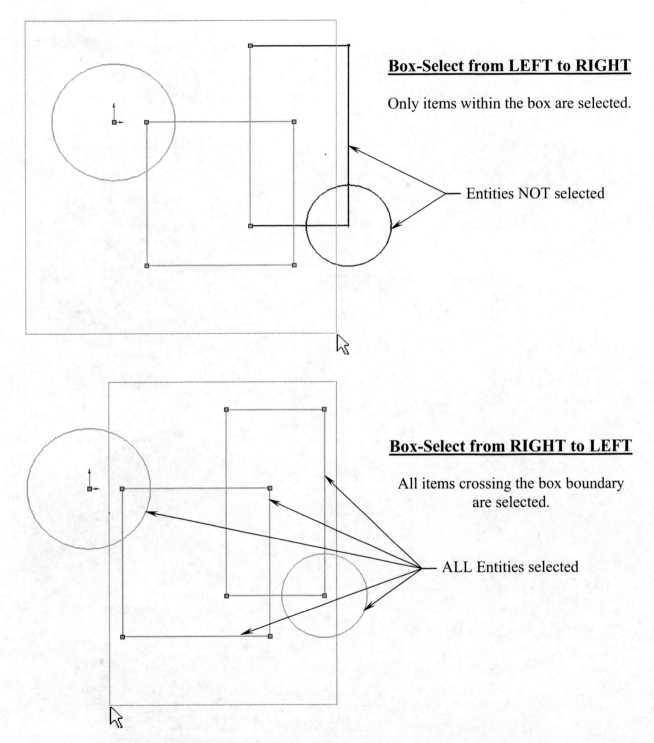 to drag a selection box around items.

<u>Box-Select from LEFT to RIGHT</u>

Only items within the box are selected.

Entities NOT selected

<u>Box-Select from RIGHT to LEFT</u>

All items crossing the box boundary are selected.

ALL Entities selected

The default geometry type selected is as follows:

* Part documents – edges * Assembly documents – components * Drawing documents - sketch entities,

dims & annotations. * To select multiple entities, hold down **Ctrl** while selecting after the first selection.

The new <u>Mouse Gestures</u> for Sketches, Drawings and Parts

- Similar to a keyboard shortcut, you can use a Mouse Gesture to execute a command. A total of 8 keyboard shortcuts can be independently mapped and stored in the Mouse Gesture Guides.

- To activate the Mouse Gesture Guide, **right-click-and-drag** to see the current eight-gestures, then simply select the command that you want to use.

Mouse Gestures for Sketches   **Mouse Gestures for Parts & Assemblies**   **Mouse Gestures for Drawings**

- To customize the Mouse Gestures and include your favorite shortcuts, go to:

Tools / Customize.

- From the **Mouse Gestures** tab, select **All Commands** and enable the **Show only commands with Mouse Gestures assigned** checkbox.

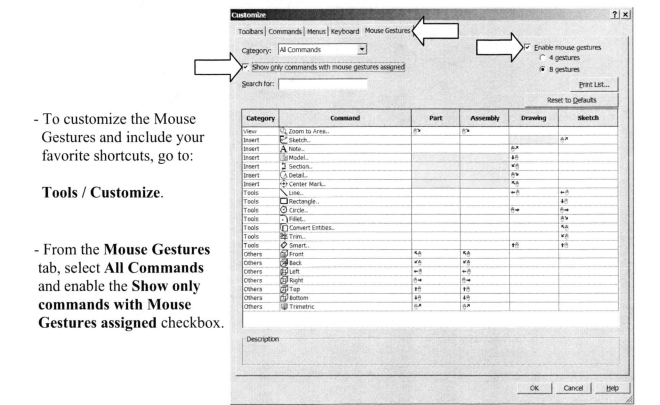

Written with SolidWorks 2010 Premium SP2.1 and Windows XP Professional SP3

CHAPTER 1

Introduction To 3D Sketch

3-D Sketch  Advanced Topics

Using SolidWorks enables you to create 3D sketches. A 3D sketch consists of lines and arcs in series and splines. You can use a 3D sketch as a sweep path, as a guide curve for a loft or sweep, a centerline for a loft, or as one of the key entities in a piping system. Geometric relations can also be added to 3-D Sketches.

Parameters

$\blacksquare_X$ **X Coordinate**

$\blacksquare_Y$ **Y Coordinate**

$\blacksquare_Z$ **Z Coordinate**

Curvature (Spline curvature at the frame point)

Tangency (In the **XY** plane)

Tangency (In the **XZ** plane)

Tangency (In the **YZ** plane)

Space Handle

When working in a 3D sketch, a graphical assistant is provided to help you maintain your orientation while you sketch on several planes. This assistant is called a *space handle*. The space handle appears when the first point of a line or spline is defined on a selected plane. Using the space handle, you can select the axis along which you want to sketch.

Introduction to 3D Sketch

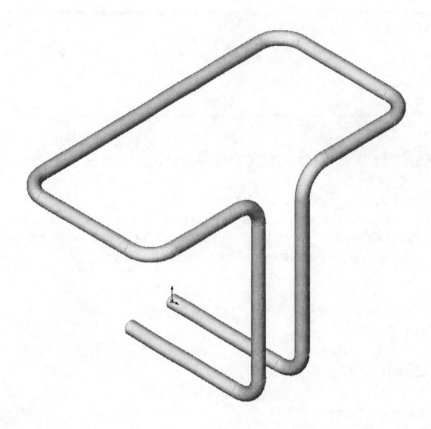

Dimensioning Standards: **ANSI**
Units: **INCHES** – 3 Decimals

Tools Needed:

3D Sketch	2D Sketch	Sketch Line
Circle	Dimension	Add Geometric Relations
Sketch Fillet	Tab Key	Base/ Boss Sweep

1. Starting a new part file: Select **File / New / Part / OK**.

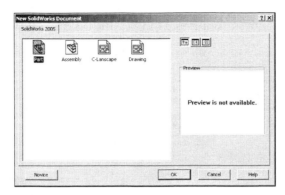

2. Using 3D Sketch:

- Click  or select **Insert / 3D Sketch**, and change to **Isometric view** .

- Select the Line tool and sketch the first line along the **X** axis.

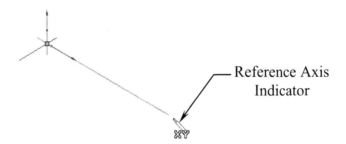

Reference Axis
Indicator

- Sketch the second line along the **Y** axis as shown.

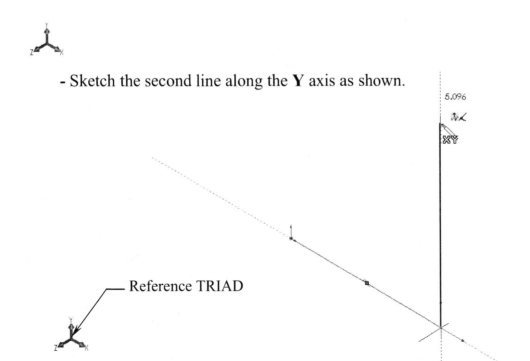

Reference TRIAD

3. Changing direction:

- By default, your sketch is relative to the default coordinate system in the model.

- To switch to one of the other two default planes, press the **TAB** key. The reference origin of the current sketch plane is displayed.

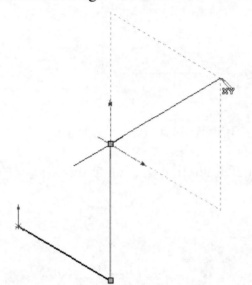

> ### The TAB key
>
> While dragging the mouse cursor (when sketching the lines), press the **TAB** key to switch to other planes/directions.

4. Completing the profile:

- Follow the axis as labeled; press **TAB** to change the direction if necessary.

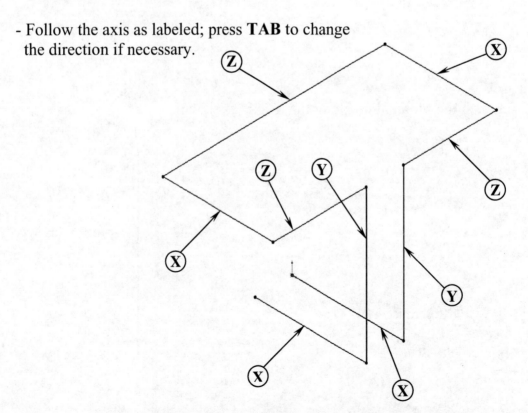

5. Adding dimensions:

- Click 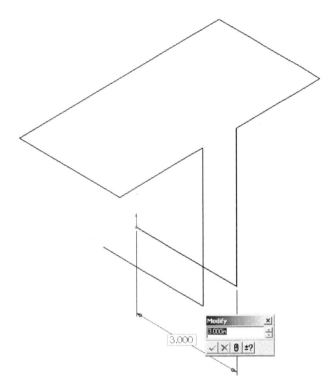 or select **Tools / Dimensions / Smart**.

- Click on the first line and add a dimension of **3.00"**.

- Continue adding the dimensions as
  shown, to fully define the 3D sketch.

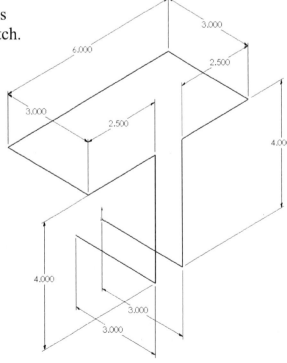

6. Adding the Sketch Fillets:

- Click  or select **Tools / Sketch Tools / Fillet**.

- Add **.500"** fillets to all the intersections as indicated.

- Enable the **Keep Constrained Corner** check box.

- Click OK when finished.

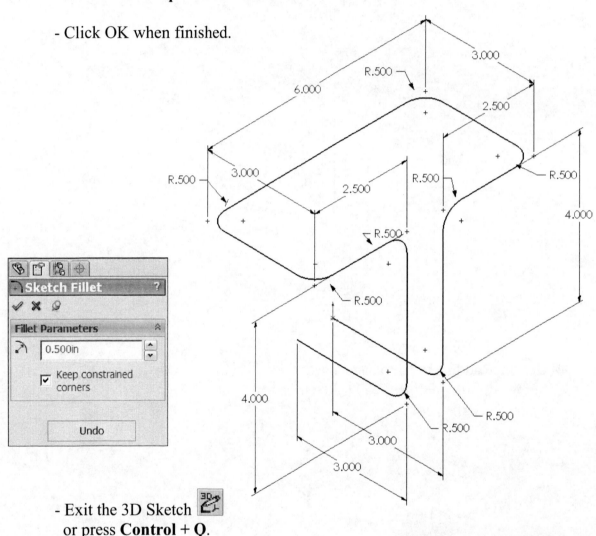

- Exit the 3D Sketch 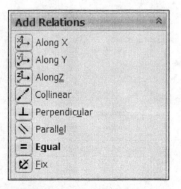 or press **Control + Q**.

💡 **Relations**

Geometric Relations such as Along Z and Equal can also be use to replace some of the duplicate dimensions.

---

7. Sketching the Sweep Profile:

- Select the RIGHT plane from the FeatureManager tree.

- Click 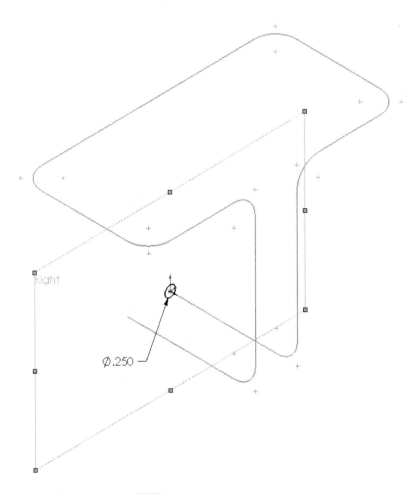 to open a new sketch or select **Insert / Sketch**.

- Sketch a Circle ⊙ using the Origin as the center. (The system automatically creates a Coincident relation between the Center of the circle and the Origin.)

Ø.250

- Add a **Ø.250** dimension ◇ to fully define the circle.

- Exit the Sketch ✎ or select **Insert / Sketch**.

Note:

- *The Sweep Profile should be Pierced or Coincident with the Sweep Path.*
- *The Swept Boss/Base command is only available when the sketch pencil is off.*

8. Creating the Swept feature:

- Click 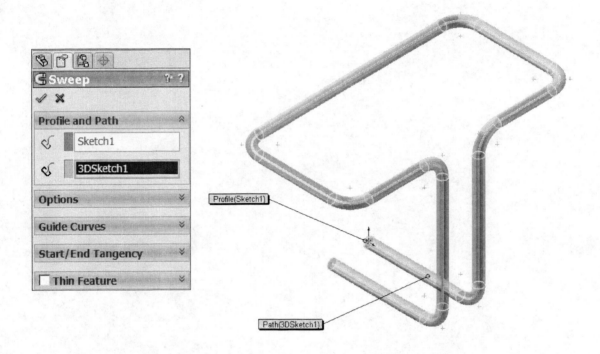 or select **Insert / Boss-Base / Sweep**.

- Select the Circle as Sweep Profile (Sketch1)

- Click anywhere on the 3D Sketch to use as Sweep Path (3Dsketch1).

- Click **OK**.

9. Saving your work:

- Select **File / Save As / 3D Sketch / Save**.

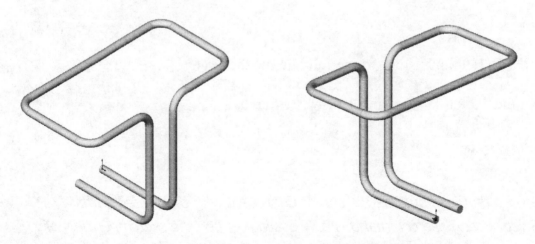

Questions for Review

3D Sketch

1. When using 3D Sketch, you do not have to pre-select a plane as you would in 2D Sketch.
   - a. True
   - b. False

2. The space handle appears only after the first point of a line is started.
   - a. True
   - b. False

3. To switch to other planes in 3D Sketch mode, press:
   - a. Up Arrow
   - b. Down Arrow
   - c. TAB key
   - d. CONTROL key

4. Dimensions cannot be used in 3D Sketch mode.
   - a. True
   - b. False

5. Geometric Relations cannot be used in 3D Sketch mode.
   - a. True
   - b. False

6. All of the sketch tools in 2D Sketch are also available in 3D Sketch.
   - a. True
   - b. False

7. 3D Sketch entities can be used to extrude a solid feature.
   - a. True
   - b. False

8. 3D Sketch entities can be used as a path in a swept feature.
   - a. True
   - b. False

1. TRUE
2. TRUE
3. C
4. FALSE
5. FALSE
6. FALSE
7. FALSE
8. TRUE

<u>Exercise</u>: Sweep with 3D Sketch

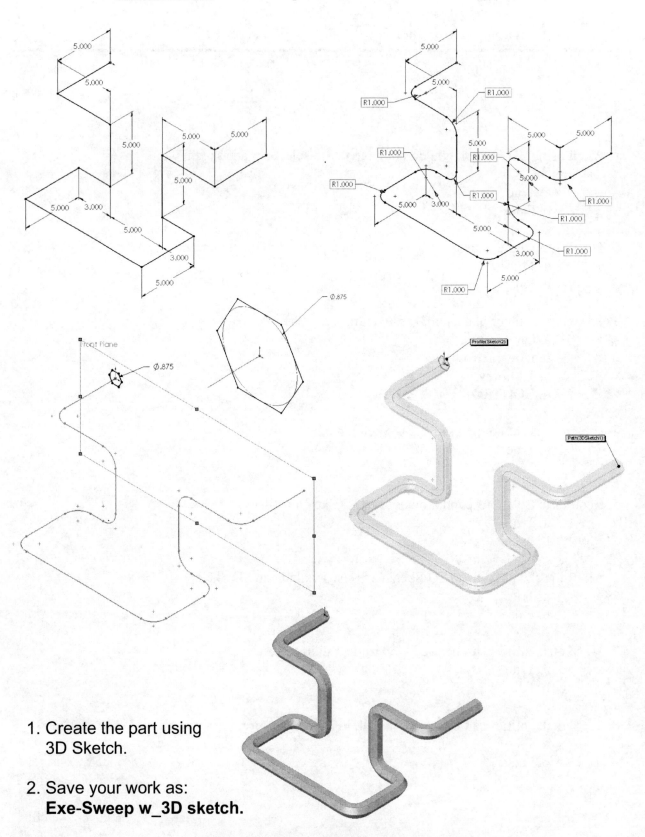

1. Create the part using
   3D Sketch.

2. Save your work as:
   Exe-Sweep w_3D sketch.

Exercise: 3D Sketch & Planes

A 3D sketch normally consists of lines and arcs in series, and splines. You can use a 3D sketch as a sweep path, as a guide curve for a loft or sweep, a centerline for a loft, or as one of the key entities in a routing system.

The following exercise demonstrates how several planes can be used to help define the directions of the 3D Sketch Entities.

1. Sketching the reference Pivot lines:

- Select the TOP plane and

open a new sketch .

- Sketch **2** Centerlines

and add Dimensions
as shown.

2. Creating the 1st 45° Planes:

- Select **Insert/Reference Geometry/Planes** .

- Click the **At Angle** Option and enter **45** as Angle .

- Select the TOP plane and the Vertical line as noted.

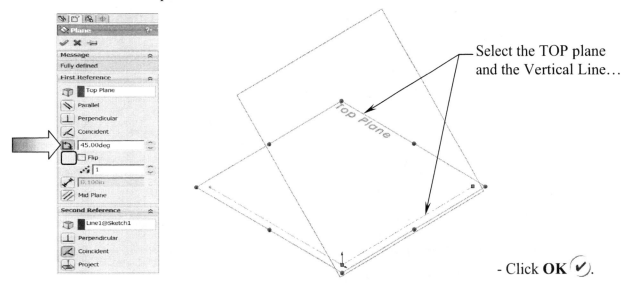

Select the TOP plane
and the Vertical Line...

- Click **OK** .

3. Creating the 2nd 45° Planes:

- Select **Insert/Reference Geometry/Planes** 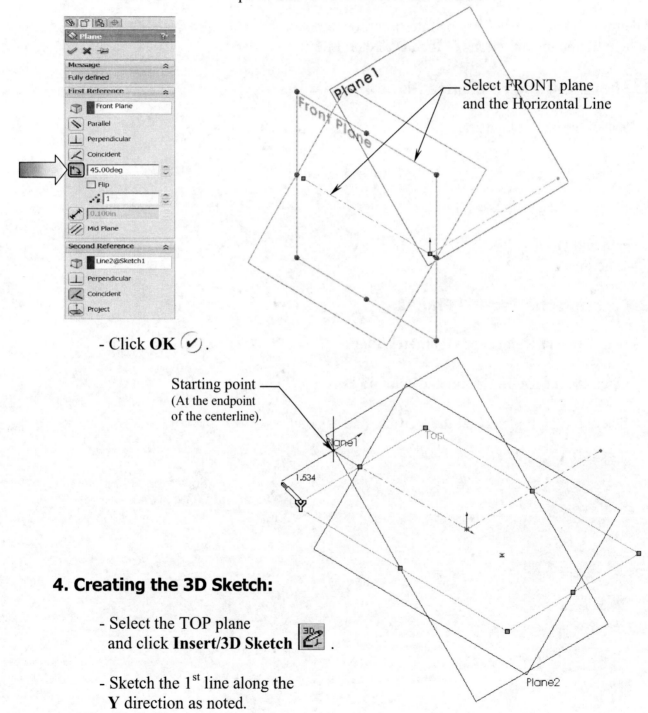.

- Click the At Angle Option and enter **45** for Angle .

- Select the FRONT plane and the Horizontal line as noted.

Select FRONT plane
and the Horizontal Line

- Click **OK** .

Starting point
(At the endpoint
of the centerline).

4. Creating the 3D Sketch:

- Select the TOP plane
and click **Insert/3D Sketch** .

- Sketch the 1st line along the
Y direction as noted.

- Select the **PLANE2** (45 deg.) from the Feature Manager tree and Sketch the 2nd line along the **Y** direction (watch the cursor feedback symbols).

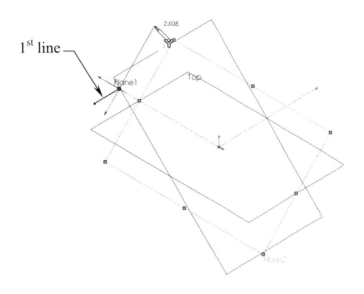

1st line

- Sketch the rest of lines on the planes as labeled.

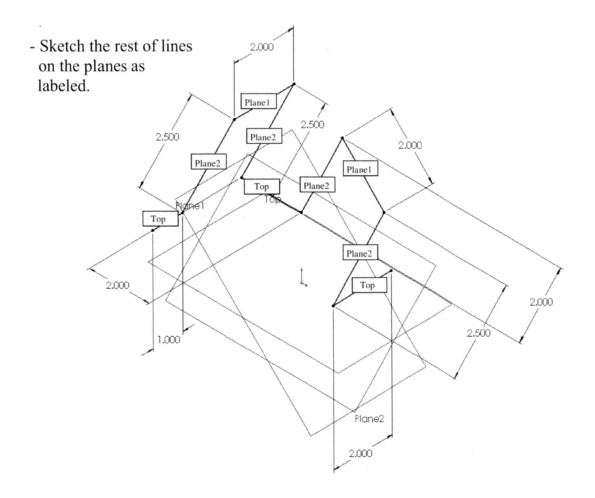

- Add **Sketch Fillets**  of **.500 in.** to all corners.

- Add Dimensions to fully define the sketch.

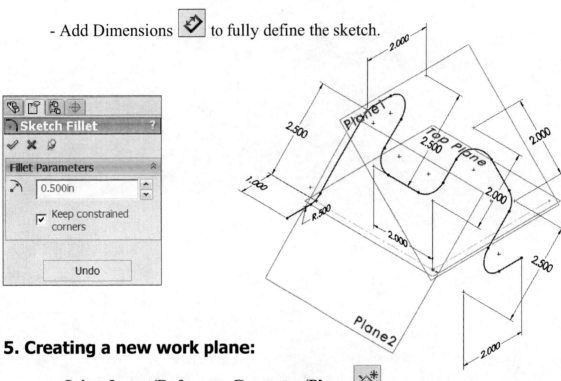

5. Creating a new work plane:

- Select **Insert/Reference Geometry/Plane** .

- Click the **Normal To Curve** option.

- Select the line approximately as shown.

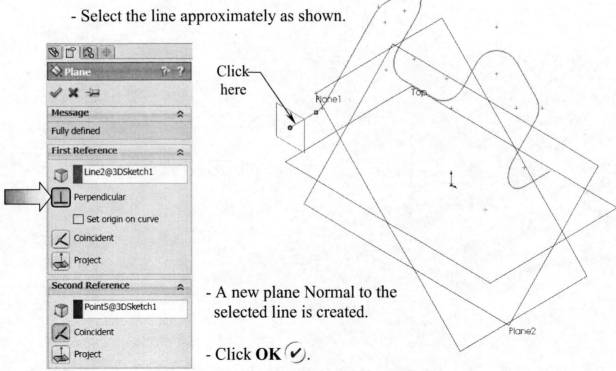

- A new plane Normal to the selected line is created.

- Click **OK** ✔.

6. Sketching the Sweep Profile:

- Select the new plane
  (Plane3) and open a new sketch 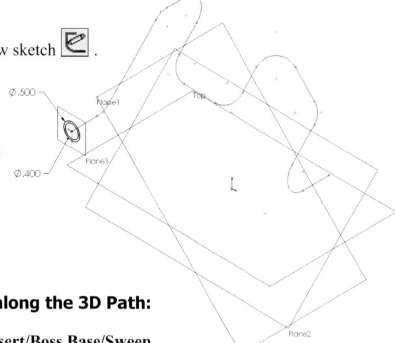.

- Sketch 2 Circles
  on the same center and
  add the dimensions as
  shown to fully define
  the sketch.

7. Sweeping the Profile along the 3D Path:

- Click ⏚ or Select **Insert/Boss Base/Sweep**

- Select the Circles as the Sweep Profile.

- Select the 3D Sketch as the Sweep Path.

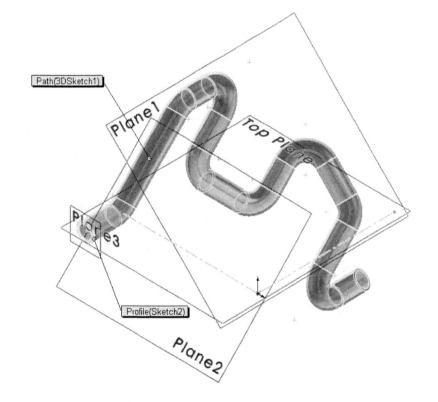

- Click **OK** ✔.

- The resulting Swept feature.

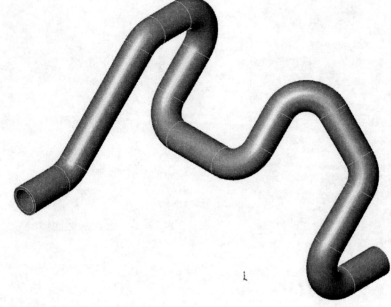

8. Hiding the Planes:

- From the menu, select **View/Planes**.

- The planes are temporarily put away from the scene.

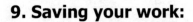

9. Saving your work:

- Click **File/Save As:**

  3D-Sketch-Planes.

- Click **Save**.

Exercise: 3D Sketch & Composite Curve

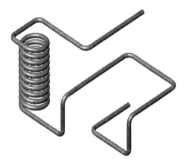

A 3D sketch normally consists of lines and arcs in series, and Splines. You can use a 3D sketch as a sweep path, as a guide curve for a loft or sweep, a centerline for a loft, or as one of the key entities in a routing system.

The following exercise demonstrates how several 3D Sketches can be created and combined into 1 continuous Composite Curve for use as a Sweep Path.

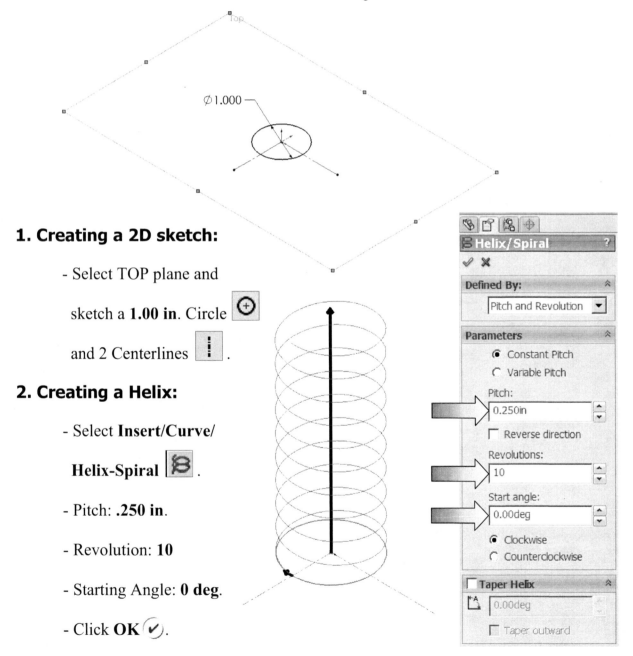

Ø1.000

1. Creating a 2D sketch:

- Select TOP plane and

sketch a **1.00 in**. Circle ⊕

and 2 Centerlines ⋮ .

2. Creating a Helix:

- Select **Insert/Curve/**

Helix-Spiral 🕉 .

- Pitch: **.250 in**.

- Revolution: **10**

- Starting Angle: **0 deg**.

- Click **OK** ✔.

Helix/Spiral

Defined By:
Pitch and Revolution

Parameters
- Constant Pitch
- Variable Pitch

Pitch:
0.250in

☐ Reverse direction

Revolutions:
10

Start angle:
0.00deg

- Clockwise
- Counterclockwise

☐ **Taper Helix**
0.00deg
☐ Taper outward

3. Creating the 1st 3D sketch:

- Select **Insert/3D Sketch** .

- Select the Line command and sketch the 1st line along the X direction.

On-Plane relation
(End point & Right plane)

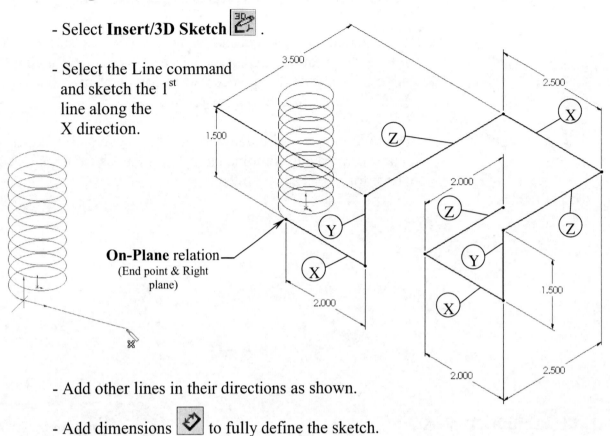

- Add other lines in their directions as shown.

- Add dimensions to fully define the sketch.

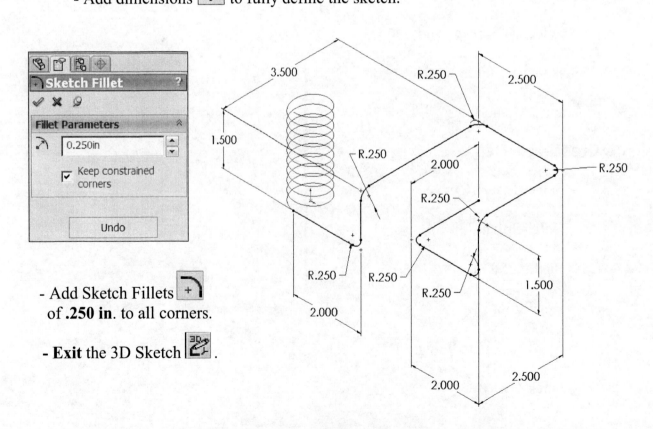

- Add Sketch Fillets of **.250 in**. to all corners.

- **Exit** the 3D Sketch .

4. Creating the 2nd 3D sketch:

- Select **Insert/3D Sketch**

- Select the Line command and sketch the 1st line along the X direction.

- Sketch the rest of the lines following their directions shown below.

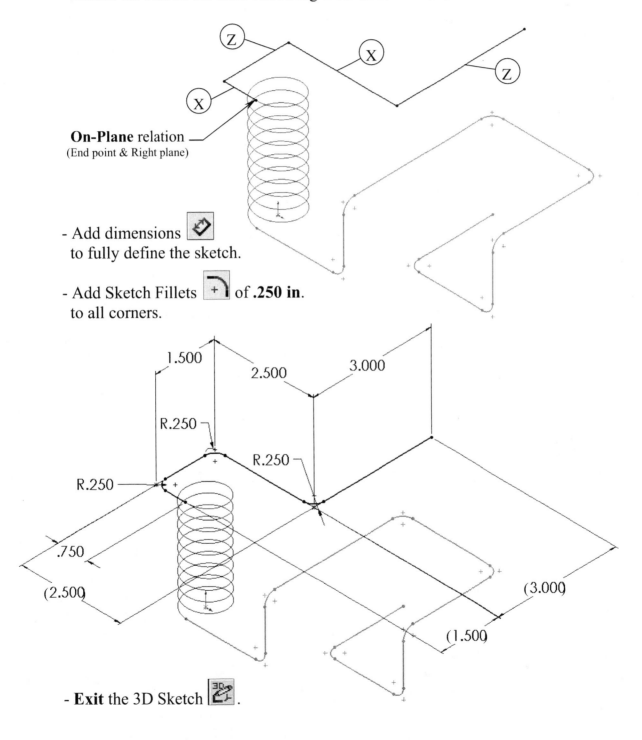

On-Plane relation
(End point & Right plane)

- Add dimensions
  to fully define the sketch.

- Add Sketch Fillets of **.250 in**.
  to all corners.

- **Exit** the 3D Sketch .

5. Combining the 3 sketches into 1 curve:

- Select **Insert/Curve/Composite** 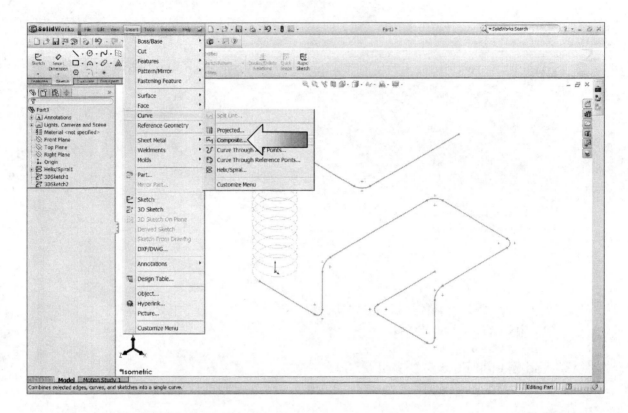.

- Select the 3 Sketches either from the Feature Manager tree – or – directly from the graphics area.

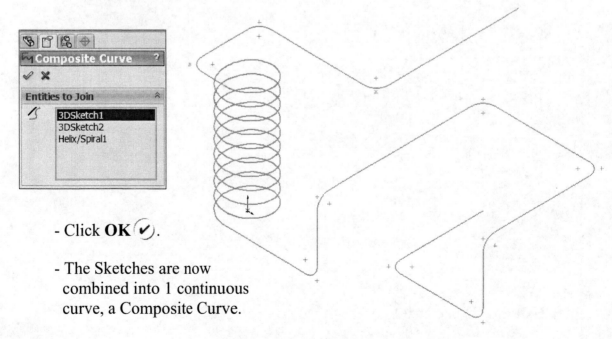

- Click **OK** ✔.

- The Sketches are now combined into 1 continuous curve, a Composite Curve.

6. Creating a new work plane:

- Select **Insert/Reference Geometry/Plane** .

- Click the **Normal To Curve** option and select the edge and the endpoint as noted.

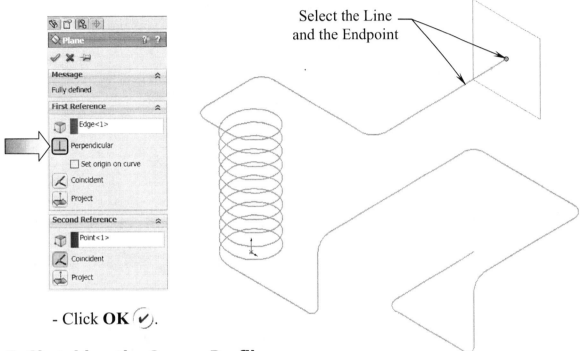

Select the Line and the Endpoint

- Click **OK** .

7. Sketching the Sweep Profile:

- Select the new plane (Plane1) and open a new sketch .

- Sketch a Circle and add a **.165** dia. dimension .

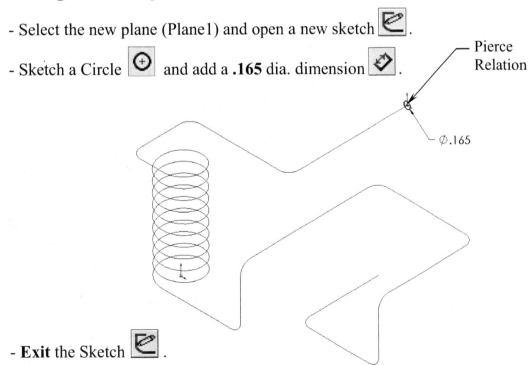

Pierce Relation

Ø.165

- **Exit** the Sketch .

8. Sweeping the Profile along the Path:

- Select **Insert/Boss Base/ Sweep** 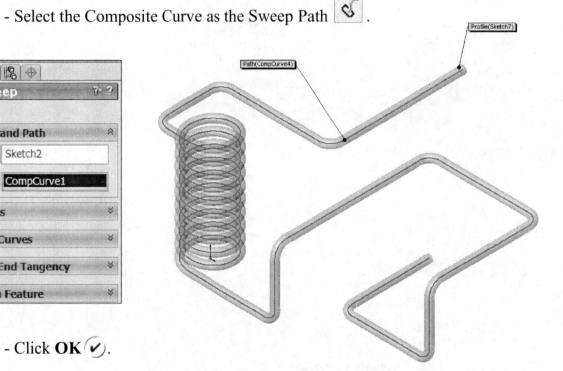.

- Select the Circle as the Sweep Profile .

- Select the Composite Curve as the Sweep Path .

- Click **OK** .

9. Saving your work:

- Click **File/Save As**.

- Enter **3D Sketch – Composite Curve**

- Click **Save**.

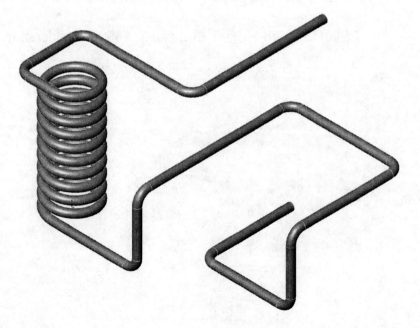

CHAPTER 2

Plane Creation

Planes Advanced Topics

- In SolidWorks, planes are not only used to sketch the geometry, but they Are also used to create the section views of a model or an assembly, or as an end conditions to extrude features, or as a neutral plane to define the draft angles, etc.

- There are several options to create planes:

 Parallel Plane.   At Angle Plane.

 Perpendicular Plane.   Offset Distance Plane.

 Coincident Plane.   Mid Plane.

 Project Plane.

- Each plane requires slightly different types of references, some of them may requires only one reference and some others may require two or three references.

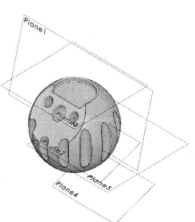

- This chapter discusses how planes are created Using the sketch geometry and features available in the model as references.

Plane Creation

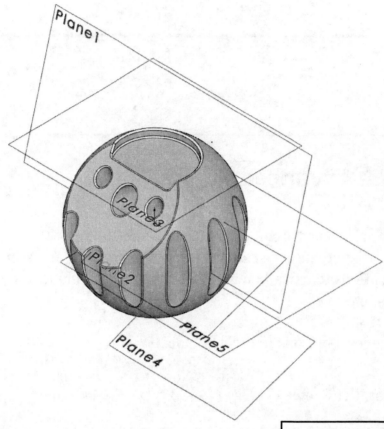
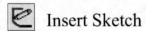
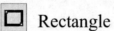

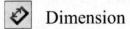

Dimensioning Standards: **ANSI**

Units: **INCHES** – 3 Decimals

Tools Needed:

Insert Sketch	Rectangle	Circle
Planes	Add Geometric Relations	Dimension
Sketch Mirror	Offset Entities	Boss/Base Revolve
Circular Pattern	Extruded Cut	Fillet/Round

1. Starting with a new Part document:

- Start with the Base profile.

- Select the FRONT plane from the FeatureManager tree.

- Click 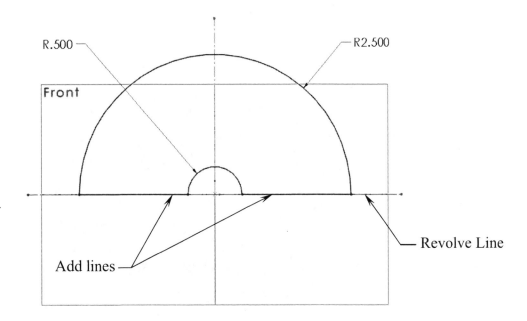 or select **Insert / Sketch**.

- Sketch the profile below and add dimensions as shown.

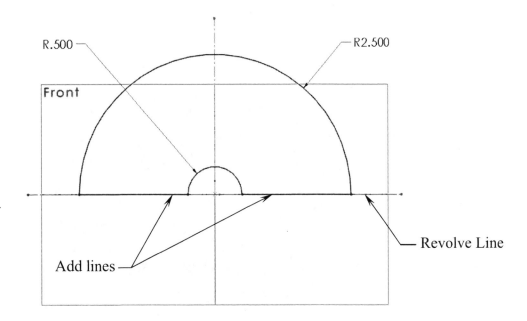

2. Revolving the Base:

- Click or select **Insert / Boss Base / Revolve**

- Set Revolve Type to: **One Direction**.

- Set Revolve Angle to: **360 deg**.

- Click **OK**.

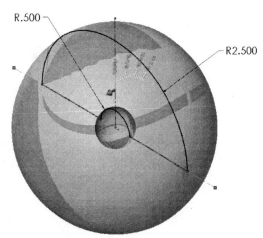

3. Creating a flat surface:

- Select the RIGHT plane from the FeatureManager tree.

- Click 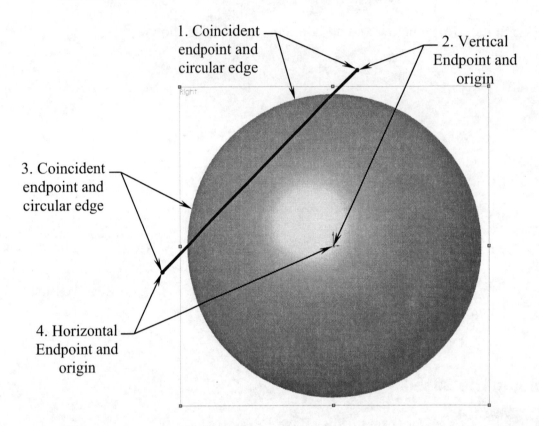 or select **Insert / Sketch** and switch to the right view (Ctrl+4).

- Sketch a Line and add the Relations as shown.

1. Coincident endpoint and circular edge

2. Vertical Endpoint and origin

3. Coincident endpoint and circular edge

4. Horizontal Endpoint and origin

4. Extruding a Cut:

- Click 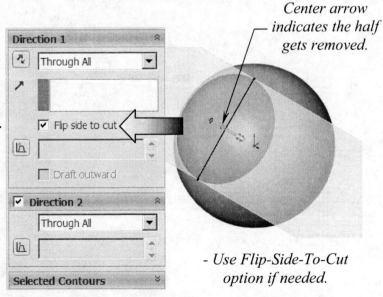 or select:

Insert / Cut / Extrude.

- Use **Through All** for both Direction 1 and Direction 2.

- Click **OK** ✓.

Center arrow indicates the half gets removed.

- Use Flip-Side-To-Cut option if needed.

Direction 1
Through All
☑ Flip side to cut
☐ Draft outward
☑ Direction 2
Through All
Selected Contours

5. Creating a Plane-At-Angle:

(Requires a Reference Plane, a Reference Axis, and an Angular Dimension).

- Select the FRONT plane from FeatureManager tree.

- Click 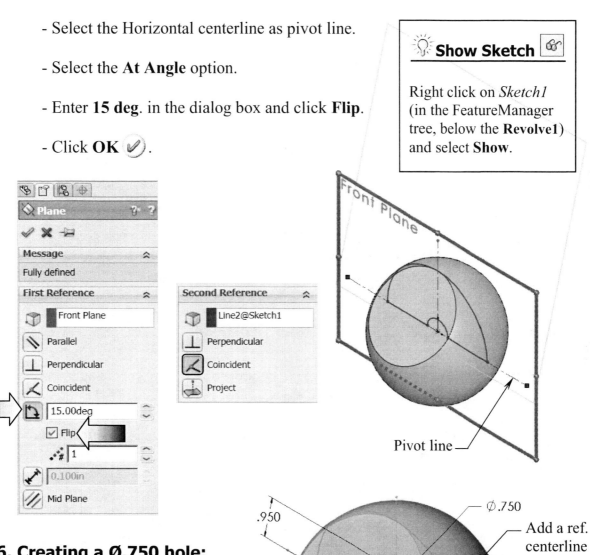 or select **Insert / Reference Geometry / Plane**.

- Select the Horizontal centerline as pivot line.

- Select the **At Angle** option.

- Enter **15 deg**. in the dialog box and click **Flip**.

- Click **OK** ✓.

> 💡 **Show Sketch** 👓
>
> Right click on *Sketch1* (in the FeatureManager tree, below the **Revolve1**) and select **Show**.

Pivot line

6. Creating a Ø.750 hole:

- Select the new plane (PLANE1).

- Click 📝 or select **Insert / Sketch**.

- Sketch a Circle ⊕ and add the

Dimensions 🖊 as shown.

.950

Ø.750

Add a ref. centerline to use later in step 8.

Vertical

- Click 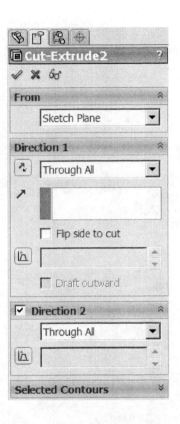 or select **Insert / Cut / Extrude**.

- Direction 1: **Through All**

- Direction 2: **Through All**

- Click **OK**.

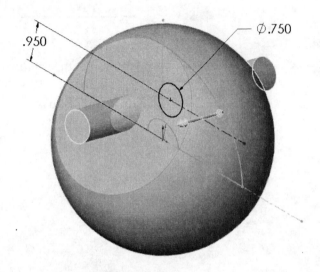

7. Showing the Sketches:

- Expand the Cut-Extrude1 (click the + symbol) in the FeatureManager tree, right click on **Sketch2**, and select **Show**.

- Expand the Cut-Extrude2 (click the + symbol), right-click on **Sketch3**, and select **Show**, also Hide the Sketch1.

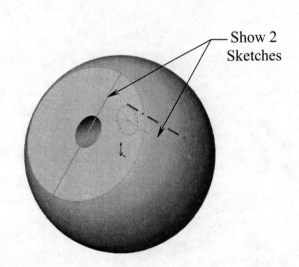

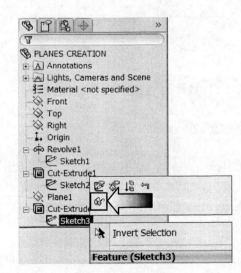

8. Creating a Plane-Through-Lines/Points: (Requires a Reference Line and a Sketch Point or a Vertex).

- Click 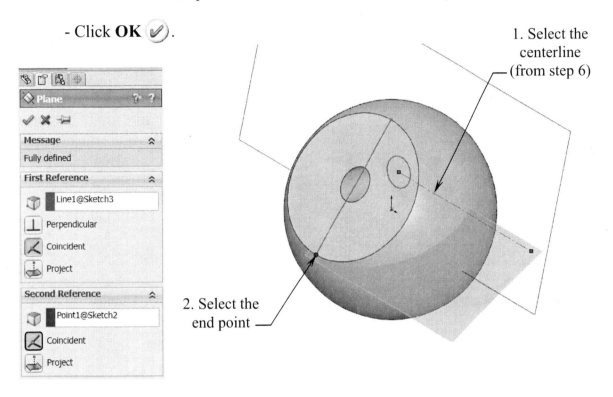 or select **Insert / Reference Geometry / Plane**.

- Select the Line and the Endpoint as indicated.

- The **Coincident** option should be selected automatically.

- Click **OK**.

1. Select the centerline (from step 6)

2. Select the end point

9. Creating the Ø.500 holes:

- Select the new plane (PLANE2).

- Click or select **Insert / Sketch**.

- Sketch a Circle and Mirror it

- Add Dimensions

as shown to fully

define the sketch.

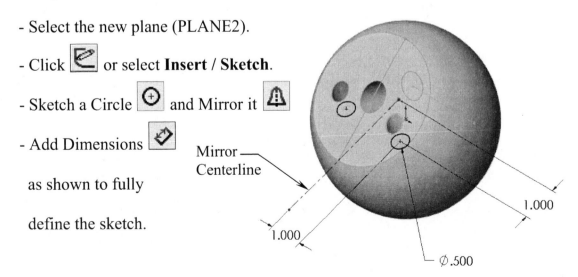

Mirror Centerline

1.000

1.000

Ø.500

- Click  or select **Insert / Cut / Extrude**.

- Direction 1:   **Through All**

- Direction 2:   **Through All**

- Click **OK** ✓.

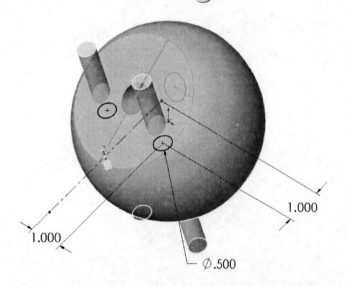

10. Creating a Parallel-Plane at-Point: (Requires a Reference Plane and Reference Point).

- Click �'✶ or select **Insert / Reference Geometry / Plane**.

- Select the TOP plane and the Endpoint as indicated.

- Based on your selection, the system selects the **Parallel Plane** option.

- Click **OK** ✓.

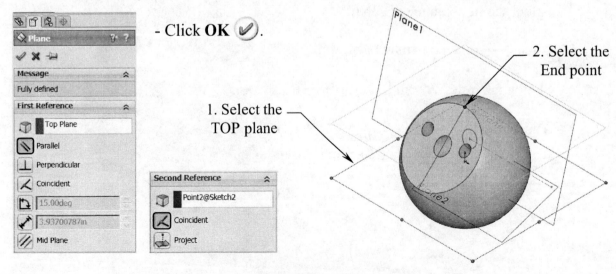

1. Select the TOP plane

2. Select the End point

11. Creating the Ø2.500 Recess:

- Select the new Plane (PLANE3) and insert a new sketch .

- Sketch a Circle ⊕ and add Dimension ◇ .

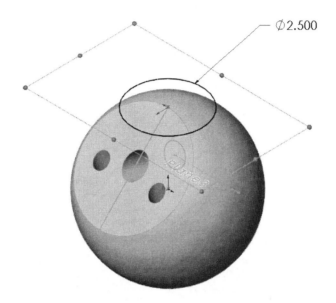

Ø2.500

- Click 🔲 or select **Insert / Cut / Extrude**.

- End Condition: **Blind**

- Extrude Depth: **.625** in.

- Click **OK** ✓ .

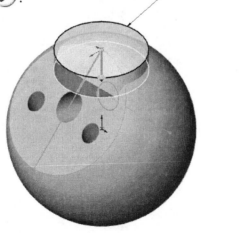

Ø2.500

- Hide the Sketch2 and Sketch3 👓 .

12. Creating a Plane-Offset-Distance: (Requires a Reference Plane and a Distance Dimension).

- Click 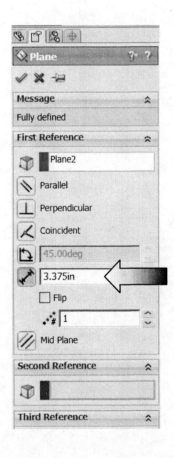 or select **Insert / Reference Geometry / Plane**.

- Select PLANE2 (from the FeatureManager tree) to offset from.

- The **Offset Distance** option is automatically selected.

- Enter **3.375** for Offset Distance value.

- Make sure the new plane is placed below the PLANE2.

- Click **OK** ⊘.

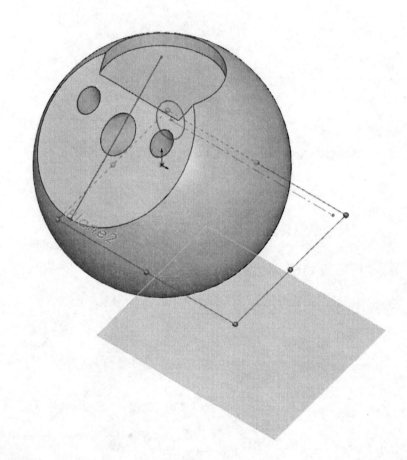

13. Creating the Bore holes:

- Select the new plane (PLANE4) and insert a new sketch.

- Select the *circular edge* of the hole and press Offset-Entities.

- Enter **.100 in**. for Offset Distance (Only one offset can be done at a time, since the 2 circles are not connecting with each other).

- Click **OK** ✅.

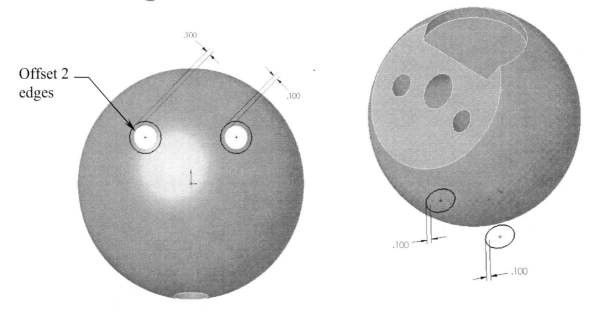

Offset 2 edges

- Click 🗐 or select **Insert / Cut Extrude**.

- End Condition: **Blind**.

- Extrude Depth: **1.500** in.

- Click **OK** ✅.

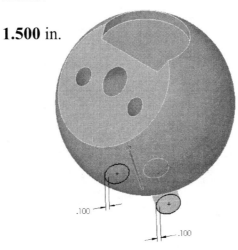

14. Creating a Plane-Normal-To-Curve: (Requires a Reference Line or Curve).

- Click 🖉 or select **Insert / Reference Geometry / Plane**.

- Select the Arc and the End point as noted.

- The **Normal To Curve** option is selected.

- Click **OK** ✅.

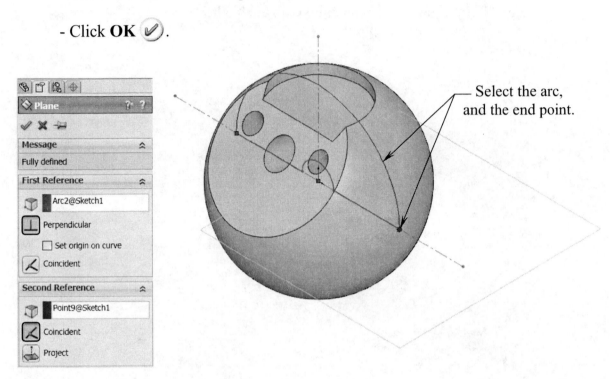

Select the arc,
and the end point.

15. Creating the side-grips:

- Select the new plane (PLANE5) and insert a new sketch ✏️ .

- Sketch a Circle and add a **Ø.625** dimension.

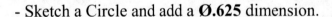
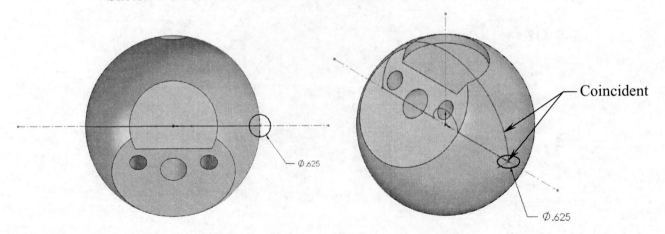

Coincident

Ø.625

Ø.625

- Click 🔳 or select **Insert / Cut Extrude**.

- Direction 1: **Through All**.

- Direction 2: **Through All**.

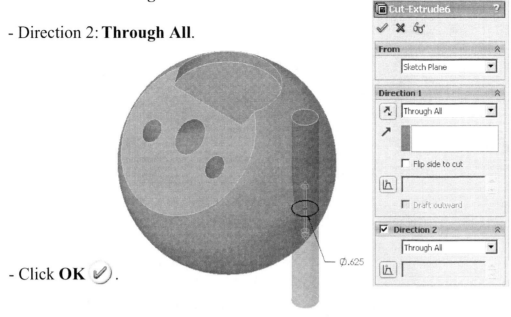

- Click **OK** .

16. Creating a Circular Pattern of the Grips:

- Click or select **Insert / Pattern Mirror / Circular Pattern**.

- Click **View / Temporary Axis** and select the center axis as indicated.

- Equal Spacing: **Enabled**.

- Total Angle: **360 deg**.

- Number of instances: **12**.

- Select the Cut as Feature To Pattern.

- Click

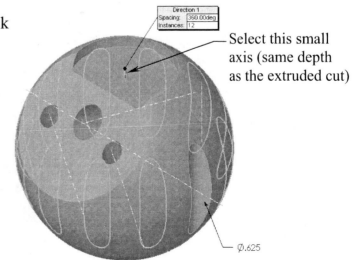

Select this small axis (same depth as the extruded cut)

17. Adding the center hole:

- Select the upper face of the Recess and insert a new sketch .

- Sketch a Circle and add a **Ø.500** dimension.

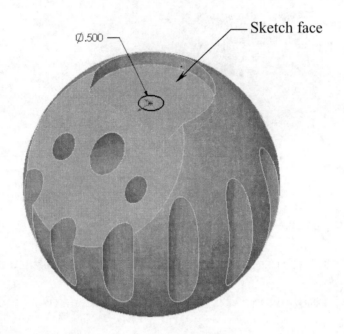

Ø.500 — Sketch face

- Click 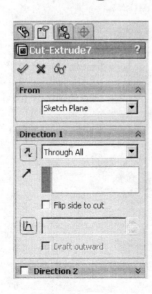 or select **Insert / Cut / Extrude**.

- End Condition: **Through All**

- Click **OK** ✓.

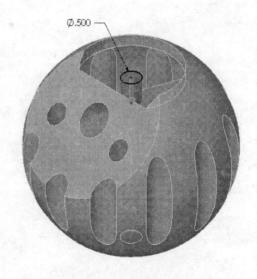

18. Adding a recess:

- Select the upper face of the Recess and insert a new sketch .

- Select the Edge of the Ø.500 hole and click **Offset Entities** .

- Enter **.625** for Offset Distance.

- Click **OK** .

Offset this Edge — — Sketch face

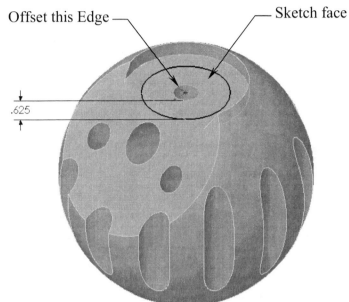

- Click or select **Insert / Cut Extrude**.

- End Condition: **Blind**.

- Extrude Depth: **.175** in.

- Click **OK** .

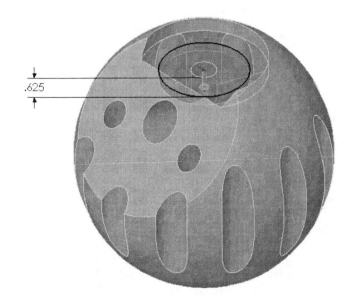

19. Adding Fillets to all edges:

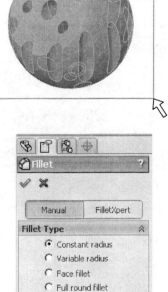

- Drag a box around the part (window select), to group all of its edges.

- Click 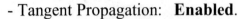 or select **Insert Features / Fillet-Round**.

- Enter **.040** for Radius [0.040in]

- Tangent Propagation: **Enabled**.

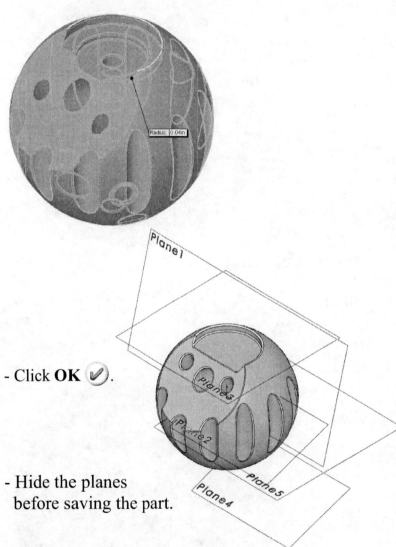

- Click **OK** ✓.

- Hide the planes before saving the part.

20. Saving your work:

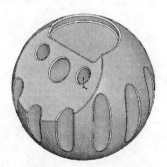

- Click **File / Save As / Planes Creation / Save**.

Questions for Review

Plane Creation

1. Planes can be used to section a part or an assembly.
   - a. True
   - b. False

2. A sketch can be extruded to a plane as the end condition by using the Up-To-Surface option.
   - a. True
   - b. False

3. Which one of the options below is not a valid command?
   - a. Parallel plane at Point.
   - b. Offset plane at Distance.
   - c. Perpendicular to another plane at Angle.
   - d. Normal to Curve.

4. To create a plane at Angle, you will need:
   - a. The Angle and a Reference plane.
   - b. The Angle and a pivot Line.
   - c. The Angle, a pivot Line, and a Reference plane.

5. To create a plane through Lines/Points, you will need at least:
   - a. One line and a point
   - b. Two lines and a point
   - c. Two lines and Two points

6. To create a Parallel Plane At Point, you will need a reference plane and a point.
   - a. True
   - b. False

7. When creating a Plane Normal To Curve, you can select:
   - a. A linear model edge
   - b. A straight line.
   - c. A 2D or 3D curve
   - d. All of the above

1. TRUE 2. TRUE
3. C 4. C
5. A 6. TRUE
7. D

Exercise: Create new Work Planes

1. Create a reference sketch as shown.

2. Create 3 new planes using the references as indicated.

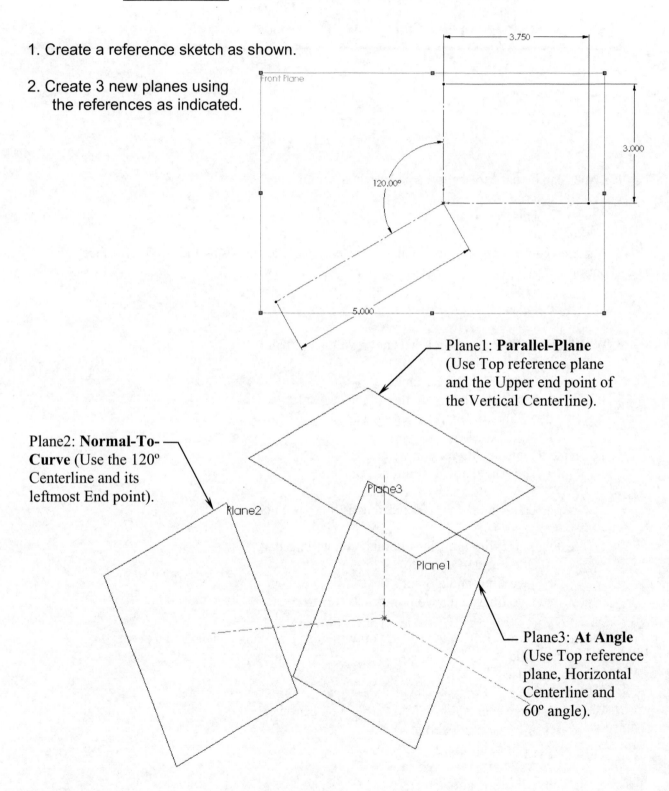

Plane1: **Parallel-Plane** (Use Top reference plane and the Upper end point of the Vertical Centerline).

Plane2: **Normal-To-Curve** (Use the 120° Centerline and its leftmost End point).

Plane3: **At Angle** (Use Top reference plane, Horizontal Centerline and 60° angle).

3. Save your work as: **Exe-New Work Planes**.

CHAPTER 3

Advanced Modeling

Advanced Modeling – 5/8" Spanner

- The draft option is omitted in this lesson to help focus in other areas.

- The arc conditions Min / Max are options that help placing dimensions on the tangents of the arcs or circles. Once a dimension is created, the arc conditions can be changed by right clicking on the dimension and selecting the Leaders tab and chose the condition for each arc.

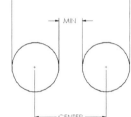

- Two conditions can be specified at a time.

- Adding text [A] on the model is another unique feature in SolidWorks. This option allows the letters to be extruded as boss or a cut, similar to other extruded features.

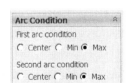

- All letters in the same sketch are considered one entity, they will be extruded at the same time and will receive the same extrude depth.

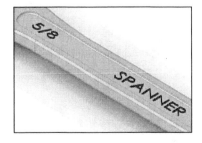

- This lesson will guide us through some of advanced modeling techniques to create the spanner. The same model will be used again in a future chapter, where we will learn to perform some stress analysis and see how much load the part can withstand.

5/8" Spanner
Advanced Modeling

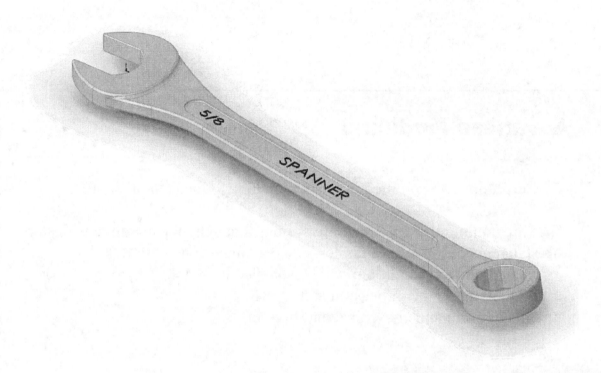

Dimensioning Standards: **ANSI**

Units: **INCHES** – 3 Decimals

Tools Needed:

Insert Sketch	Line	3 Point Arc
Text	Add Geometric Relations	Dimension
Sketch Fillet	Polygon	Plane
Base/Boss Extrude	Extruded Cut	Fillet/Round

1. Creating the Open-end sketch:

- Select TOP plane from Feature Manager Tree.

- Click 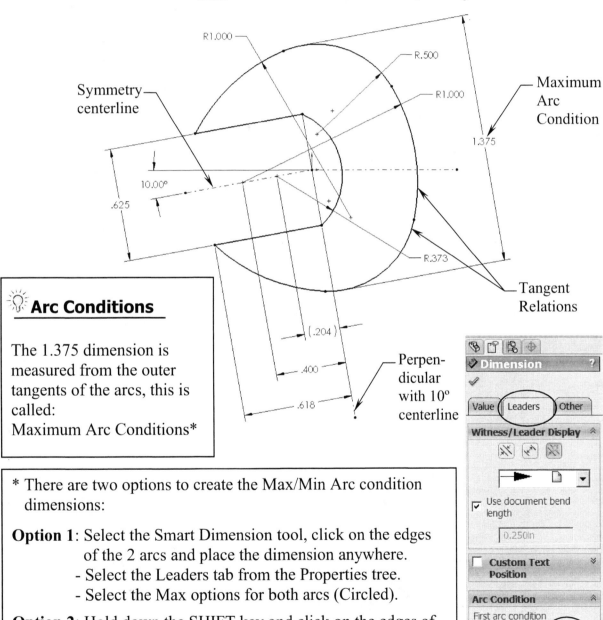 or select **Insert / Sketch**.

- Sketch the profile shown below using Lines and 3-Point Arcs.

- Add Dimensions and Relations needed, to fully define the sketch.

⬙ **Arc Conditions**

The 1.375 dimension is measured from the outer tangents of the arcs, this is called:
Maximum Arc Conditions*

---

* There are two options to create the Max/Min Arc condition dimensions:

Option 1: Select the Smart Dimension tool, click on the edges of the 2 arcs and place the dimension anywhere.
  - Select the Leaders tab from the Properties tree.
  - Select the Max options for both arcs (Circled).

Option 2: Hold down the SHIFT key and click on the edges of the 2 arcs, the dimension leader lines are snapped to the arc tangents automatically.

2. Extruding the base feature:

- Click  or select **Insert / Boss-Base / Extrude**.

- End Condition: **Mid Plane**

- Extrude Depth: **.250 in**.

- Click **OK** ✅ .

💡 **Renaming Features**

Slow double click on each feature's name and rename them to something more descriptive like: Open-End, Transition-Body, Closed-End, etc...

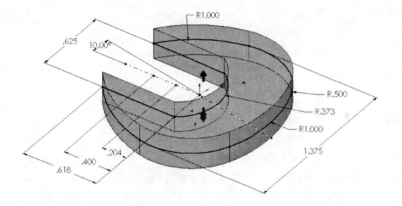

3. Creating the transition sketch:

- Select TOP plane from Feature manager tree.

- Click 📝 or select **Insert / Sketch**.

- Sketch the profile below using Lines 🖊 (Note: only add the fillets after the sketch is fully defined).

- Add dimensions 🔷 or Relations 🔩 as needed.

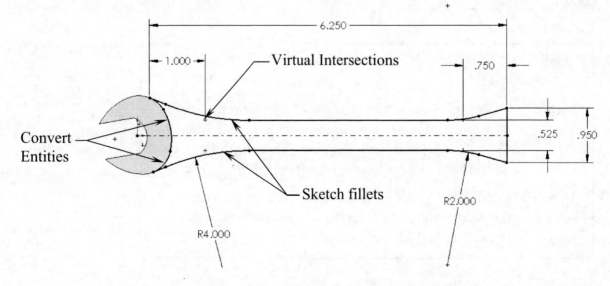

Virtual Intersections

Convert Entities

Sketch fillets

4. Extruding the Transition feature:

- Click  or select **Insert / Boss-Base / Extrude**.

- End Condition: **Mid Plane**

- Extrude Depth: **.175 in**.

- Click **OK** ✅.

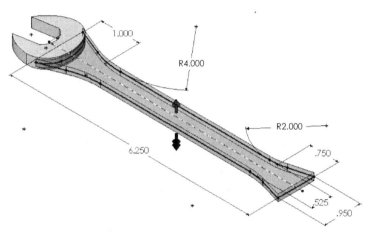

5. Adding the reference geometry:

- Select the face as indicated.

- Click 📝 or select **Insert / Sketch**.

- Sketch a Centerline ⫶ at the mid-point of the two vertical edges.

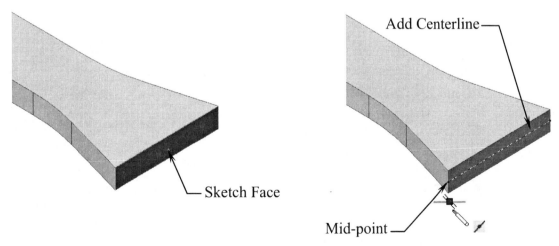

- Exit the Sketch 📝 or select **Insert / Sketch**.

6. Creating a new work plane: Plane at Angle

- Click ⬚ or select **Insert / Reference Geometry / Plane**.

- For Reference Entities ⬚ Select the *Sketch4* (centerline) and the ***upper face*** of the Transition.

- In the **At Angle** dialog, type **10 deg**. (arrow).

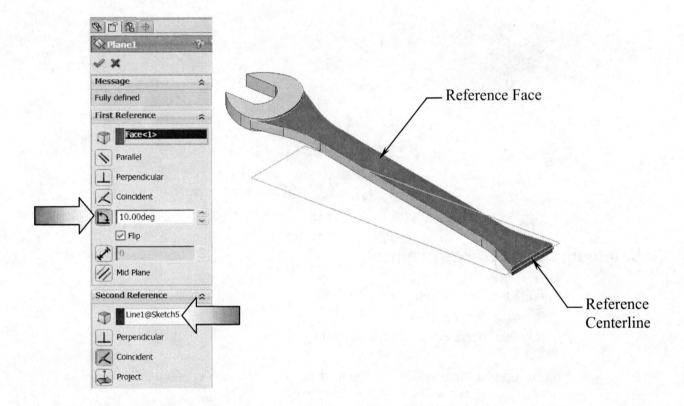

Reference Face

Reference Centerline

- Click **OK** ✓.

- The system creates a plane that starts from the reference face and pivots around the centerline.

- The preview of the new 10 deg. plane.

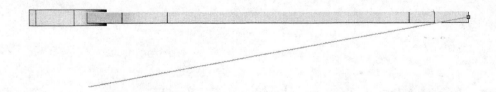

7. Creating the Closed-End sketch:

- Select the new **10° plane** from FeatureManager tree.

- Click 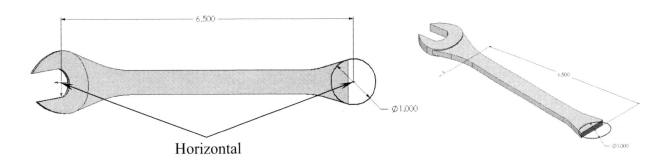 or select **Insert / Sketch**.

- Sketch a circle and add dimensions as shown.

Horizontal

8. Extruding the Closed-end feature:

- Click or select **Insert / Boss-Base / Extrude**.

- **Direction 1:**   **Blind**

- Extrude Depth: **.200 in**.

- **Direction 2:**   **Blind**

- Extrude Depth: **.130 in**.

- Click **OK**.

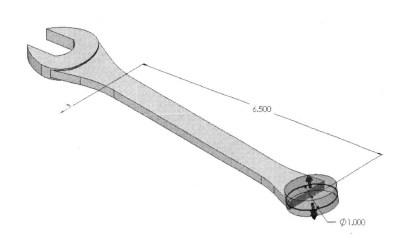

9. Adding a 12-Sided polygon hole:

- Select the face indicated as sketch plane.

- Click 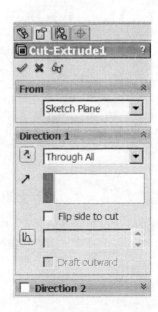 or select **Insert / Sketch**.

- Sketch a Polygon ⬡ with **12 sides** Ⓝ (arrow).

- Add a **.625 Dia.** Dimension to the inside construction circle.

- Add a **Concentric** relation ⊥ as shown.

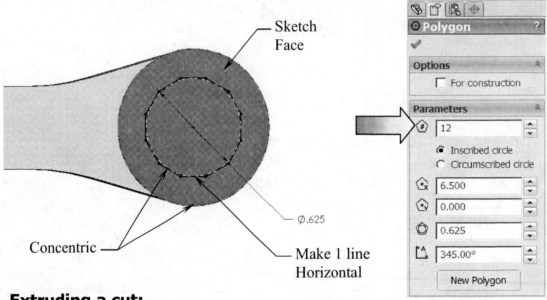

Sketch Face

Ø.625

Concentric

Make 1 line Horizontal

Polygon

Options

☐ For construction

Parameters

⟨#⟩ 12

⦿ Inscribed circle
○ Circumscribed circle

⟨x⟩ 6.500

⟨y⟩ 0.000

⬠ 0.625

345.00°

New Polygon

10. Extruding a cut:

- Click 🔲 or select **Insert / Cut / Extrude**.

- End Condition: **Through All**

- Click **OK** ✓.

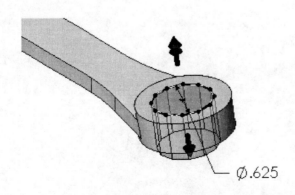

Ø.625

Cut-Extrude1

From

Sketch Plane ▼

Direction 1

Through All ▼

☐ Flip side to cut

☐ Draft outward

☐ **Direction 2**

11. Creating the Recess profile:

- Select the face indicated as sketch plane.

- Click or select **Insert / Sketch**.

- Sketch the profile shown below using Lines ◿ and Tangent Arcs ⊃ .

- Add Dimensions ✐ and Relations ⊥ to fully define the sketch.

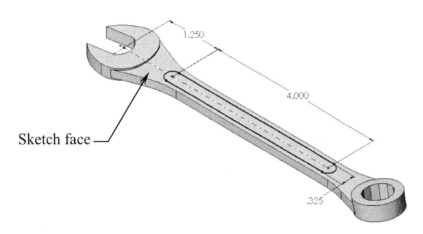

Sketch face

12. Extruding the Recessed feature:

- Click 回 or select **Insert / Cut / Extrude**.

- End Condition: **Blind**

- Extrude Depth: **.030 in**.

- Click **OK** ✅.

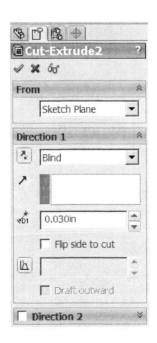

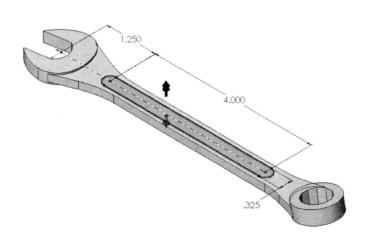

13. Mirroring the Recessed feature:

- Hold down the CONTROL key, then select the TOP reference plane and the Recessed feature from Feature Manager tree.

- Click 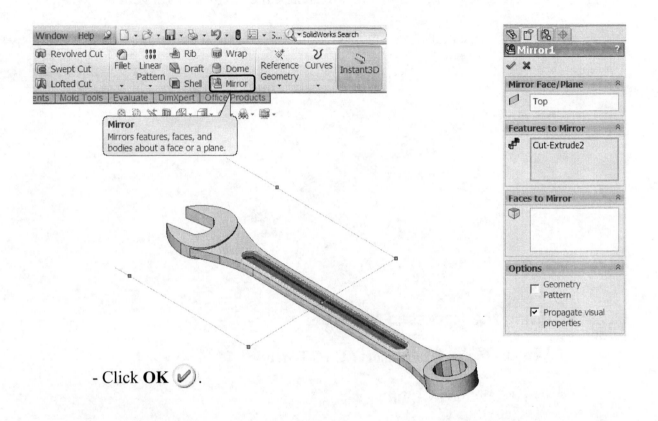 or select **Insert / Pattern Mirror** menu, then select **Mirror**.

- Click **OK** ✅.

- Rotate 🔄 the model to verify the results.

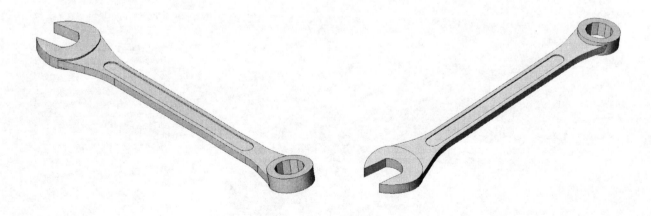

14. Adding the .030" fillets:

- Click 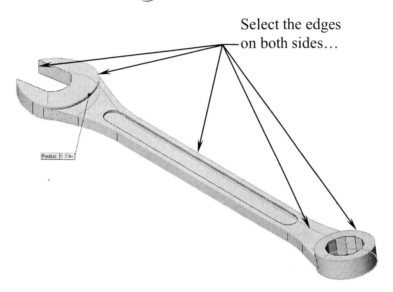 or select **Insert / Features / Fillet/Round**.

- Enter **.030 in**. for Radius.

- Select the edges as shown for Edges to fillet.

- Tangent Propagation: **Enabled**

- Click **OK** .

Select the edges on both sides…

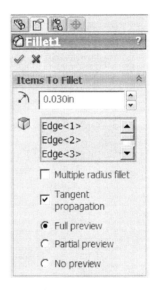

15. Adding the .050" fillets:

- Repeat step 14 and add a **.050"** fillet to the 4 edges shown below.

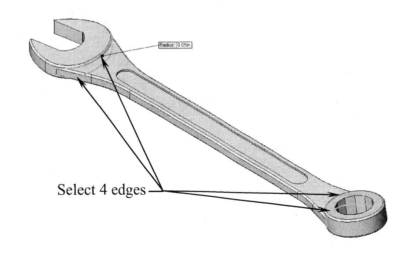

Select 4 edges

16. Adding the .015" fillets:

- Click 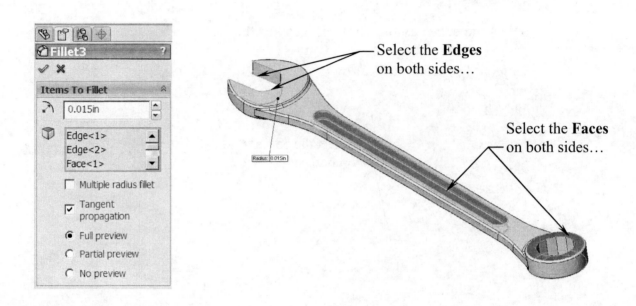 and add a **.015"** fillet to the edges and faces shown below.

Select the **Edges**
on both sides...

Select the **Faces**
on both sides...

- Click **OK** ⊘.

- Verify your fillets with the model shown below.

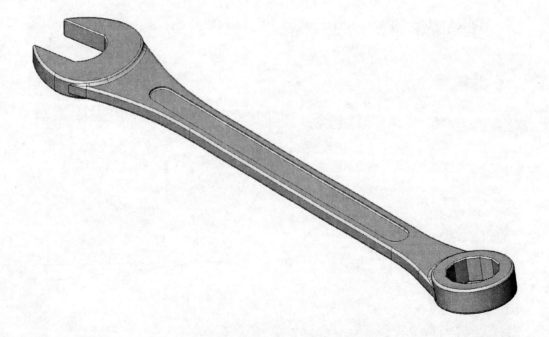

17. Adding text in the recessed area:

- Select the face indicated as sketch plane.

- Click 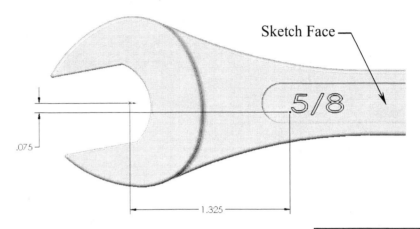 or select **Insert / Sketch**.

- Click and type **5/8** in the text dialog box.

- Add dimensions to position the text.

- Uncheck Use document's font check box .

- Change Width factor to **150%** .

- Leave Spacing at **100%** .

- Font: **Century Gothic** .

- Style: **Regular**.

- Points size: **14 pt**.

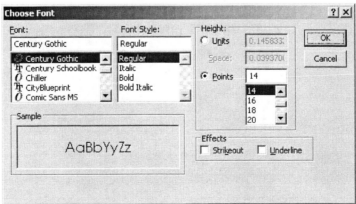

18. Extruding the text:

- Click 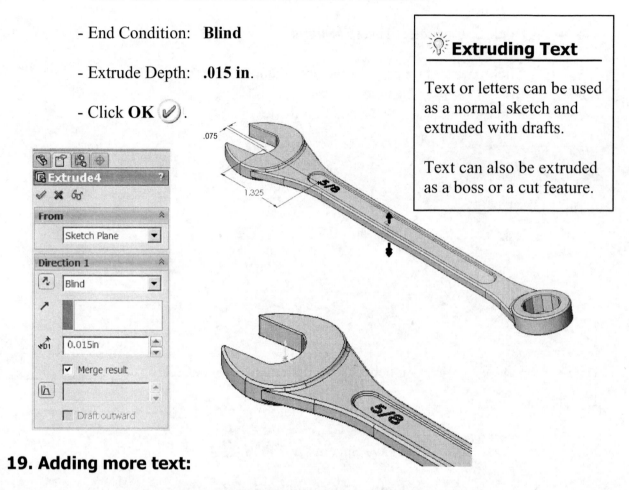 or select **Insert / Boss-Base / Extrude**.

- End Condition: **Blind**

- Extrude Depth: **.015 in**.

- Click **OK**.

> 💡 **Extruding Text**
>
> Text or letters can be used as a normal sketch and extruded with drafts.
>
> Text can also be extruded as a boss or a cut feature.

19. Adding more text:

- Select the indicated face as sketch plane.

- Click or select **Insert / Sketch**.

- Click and type SPANNER in the Text dialog box.

- Add dimensions to fully position the text.

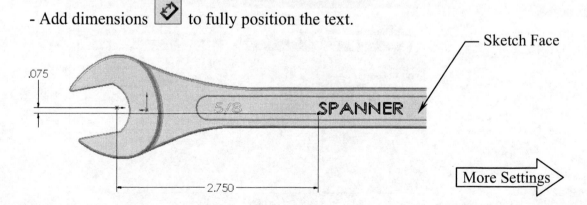

— Sketch Face

.075

2.750

More Settings

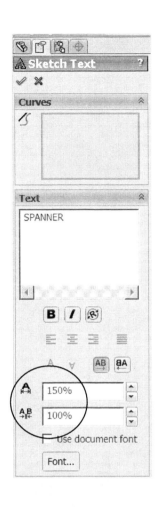

- Uncheck Use document's font check box ☐ Use document's font .

- Change Width factor to **150%** [A] .

- Leave Spacing at **100%** [AB] .

- Font: **Century Gothic** [Font...] .

- Style: **Regular**.

- Points size: **14 pt**.

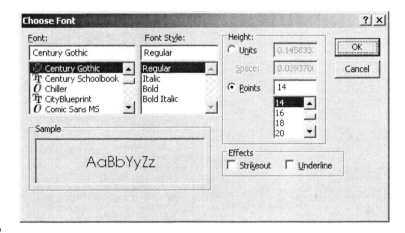

20. Extruding the text:

- Click [icon] or select **Insert / Boss-base / Extrude**.

- End Condition: **Blind**

- Extrude Depth: **.015 in**.

- Click **OK** ✓.

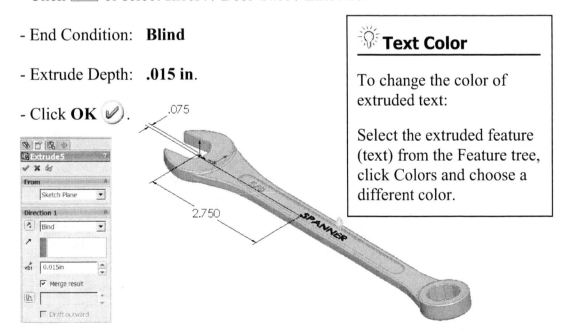

.075

2.750

💡 Text Color

To change the color of extruded text:

Select the extruded feature (text) from the Feature tree, click Colors and choose a different color.

21. Saving your work:

- Select **File** / **Save as** / **Spanner** / **Save**.

22. Optional:

- Repeat step 17 through 20 to add text to the other side of the part.

Questions for Review

Advanced Modeling

1. The Min / Max conditions can be selected from the dimensions properties, under the Leaders tab.
   - a. True
   - b. False

2. The Mid-Plane extrude type protrudes the sketch profile to both directions equally.
   - a. True
   - b. False

3. It is sufficient to create a plane at angle with a surface and an angular dimension.
   - a. True
   - b. False

4. When sketching a polygon, the number of sides can be changed on the Properties tree.
   - a. True
   - b. False

5. A 3D solid feature can be mirrored using a centerline as the center of mirror.
   - a. True
   - b. False

6. Text cannot be used to extrude as a boss or a cut feature.
   - a. True
   - b. False

7. Extruded text can be mirrored just like any other 3D features.
   - a. True
   - b. False

8. Text in a sketch can be extruded with drafts, inward or outward.
   - a. True
   - b. False

7. TRUE   8. TRUE
5. FALSE   6. FALSE
3. FALSE   4. TRUE
1. TRUE   2. TRUE

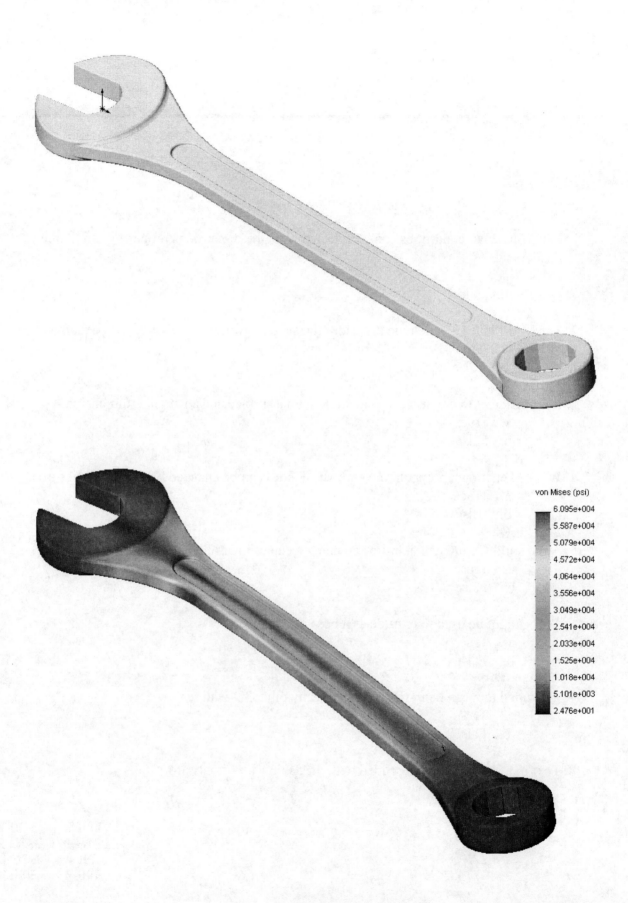

von Mises (psi)

6.095e+004
5.587e+004
5.079e+004
4.572e+004
4.064e+004
3.556e+004
3.049e+004
2.541e+004
2.033e+004
1.525e+004
1.018e+004
5.101e+003
2.476e+001

CHAPTER 4

Sweep with Composite Curves

Sweep Ⓖ with Composite Curves

Unlike extruded or revolved shapes, the sweep option offers a more advanced way of creating complex geometry, where a single profile can be swept along 2D guide paths or 3D curves to define the shape.

One of the easier methods of creating a swept feature is to create the Sweep Path first and a single closed sketch Profile after.

The Profile will be related to the Sweep Path with the PIERCE relations.

When the Profile is swept, the Sweep Path and (Guide Curves) help control the shape and its behaviors such as twisting, tangencies, etc.

The Composite Curve 🗠 option allows multiple sketches or model edges to be jointed into one continuous path for use in sweep features.

This lesson will guide you through the creation of a helical extension spring; where several 2D sketches will get combined with a 3D helix to create one continuous curves.

This curve is called: **Composite Curve**.

Helical Extension Spring
Sweep with Composite Curves

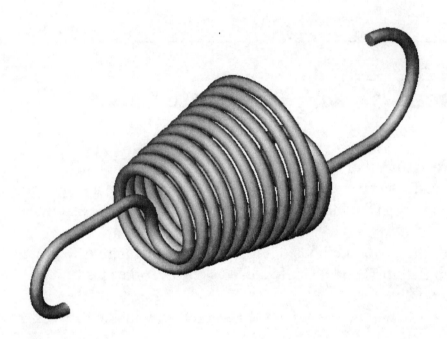

Dimensioning Standards: **ANSI**
Units: **INCHES** – 3 Decimals

Tools Needed:

🖉	Insert Sketch	╲	Line	⊕	Circle
⊃	Tangent Arc	⌂	3 Point Arc	⊥	Add Geometric Relations
◇	Dimension	⌐	Composite Curve	�G	Sweep

1. Sketching the first profile:

- Select the **FRONT** plane from the FeatureManager Tree.

- Click 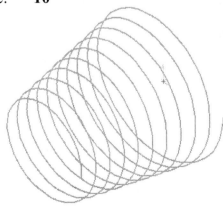 or **Insert / Sketch**.

- Sketch a circle ⊕ and dimension �️ as shown:

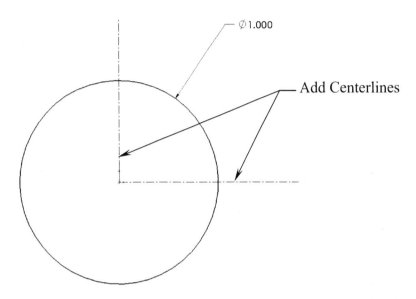

∅1.000

Add Centerlines

2. Converting the circle into a Helix (the sweep path):

- Select **Insert / Curve / Helix / Spiral**.

Defined by:	**Pitch and Revolution**
Pitch:	**.100**
Revolution:	**10**
Starting angle:	**0°**
Taper helix:	**Enabled**
Taper angle:	**10°**

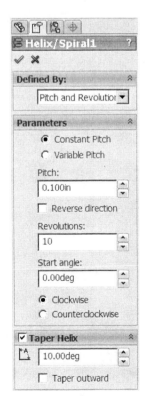

- Click **OK** ✅.

3. Creating a 2-degree plane:

- Show the previous sketch (Sketch1).

- Click or select **Insert/Reference Geometry/ Plane**.

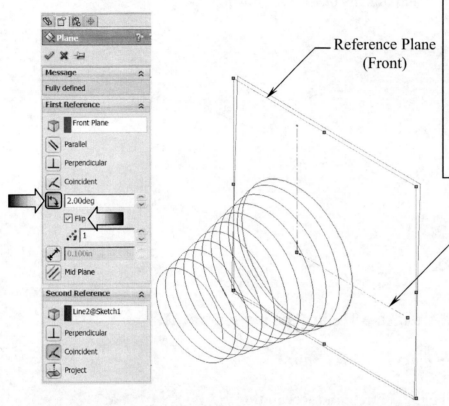

Reference Plane (Front)

Pivot Line

- Select the **Horizontal Centerline** as Pivot Line.

- Select **Plane at Angle** option.

- Enter **2.00deg**. for Angle.

- Enable the **Flip** option.

(Make sure the new plane

leans to the right).

- Click **OK** ✅.

- Hide the Sketch1.

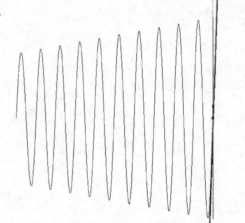

Plane1

2° Plane

4. Sketching the large loop:

- Select the **Plane1** from the Feature Manager Tree.

- Click [icon] or select **Insert / Sketch**.

- Sketch a 3-point Arc [icon] and add dimension as shown:

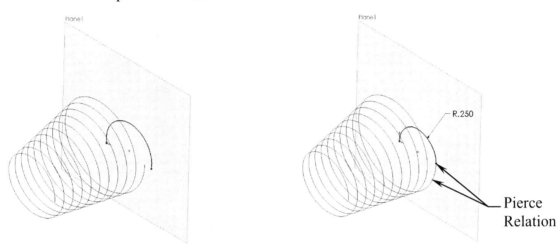

- Add a **Pierce** relation between the end point of the Arc and the Helix.

- Exit the sketch [icon] or select **Insert / Sketch**.

5. Sketching the large hook:

- Select the **RIGHT** plane from the FeatureManager Tree.

- Click [icon] or select **Insert / Sketch**.

- Sketch the profile and add Dimension and Relations as shown below:

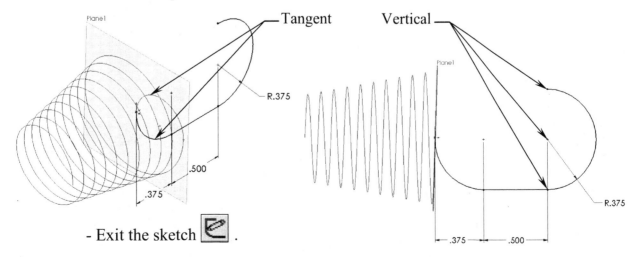

- Exit the sketch [icon] .

6. Creating a new plane for the small loop:

- Select the **Plane1** from the FeatureManager Tree.

- Click 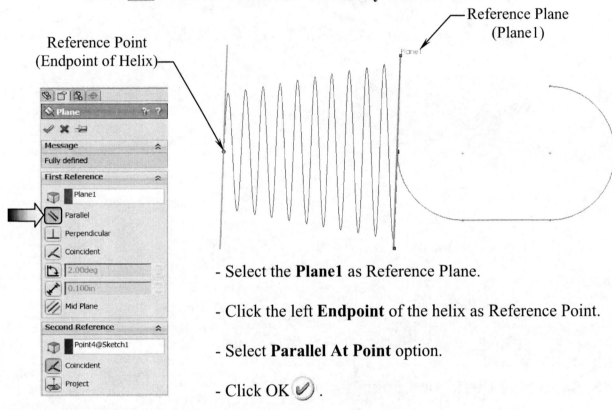 or **Insert / Reference Geometry / Plane**.

- Select the **Plane1** as Reference Plane.

- Click the left **Endpoint** of the helix as Reference Point.

- Select **Parallel At Point** option.

- Click OK.

7. Adding the small loop:

- Select the new plane (**Plane2**) from the Feature Manager Tree.

- Click 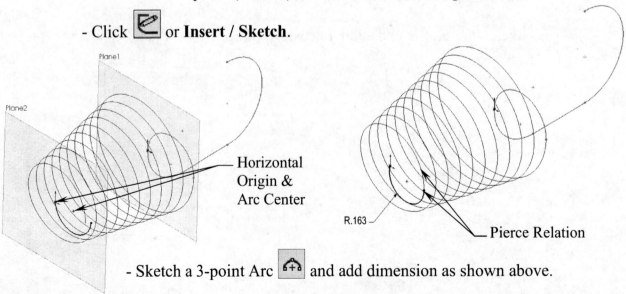 or **Insert / Sketch**.

- Sketch a 3-point Arc and add dimension as shown above.

- Add a **Pierce** relation 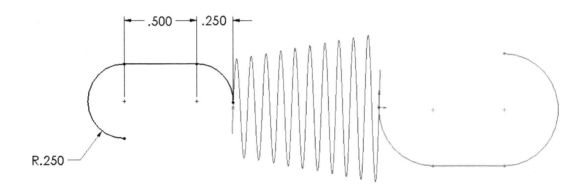 between the endpoint of the Arc and the Helix.

- Exit the sketch or **Insert / Sketch**.

8. Creating a small hook:

- Select the **RIGHT** plane from the FeatureManager Tree.

- Click or **Insert / Sketch**.

- Sketch the profile and add dimensions as shown.

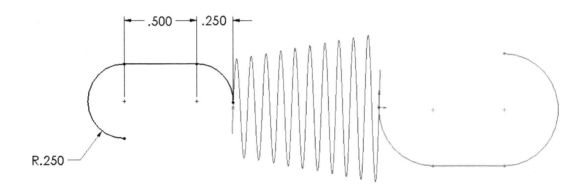

- Add the relations Vertical and Tangent to the indicated entities.

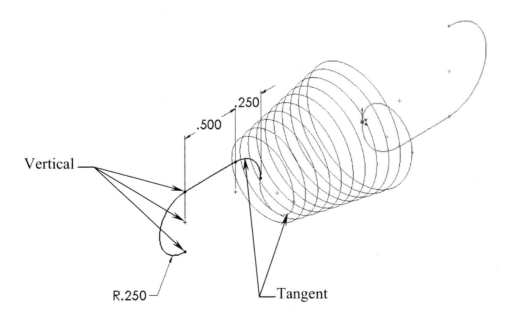

- Exit the sketch or Click **Insert / Sketch**.

9. Combining all sketches into one, using Composite Curve option:

- Click 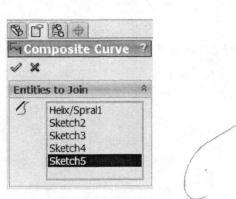 or **Insert / Curve / Composite**.

- Select all sketches as indicated.

- Click **OK** ✅.

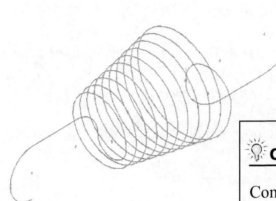

> 💡 **Composite Curve**
>
> Composite Curve option allows multiple sketches or model edges to be jointed into one continuous path for use in sweep features.

10. Creating a perpendicular plane:

- Click 🗙 or **Insert / Reference Geometry / Plane**.

- Click the edge and the endpoint as noted.

- Select **Normal to Curve** option (arrow).

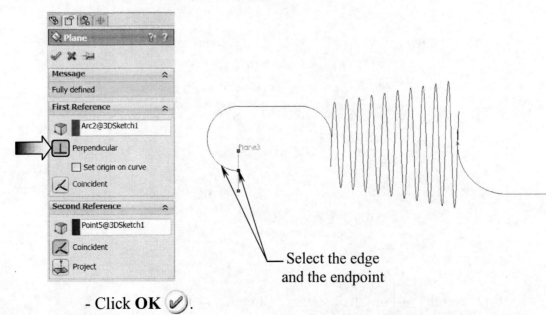

Select the edge and the endpoint

- Click **OK** ✅.

11. Sketching the sweep profile (wire diameter):

- Select the new plane (**Plane3**) from the Feature Manager Tree.

- Click  or **Insert / Sketch**.

- Sketch a circle at the end of the hook.

- Add a **Piece** Relation to fully define the sketch.

- Exit the sketch or **Insert / Sketch**.

Pierce
relation

Ø.080

12. Sweeping the profile along the path:

- Click or **Insert / Boss-Base / Sweep**.

- Select the small circle as sweep profile .

- Select the composite curve as sweep path .

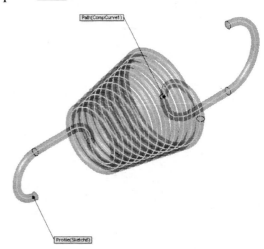

- Click **OK** .

13. Saving your work:

- Click **File / Save As / Helical Extension Spring / Save**.

<u>Other Examples:</u>

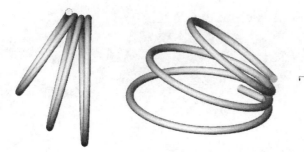

<u>Conical Spring</u>

<u>V-Shaped</u>

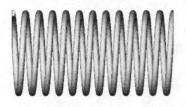

<u>Ground-End</u>

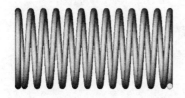

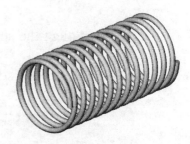

<u>Closed-End</u>

<u>Expanded</u>

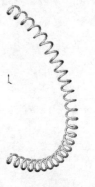

Questions for Review

Sweep with Composite Curve

1. Beside Pitch and Revolution, a helix can be defined with Pitch and Height.
    a.   True
    b.   False

2. It is sufficient to create an Offset Distance plane using a reference plane and a distance.
    a.   True
    b.   False

3. The sweep profile should have a Pierce relation with the sweep path.
    a. True
    b. False

4. Several sketches or model edges can be combined to make a Composite curve.
    a. True
    b. False

5. A Composite curve cannot be used as a sweep path.
    a. True
    b. False

6. The system allows multiple sweep paths and only one guide curve when creating a
   a swept feature.
    a. True
    b. False

7. In a sweep feature, the system allows only one sweep path, but multiple guide curves
   can be used.
    a. True
    b. False

8. Several sketch profiles can be used to sweep along a path.
    a. True
    b. False

7. TRUE   8. FALSE
5. FALSE   6. FALSE
3. TRUE   4. TRUE
1. TRUE   2. TRUE

Exercise: Circular Spring - Expanded

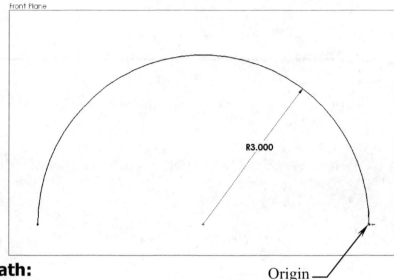

1. Sketching the Sweep Path:

- Select the FRONT plane and open a new sketch.

- Sketch an Arc as shown and add dimensions and relations needed to fully define the sketch.

- EXIT the sketch.

2. Sketching the Sweep Profile:

- Select the RIGHT plane and open a new sketch.

- Sketch a Horizontal line towards the right.

- Add a **.250 in**. dimension.

- EXIT the sketch.

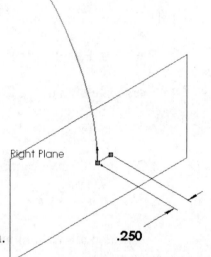

3. Creating a Swept Surface: (Surface)

- Click 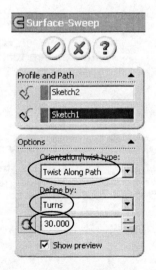 or select **Insert / Surface / Sweep**.

- Select the **Horizontal-Line** for use as the Sweep Profile.

- Select the **Arc** as the Sweep Path.

- Expand the **OPTIONS** dialog box.

- Select **Twist Along Path**, under Orientation / Twist Type.

- For Define By: Select **TURNS**.

- For number of Turns: Enter **30**.

- Click **OK** ✅.

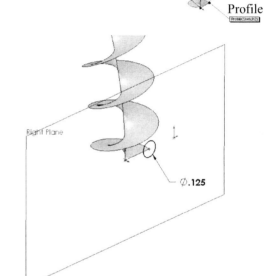

4. Sketching the Wire-Diameter:

- Select the RIGHT plane and open a new sketch.

- Sketch a Circle at the right end of the swept surface.

- Add a **Ø.125 in**. dimensions.

- **EXIT** the sketch.

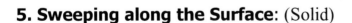

5. Sweeping along the Surface: (Solid)

- Click 🔁 or select **Insert / Bose-Base / Sweep**.

- Select the **Circle** for use as the Sweep Profile.

- For Sweep Path, select the **Edge** of the Swept-Surface.

- Click **OK** ✅.

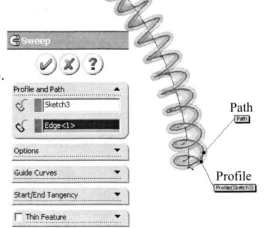

6. Hide the Swept-Surface:

- Right click over the Swept-Surface

and select HIDE 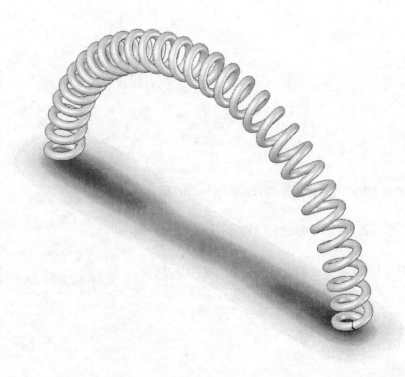 .

Right click
& HIDE.

7. Save your work:

- Select **File / Save As.**

- For file name, enter **Expanded Circular Spring.**

- Click **Save**.

CHAPTER 4 (cont.)

Sweep with Composite Curve

Sweep  with Composite Curve

- In a Sweep feature, there is only one Sweep Profile, one Sweep Path, and one or more Guide Curves.

- The Sweep Profile describes the feature's cross-section.

- The Sweep Path controls the twisting and how the Sweep Profile moves along the path.

- The Sweep path can be a 2D or 3D sketch, the edges of the part, or a Composite Curve.

- The Composite Curve option allows users to combine 2D or 3D curves, sketch geometry, and model edges into a single curve.

- The Composite Curves are used as Guide Curves when creating a loft or a sweep.

- The Guide Curves will be further discussed in the next chapter.

- This chapter focuses on the creation of a multiple pitch, closed-end spring, and composite curves. Even though the same part cam be made easily with the Variable Pitch option, but instead, we will use a slightly different method to help focus on the use of the Composite Curve command.

Multi-Pitch Spring with Closed Ends
Sweep with Composite Curve

Dimensioning Standards: **ANSI**	
Units: **INCHES** – 3 Decimals	

Tools Needed:

 Insert Sketch

 Plane

 Dimension

 Add Geometric Relations

Composite Curve

Base/Boss Sweep

1. Creating new work planes:

- Click or select **Insert / Reference Geometry / Planes.**

- Select **Offset Distance**; use the FRONT reference plane and create 2 new planes as shown below.

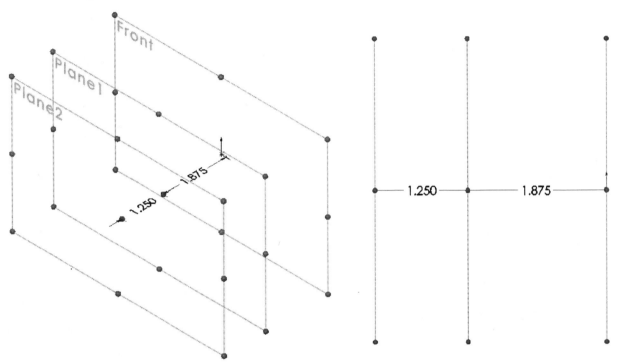

2. Creating the 1ˢᵗ helix:

- Select the FRONT plane and open a sketch or select **Insert / Sketch.**

- Sketch a Circle from the Origin and add a **Ø1.00"** dimension.

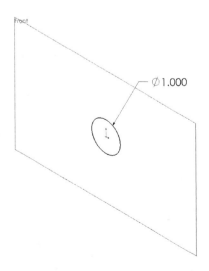

- Select **Insert / Curve / Helix-Spiral**.

- Enter the following parameters:

Pitch:	**.375 in**.
Revolution:	**5**
Starting Angle:	**0 deg**.
Clockwise.	

- Click **OK** 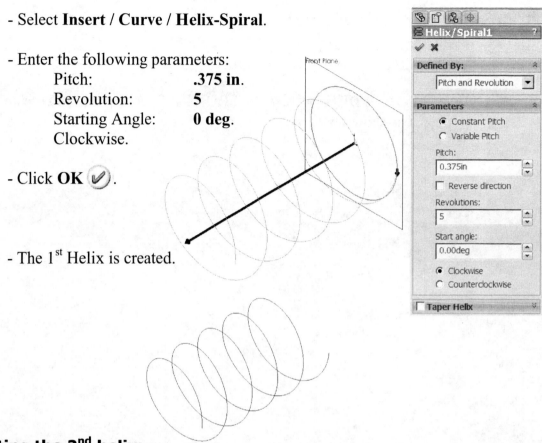.

- The 1ˢᵗ Helix is created.

3. Creating the 2ⁿᵈ helix:

- Open a new sketch on the FRONT plane or select **Insert / Sketch.**

- Sketch a Circle ⊕ starting at the Origin and add a **Ø1.00"** dimension .

(Note: Convert the previous sketch to link the two diameters automatically).

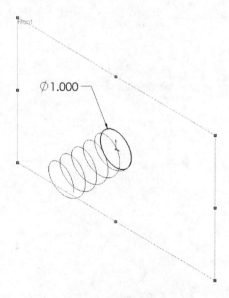

- Select **Insert / Curve / Helix-Spiral.**

- Enter the following parameters:
    Pitch: **.115 in**.
    Revolution: **1.5**
    Starting Angle: **0 deg**.
    Reverse Direction: **Enabled**.
    Counter Clockwise.

- Click **OK** .

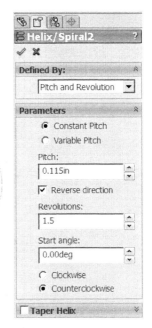

- The 2nd Helix is created.

4. Creating the 3rd helix:

- Select the PLANE1 from the FeatureManager tree and open a new sketch .

- Sketch a new Circle ⊕ starting at the Origin.

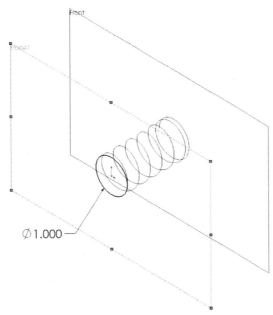

Ø 1.000

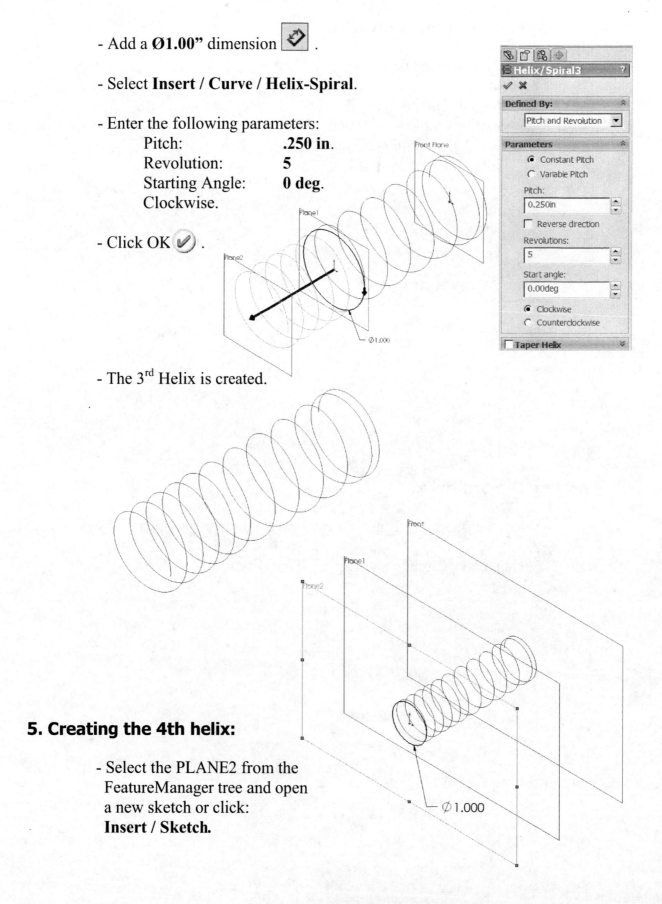

- Add a Ø**1.00"** dimension .

- Select **Insert / Curve / Helix-Spiral**.

- Enter the following parameters:
  Pitch: **.250 in**.
  Revolution: **5**
  Starting Angle: **0 deg**.
  Clockwise.

- Click OK .

- The 3rd Helix is created.

5. Creating the 4th helix:

- Select the PLANE2 from the
  FeatureManager tree and open
  a new sketch or click:
  Insert / Sketch.

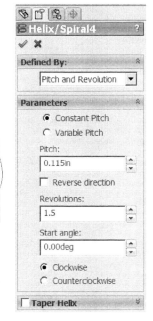

- Sketch a Circle 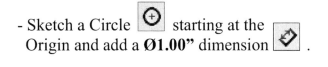 starting at the
  Origin and add a **Ø1.00"** dimension [icon] .

- Select **Insert / Curve / Helix-Spiral.**

- Enter the following parameters:
    Pitch: **.115 in**.
    Revolution: **1.5**
    Starting Angle: **0 deg**.
    Clockwise.

- Click **OK** [icon].

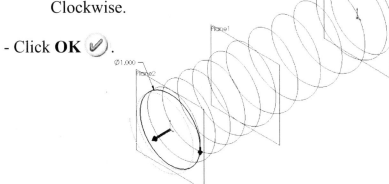

- The 4th Helix is created.

5. Combining the helixes into one continuous curve:

- Click [icon] on the Curves toolbar or
  select **Insert / Curve / Composite.**

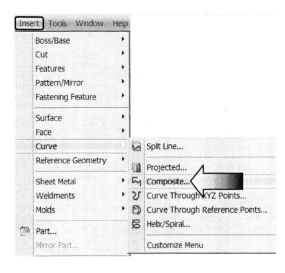

- Select the 4 helixes from the Graphics area.

- Click **OK** .

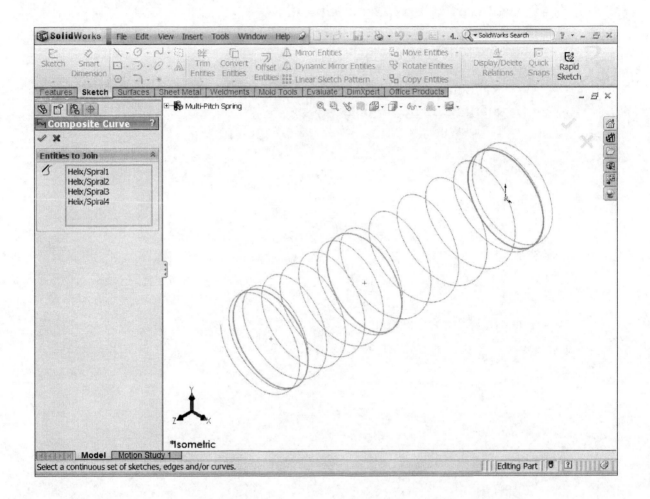

- A Composite Curve is created.

NOTE:

If the composite curve fails, check the start angle of each helix, they must start or end at the exact same location.

7. Sketch the Sweep Profile:

- Select the TOP reference plane from Feature Manager tree and open a new sketch 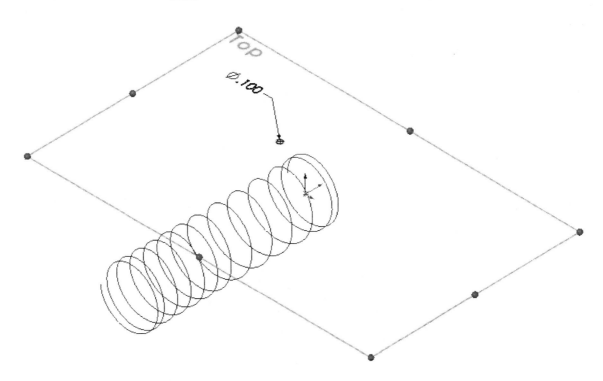.

- Sketch a Circle ⊕ and add a Ø.100" dimension ◇ .

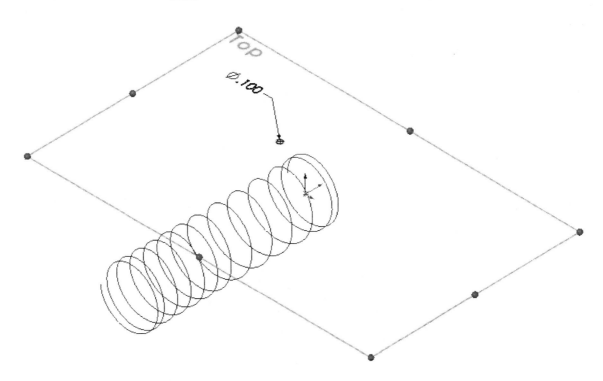

- Add a PIERCE relation between the Center of the circle and the composite-curve.

PIERCE Relation

Ø.100

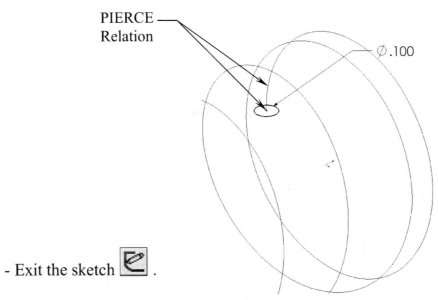

- Exit the sketch .

8. Sweep the Profile along the Composite Curve:

- Click 🔲 or select **Insert / Boss-Base / Sweep.**

- Select the small circle for use as Sweep Profile 🔲 .

- Select the Composite Curve as Sweep Path 🔲 .

- Click **OK** 🔲 .

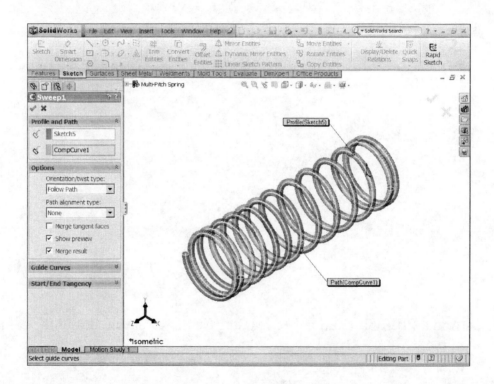

9. Saving your:

- Click **File / Save As / Multi-Pitch Spring / Save.**

Note: To add the Flat ground ends, simply sketch a pair of rectangles on both ends and extrude a Though All cut using both Direction 1 and Direction 2.

Questions for Review

Sweep w/Composite Curve

1. Multiple Sweep Profiles can be used in a sweep feature.
    a. True
    b. False

2. Multiple Sweep Paths can be used in a sweep feature.
    a. True
    b. False

3. Only one Sweep Profile and one Sweep Path can be used in a sweep.
    a. True
    b. False

4. A Helix can be defined by:
    a. Pitch and Revolution
    b. Height and Revolution
    c. Height and Pitch
    d. Spiral
    e. All of the above

5. Several connected Helixes can be combined into one single Composite Curve.
    a. True
    b. False

6. The Sweep Profile sketch should be related to the Sweep Path using the relation:
    a. Perpendicular
    b. Parallel
    c. Coincident
    d. Pierce

7. The Sweep Path controls the twisting and how the Sweep Profile moves along it.
    a. True
    b. False

8. The Edges of the part can also be used as the Sweep Path.
    a. True
    b. False

7. TRUE   8. TRUE
5. TRUE   6. D
4. E
3. TRUE
1. FLASE   2. FLASE

Exercise: Projected Curve & Composite Curve

1. Create the part based on the drawing as shown.
2. Dimensions are in inches, 3 decimal.
3. Focus on Projected Curve & Composite Curve options.

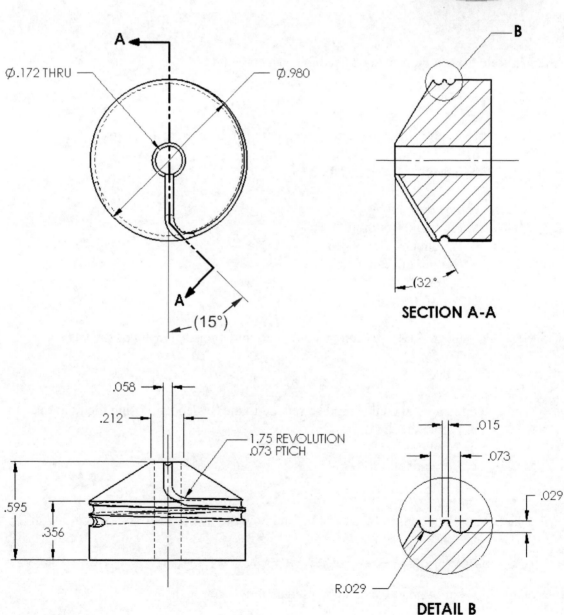

A
A

Ø.172 THRU
Ø.980

(15°)

B

SECTION A-A

(32°)

.058
.212

1.75 REVOLUTION
.073 PTICH

.595
.356

.015
.073
.029

R.029

DETAIL B

4. Save your work as: **Sweep with Composite Curve Exe.**

CHAPTER 5

Sweep & Loft

Advanced Modeling - Sweep vs. Loft

* The Sweep option creates a solid, a thin, or a surface feature by moving a single closed sketch profile along a path and guided with one or more guide curve(s).

* In order to create a sweep feature properly, a set of rules should be taken into consideration:

- o The Sweep option uses only one sketch profile, and it must be closed and non-intersecting contour to make a **solid** feature.
- o The sketch profile can be either closed or open for a **surface** feature.
- o Only one path, and it can be open or closed.
- o One or more guide-curves can be used to guide the sketch profile.
- o The sketch profile must be drawn on a new plane starting at the end point of the path.

---

* The Loft option creates a solid, a thin, or a surface feature by making transition between the sketch profiles.

* Keep in mind the following requirements with creating a loft feature:

- o The Loft option uses multiple sketch profiles, and they must be closed, and non-intersecting, to make a **solid** feature.
- o The sketch profiles can be either closed or open, for a **surface** feature.
- o Use the Centerline Parameter option to guide the profiles from the inside.
- o Use Guide Curves option to guide the sketch profiles from the outside.
- o The Guide Curves can be either a 2D or a 3D sketch.

Water Pump Housing
Advanced Modeling - Sweep & Loft

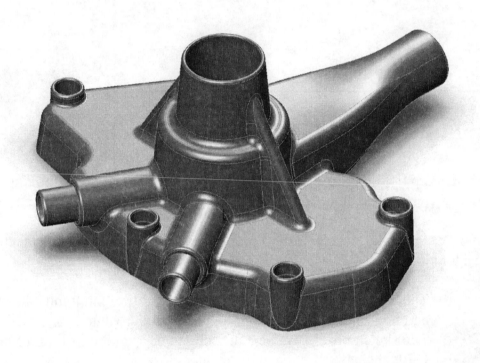

| Dimensioning Standards: **ANSI** |
| Units: **INCHES** – 3 Decimals |

Tools Needed:

Insert Sketch	Split Entities	Add Geometric Relations
Rib	Plane	Revolved Boss/Base
Extruded Boss/Base	Swept Boss/Base	Lofted Boss/Base

Understanding the Draft Options

- Drafts are normally required in most plastic injection molded parts to ensure proper part removal from the mold halves.
- The Draft option in SolidWorks adds tapers to the faces using the angles specified by the user.
- Drafts can be inserted in an existing part or added to a feature While being extruded.
- Drafts can be applied to solid parts as well as the surface models.
- There are several types of draft available:

  * Neutral Plane
  * Parting Line
  * Step Draft

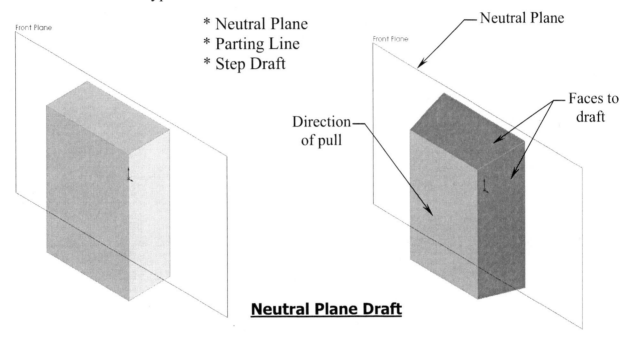

Neutral Plane Draft

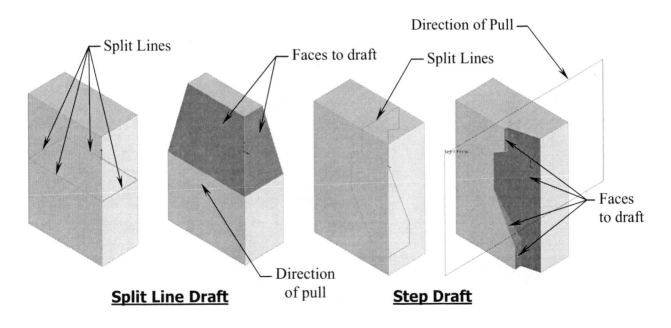

Split Line Draft   **Step Draft**

1. Creating the base Sketch: (or open a copy from the Training CD)

- Select the TOP plane and open a new sketch 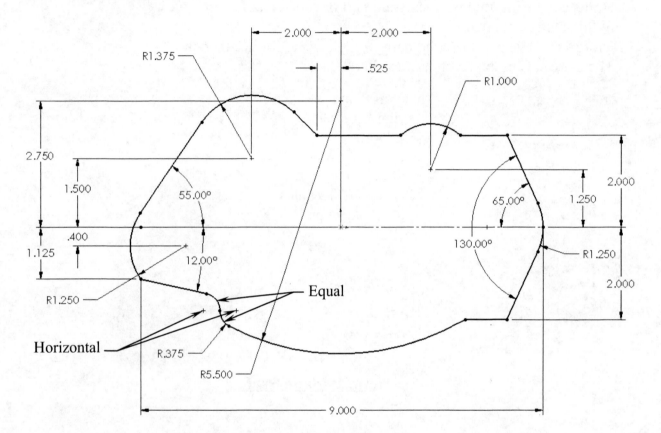.

- Sketch the profile as shown below; add dimensions and relations to fully define the sketch.

2. Extruding the Base:

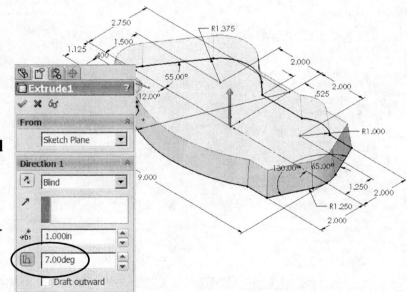

- Click **Extruded Boss/Base.**

- End Condition: **Blind**

- Depth: **1.00 in.**

- Draft: **7 deg. inward.**

- Click **OK** ✅.

3. Sketching the upper Inlet Port:

- Select the FRONT plane and open a new sketch.

- Sketch the profile as shown.

- Add the dimensions and relations as indicated.

- Add a vertical Centerline from the Origin and use as the center of the revolve in the next step.

Virtual Diameter: measured from the centerline to the endpoint of the line.

Parallel

Ø1.750

1.500

1.500

5.00°

Ø3.000

4. Revolving the upper Inlet Port:

- Click **Revolve Boss/Base** or select: **Insert / Features / Boss-Base / Revolve** from the drop down menus.

- Revolve **One Direction**.

- Revolve Angle: **360 deg**.

- Click **OK**.

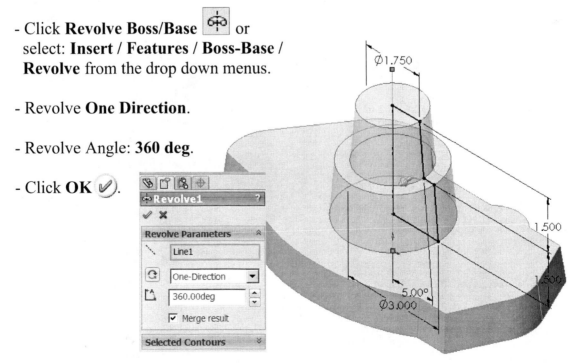

Revolve1

Revolve Parameters

Line1

One-Direction

360.00deg

☑ Merge result

Selected Contours

Ø1.750

1.500

5.00°

Ø3.000

1.500

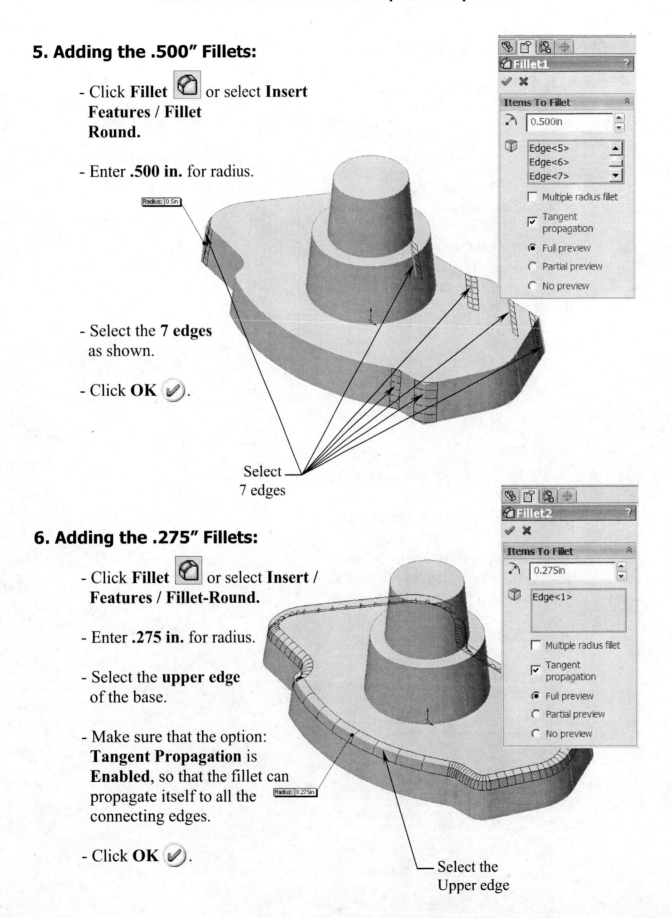

5. Adding the .500" Fillets:

- Click **Fillet** or select **Insert Features / Fillet Round.**

- Enter **.500 in.** for radius.

- Select the **7 edges** as shown.

- Click **OK**.

Select 7 edges

6. Adding the .275" Fillets:

- Click **Fillet** or select **Insert / Features / Fillet-Round.**

- Enter **.275 in.** for radius.

- Select the **upper edge** of the base.

- Make sure that the option: **Tangent Propagation** is **Enabled,** so that the fillet can propagate itself to all the connecting edges.

- Click **OK**.

Select the Upper edge

7. Creating the 1st Offset-Distance Plane:

- Click **Plane** ⬙ or select **Insert / Reference Geometry / Plane.**

- From the Flyout Feature-Manager tree, select the **FRONT** plane to offset from.

- Enter **3.000 in**. for distance.

- Place the new plane on the right side.

- Click **OK** ✅.

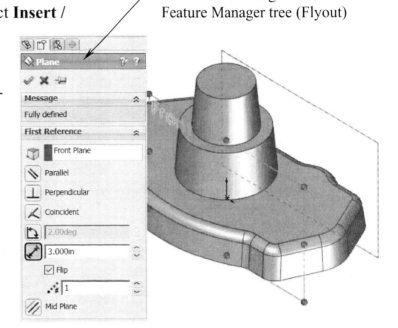

Click here to bring out the Feature Manager tree (Flyout)

8. Creating the 2nd Offset-Distance Plane:

- Click **Plane** ⬙ or select **Insert / Reference Geometry / Plane.**

- Select the **FRONT** plane again from the Flyout FeatureManager tree to offset from.

- Enter **5.000 in**. for Offset distance.

- Place the new plane also on the right side.

- Click **OK** ✅.

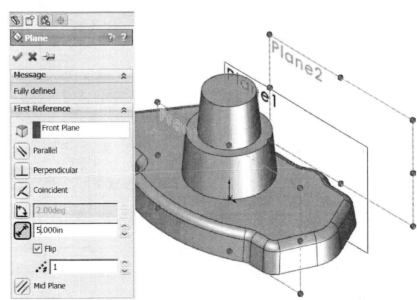

9. Creating the 3rd Offset-Distance Plane:

- Click **Plane** ⬦ or select **Insert / Reference Geometry / Plane.**

- Select the **FRONT** plane once again from the Flyout Feature Manager tree to offset from.

- Enter **6.000 in**. for offset distance.

- Place the new plane also on the right side.

- Click **OK** ✅.

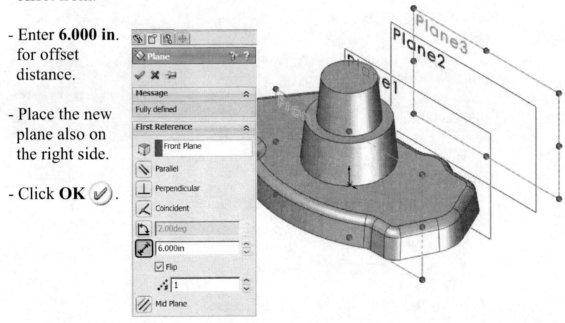

10. Sketching the 1st loft profile of the side Outlet Port:

- Select the **FRONT** plane and open a new sketch ✏️ .

- Sketch a Rectangle ☐ that's just **.125 in**. above the bottom edge of the part.

- Add the dimensions and relations as shown to fully define the sketch.

- *Exit the sketch.*

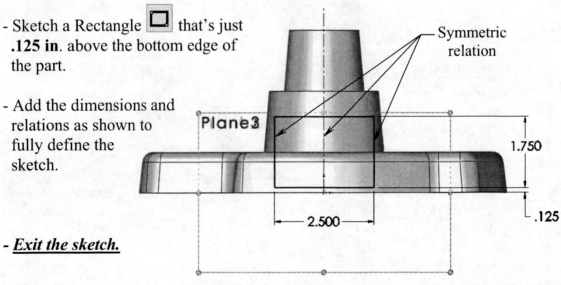

11. Sketching the 2nd loft profile of the side Outlet Port:

- Select **PLANE1** and open a new sketch 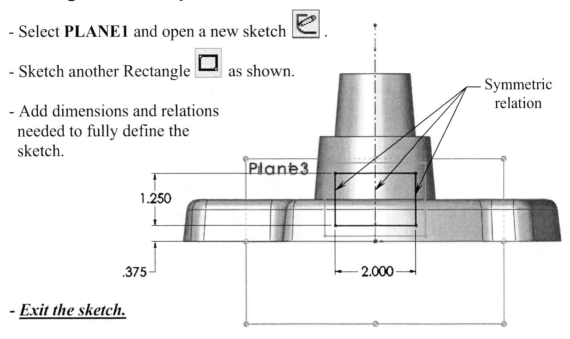.

- Sketch another Rectangle as shown.

- Add dimensions and relations needed to fully define the sketch.

Symmetric relation

Plane3

1.250

.375

2.000

- ***Exit the sketch.***

12. Sketching the 3rd loft profile of the side Outlet Port:

- Select **PLANE2** and open a new sketch .

- Sketch a Circle just above the Origin as shown below.

- Use the **Split-Entities** command and split the circle into **4 segments**.

- Add Vertical and Horizontal relations between the split points.

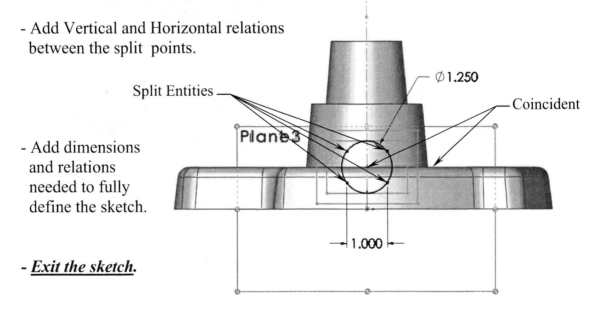

Split Entities

Ø1.250

Coincident

Plane3

- Add dimensions and relations needed to fully define the sketch.

1.000

- ***Exit the sketch.***

13. Sketching the 4th loft profile of the side Outlet Port:

- Select **PLANE3** and open a new sketch 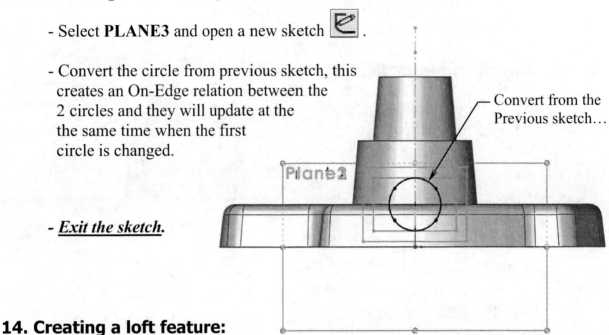.

- Convert the circle from previous sketch, this creates an On-Edge relation between the 2 circles and they will update at the the same time when the first circle is changed.

Convert from the Previous sketch...

- *Exit the sketch.*

14. Creating a loft feature:

- Click Loft or select: **Insert / Boss-Base / Loft** from the drop down menus.

- Select the 4 sketch profiles in the graphics area.

(Since there are no guide Curves to help control the loft, the profiles should be selected from the same side each time to prevent them from twisting.)

Select the 4 sketch profiles, from the same connecting points...

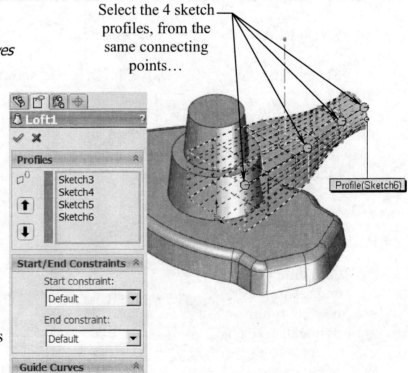

- For clarity, right click on the yellow shaded area and select one of the following options:

  * Transparent
  * Opaque
  * Clear Mesh Faces

- Click **OK**.

15. Creating the mounting bosses:

- Select the **Bottom Face** and open a new sketch.

- Sketch **5 Circles**  as shown.

- Avoid the hidden entities.

- Add a **Tangent** relation for each circle, to the outer edge of the part.

- Add an **Equal** relation to all 5 circles.

- Add dimensions to fully position the 5 circles.

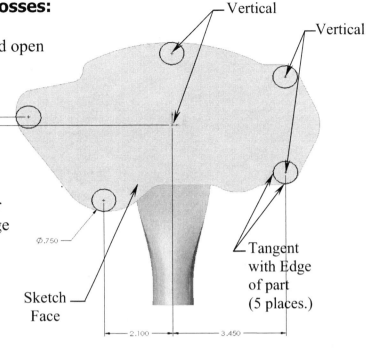

Vertical

Vertical

.275

Ø.750

Sketch Face

Tangent with Edge of part (5 places.)

2.100   3.450

16. Extruding the 5 mounting bosses:

- Click **Extrude Boss-Base** or select: **Insert / Extrude / Boss-Base**, from the drop down menus.

- Set the following:

- End Condition: **Blind**

- Depth: **1.250 in**.

- Draft: **1 deg. Inward.**

- Click **OK** .

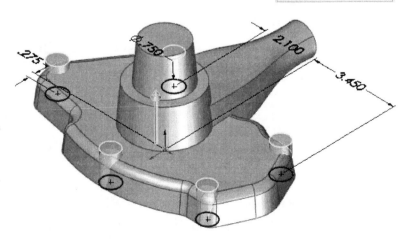

17. Sketching the rear Inlet Port:

- Select the **Upper Face** and open a new sketch.

- Sketch the profile of the Inlet at a 30° angle, one end of the profile is locked to the Origin.

- Add dimensions and other relations to fully position the sketch.

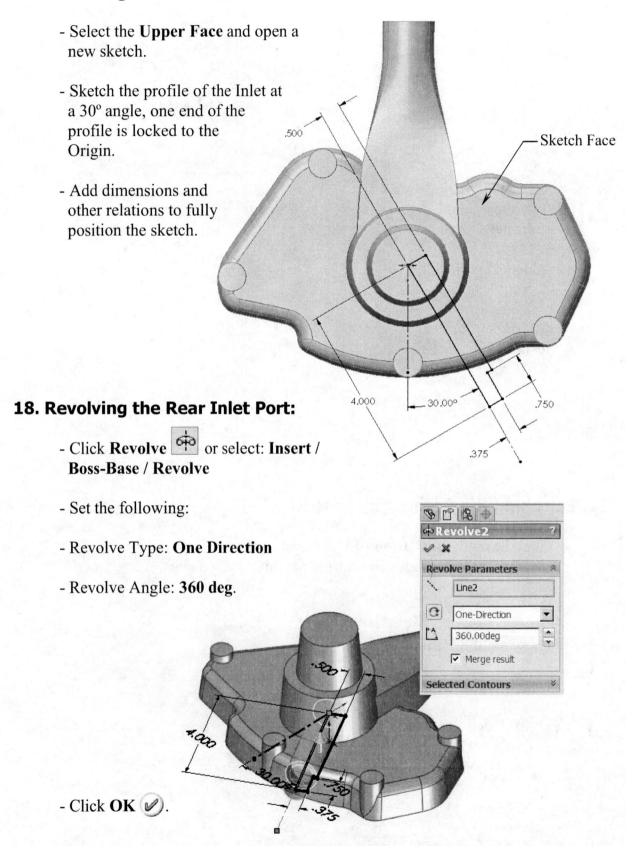

Sketch Face

18. Revolving the Rear Inlet Port:

- Click **Revolve** or select: **Insert / Boss-Base / Revolve**

- Set the following:

- Revolve Type: **One Direction**

- Revolve Angle: **360 deg**.

- Click **OK**.

19. Adding the 1ˢᵗ .250″ Face Fillet:

- Click **Fillet** 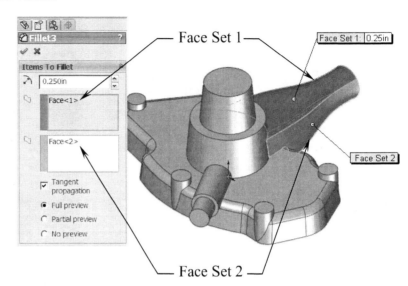 or select: **Insert / Features / Fillet-Round.**

- Enter **.250 in.** for radius value.

- For **Face Set 1**, select the **upper face** of the lofted feature.

- For **Face Set 2**, select the **side face** of the lofted feature.

- Click **OK**.

20. Adding 2ⁿᵈ the .250″ Face Fillet:

- Click **Fillet** 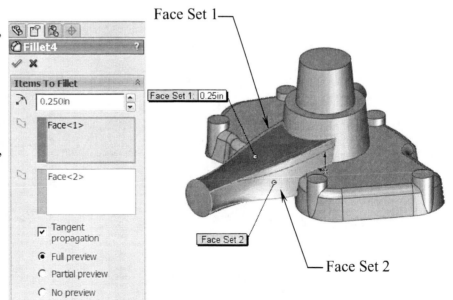 or select: **Insert / Features / Fillet-Round.**

- Enter **.250 in.** for radius value.

- For **Face Set 1**, select the **upper face** of the lofted feature.

- For **Face Set 2**, select the **side face** of the lofted feature.

- Click **OK**.

21. Adding the 3rd .150" Face Fillet:

- Click **Fillet** or select:
Insert / Features / Fillet-Round.

- Enter **.150 in.** for radius value.

- For **Face Set 1**, select the **lower face** of the lofted feature.

- For **Face Set 2**, select the **side face** of the lofted feature.

- Click **OK** .

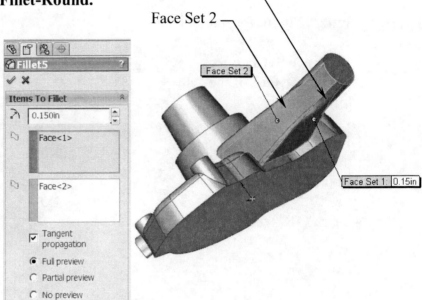

Face Set 1

Face Set 2

22. Adding the 4th .150" Face Fillet:

- Click **Fillet** or select: **Insert / Features / Fillet-Round.**

- Enter **.150 in.** for radius value.

- For **Face Set 1**, select the **lower face** of the lofted feature.

- For **Face Set 2**, select the **Side face** of the lofted feature.

- Click **OK** .

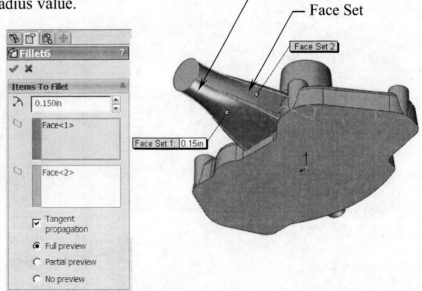

Face Set

Face Set

23. Mirroring the rear Inlet Port:

- Click Mirror 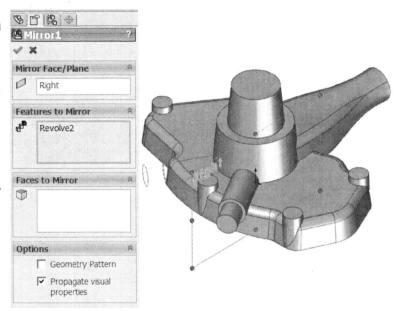 or select: **Insert / Pattern Mirror / Mirror.**

- For Mirror Face/Plane, Select the **RIGHT** plane from the flyout FeatureManager tree.

- For Features to Mirror, select the **Rear Inlet Port** either from the Graphics area or from the tree.

- Click **OK**.

24. Adding the .175" Fillets:

- Click **Fillet** 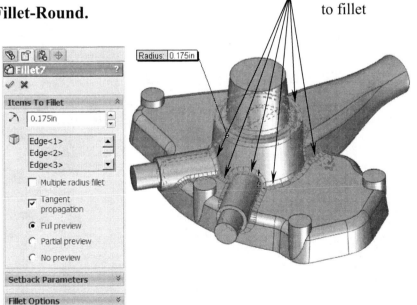 or select: **Insert / Features / Fillet-Round.**

- Enter **.175 in.** for radius value.

- Select the edges as Shown to add the fillets.

- The option Tangent-Propagation should be on by default.

- Click **OK**.

Select edges to fillet

25. Shelling the part:

- Click **Shell** 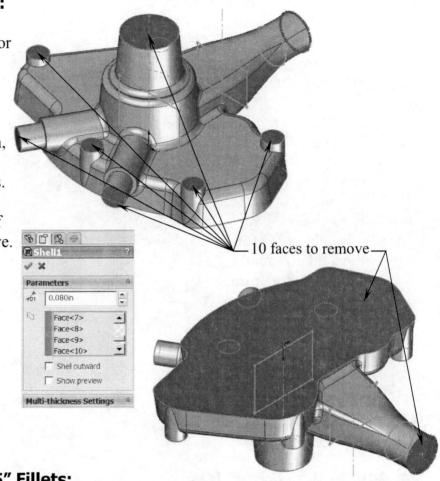 or
  select: **Insert /**
  Features / Shell.

- Under the
  Parameter section,
  enter **.080 in.**
  for wall thickness.

- Select the total of
  10 faces to remove.

- Click **OK** .

10 faces to remove

26. Adding the .0625" Fillets:

- Click **Fillet** 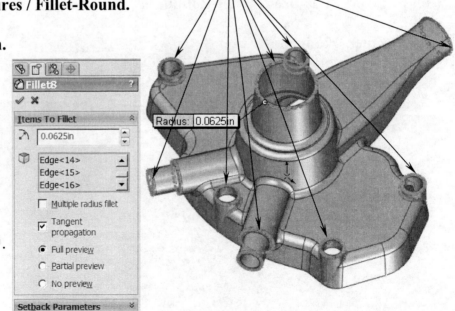 or select:
  Insert / Features / Fillet-Round.

- Enter **.0625 in.**
  for radius.

- Select the
  edges as
  shown to add
  the fillets.

- Click **OK** .

Edges to fillet
(outer edges)

27. Adding a Rib:

- Select the FRONT plane from the FeatureManager tree and open a new sketch.

- Sketch a Line  as shown.

- Add Coincident relations between the end points of the line and the edges of the part.

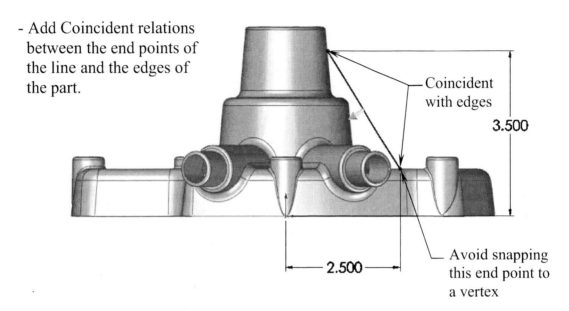

Coincident with edges

3.500

2.500

Avoid snapping this end point to a vertex

28. Extruding the Rib:

- Click **Rib** or select: **Insert / Features / Rib.**

- Select **Both Directions** under the Thickness section.

- Enter **.275 in**. for the thickness of the rib.

- Enable the Draft option and enter **1.00 deg**.

- Enable the **Draft Outward** check box.

- Click **OK** .

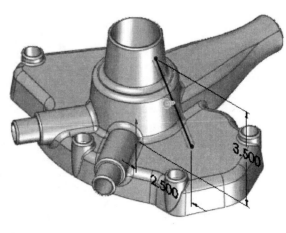

29. Creating a Full-Round fillet:

- Click **Fillet** or select: **Insert / Features / Fillet-Round.**

- Select the **Full Round** fillet option.

- For Face 1, select the left surface of the Rib.

- For Face 2, select the right surface of the Rib.

- For Face 3, select the middle surface of the Rib.

- Click **OK**.

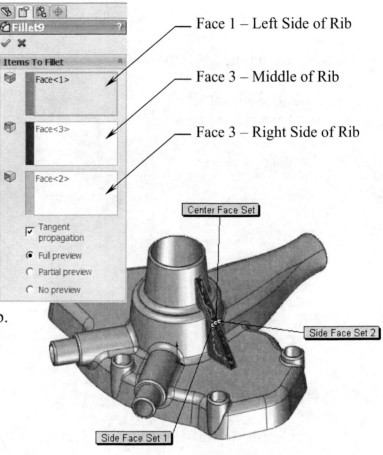

Face 1 – Left Side of Rib

Face 3 – Middle of Rib

Face 3 – Right Side of Rib

30. Mirroring the Rib:

- Click **Mirror** or select: **Insert / Pattern Mirror / Mirror**.

- For Mirror Face/Plane, select the RIGHT plane.

- For Features to Mirror, select the Rib and its fillet.

- Click **OK**.

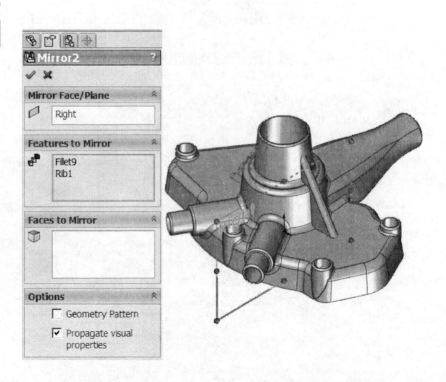

31. Adding the .025" fillets: (Removing sharp edges)

- Click **Fillet** or select: **Insert / Features / Fillet- Round.**

- Select the **Constant Radius** fillet option.

- Enter **.025 in**. for radius Value.

- Select the edges as indicated to add the fillets.

- Enable the Tangent-Propagation check box.

- Click **OK** .

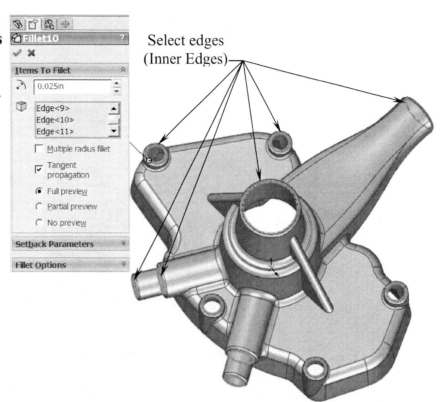

Select edges (Inner Edges)

32. Adding the .175" fillets:

- Click **Fillet** or select: **Insert / Features / Fillet-Round.**

- Enter **.175 in**. for radius value.

- Select the edges of the 2 ribs as shown.

- Click **OK** .

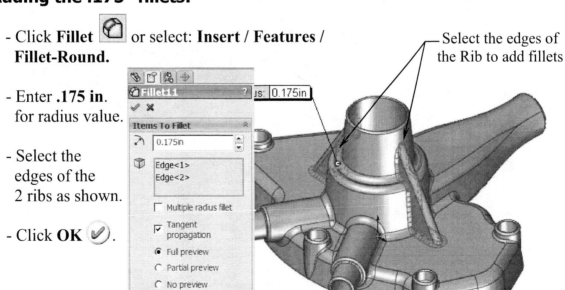

Select the edges of the Rib to add fillets

33. Saving your work:

- Click **File / Save As**.

- Enter **Water Pump Cover** as the file name.

- Click **Save.**

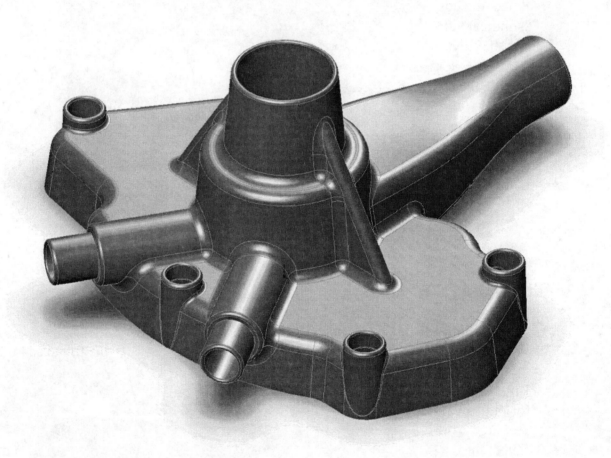

CHAPTER 6

Loft Vs. Sweep

Loft ⬱ vs. Sweep ⫶

- The Loft and the Sweep commands are normally used to create advanced, complex shapes. The differences between the two are:

  * Sweep uses a single sketched profile to sweep along a path and it is controlled by one or more guide curves.

  * Loft uses multiple sketched profiles to loft between the sections and is controlled by 1 or more guide curves or 1 Centerline Parameter.

- In order to create a solid feature, the sketch profile must be a single, closed, and non-intersecting shape.

- The guide curves can be either a 2D sketch or a 3D curve.

- The sweep paths and guide curves must be related to the sketched profiles with either Coincident or Pierce relations.

- The loft profiles should have the same number of entities or segments, so they can be connected properly during the loft transition.

- In the case where a sketch profile doesn't have the same number of entities as the others, the split entities command will be used to split the sketch entities into the desired number of connecting points.

- This lesson will guide you through the use of the Sweep, Loft and Split-Entities commands.

Water Meter Housing
Loft vs. Sweep

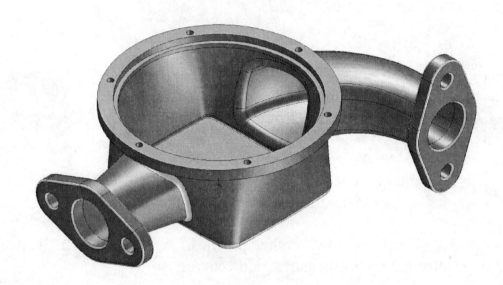

| Dimensioning Standards: **ANSI** |
| Units: **INCHES** – 3 Decimals |

Tools Needed:

Insert Sketch	Line	Split Entities
Sketch Fillet	Mirror	Add Geometric Relations
Dimension	Base/Boss Extrude	Extruded Cut
Plane	Fillet/Round	Base/Boss Loft

1. Sketching the 1st Loft Profile:

- Select the TOP plane from the FeatureManager tree.

- Click 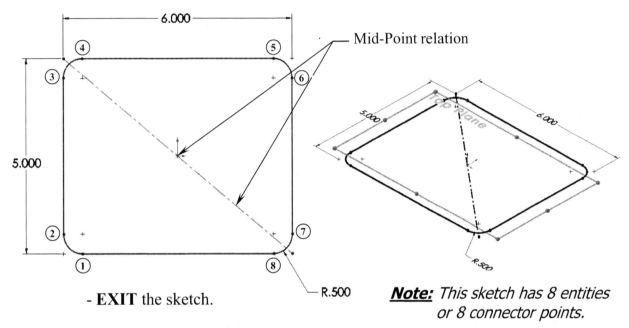 or select **Insert / Sketch**.

- Sketch a rectangle centered on the Origin, and add the dimensions as shown.

Mid-Point relation

- **EXIT** the sketch.

R.500

Note: *This sketch has 8 entities or 8 connector points.*

2. Creating an Offset Distance plane:

- Click  or select **Insert / Reference Geometry / Plane**.

- Select the TOP reference plane from the FeatureManager tree.

- Select **Offset Distance** option and enter **3.000** in.

- Click **OK** 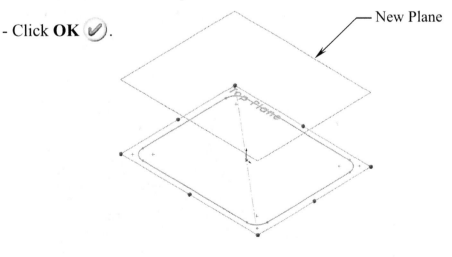.

New Plane

3. Sketching the 2ⁿᵈ Loft Profile:

- Select the new plane (**Plane1**) and open a new sketch 📝 .

- Sketch a Circle ⊕ and add dimensions ◇ and Relations ⊥ as needed.

- Select the **Split Entities** command under: **Tools / Sketch Tools**.

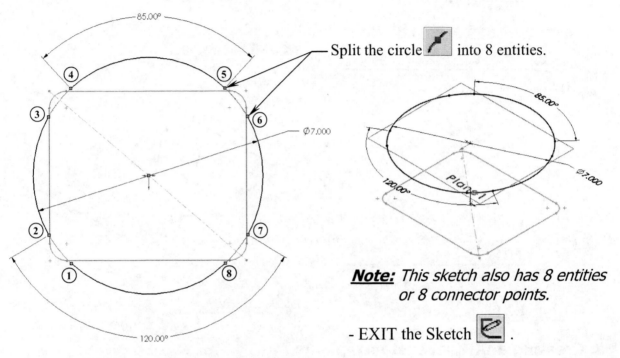

Split the circle ✂ into 8 entities.

Note: This sketch also has 8 entities or 8 connector points.

- EXIT the Sketch 📝 .

4. Creating the Lofted Base feature:

- Click 🔔 or select **Insert / Boss-Base / Loft**.

- Profiles: Select the 2 sketches as indicated.

- Move the Connector Points as needed to make a smooth transition between the 2 profiles.

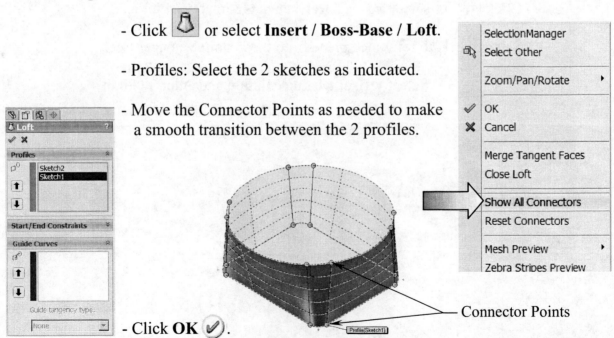

Connector Points

- Click **OK** ✓ .

5. Creating another Offset Distance plane:

- Click or select **Insert / Reference Geometry / Plane**.

- Select the FRONT reference plane from the FeatureManager tree.

- Select **Offset Distance** option and enter **5.500 in**. for distance.

- Click **OK** .

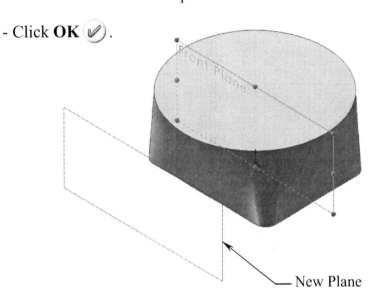

— New Plane

6. Constructing the Inlet's 1ˢᵗ Loft Profile:

- Select the FRONT plane and open a new sketch .

- Sketch a Rectangle , add Dimensions , and Sketch Fillets .

Note: This sketch has 8 entities or 8 connector points.

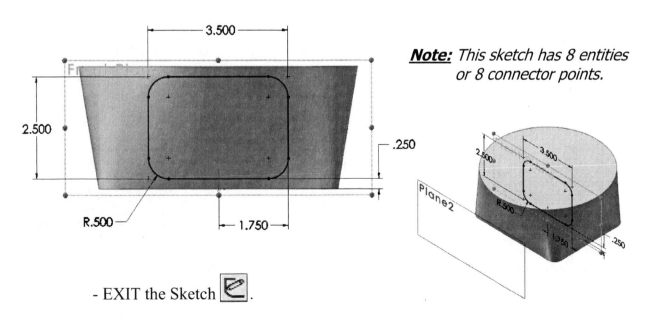

- EXIT the Sketch .

7. Constructing the Inlet's 2nd Loft Profile:

- Select the PLANE2 and open a new sketch.

- Sketch a Circle and add dimensions to fully define it.

- Click Split Entities and split the circle into 8 segments.

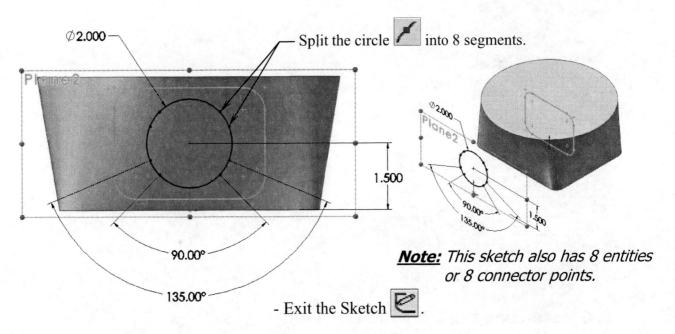

Split the circle into 8 segments.

Note: *This sketch also has 8 entities or 8 connector points.*

- Exit the Sketch.

8. Creating the Inlet solid feature:

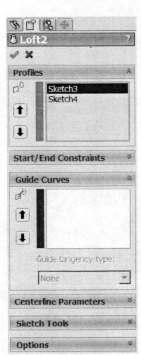

- Click or select **Insert / Boss-Base / Loft**.

- Profiles: Select the 2 sketches as indicated.

- Move the Connector Points (if needed) to create a smooth transition between the 2 profiles.

- Click **OK**.

Right click & Show-All Connectors

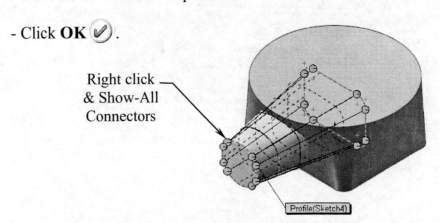

Profile(Sketch4)

9. Creating an Offset Distance plane from the Right:

- Click 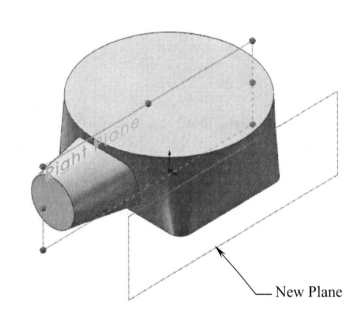 or select **Insert / Reference Geometry / Plane.**

- Select the RIGHT reference plane from the FeatureManager tree.

- Select **Offset Distance** option and enter **4.000 in**. for distance.

- Click **OK** .

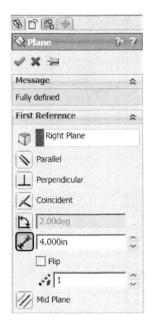

New Plane

10. Constructing the Outlet's 1ˢᵗ Loft profile:

- Select the new plane (PLANE3) and open a new sketch .

- Sketch a Circle split it into 8 segments. Add dimensions as indicated.

Split the circle into 8 segments

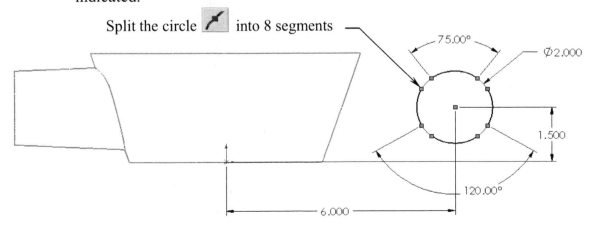

- Add the Vertical and Horizontal relations to the endpoints of the Arcs to fully define them.

Note: *This sketch has 8 entities or 8 connector points.*

- EXIT the Sketch 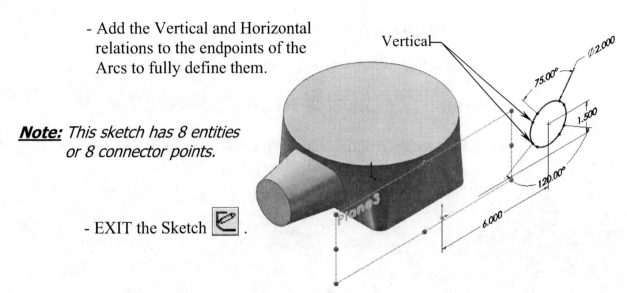.

11. "Re-Using" the previous sketch*:

- Expand the feature **Loft2** from the Manager tree (click the **+** sign).

- Locate the sketch of the Rectangle (**sketch3**), Right-click and select **SHOW** .

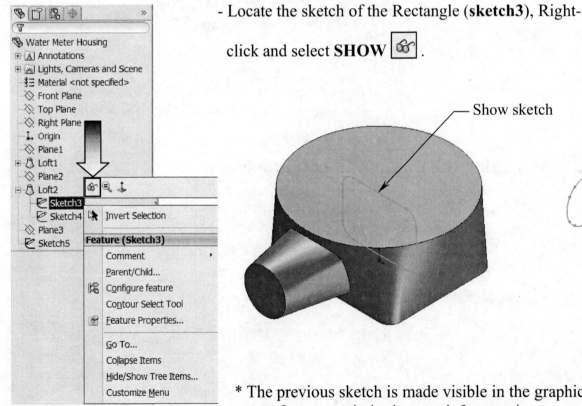

* The previous sketch is made visible in the graphics area for use again in the next loft operation.

12. Creating a plane Parallel At Point:

- Click 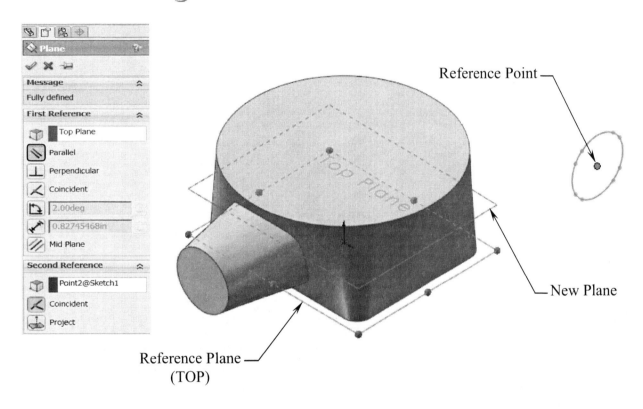 or select **Insert / Reference Geometry / Plane**.

- Select the **TOP** reference plane from the FeatureManager tree.

- Select **Parallel Plane** option.

- Click the **Center Point** of the Circle.

- Click **OK** ⊘.

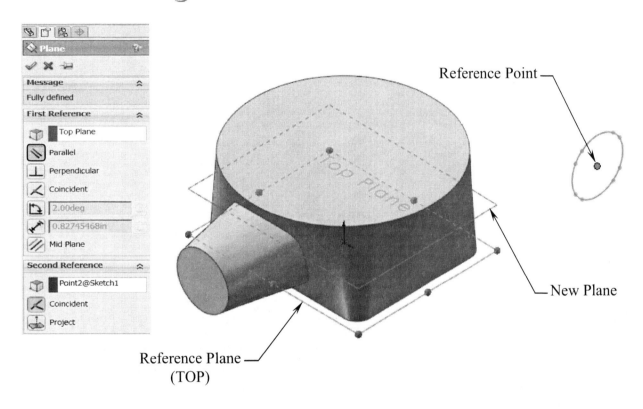

Reference Point

New Plane

Reference Plane
(TOP)

- The new plane is
   created (Plane4).

13. Constructing the Centerline Parameter:

- Select the new plane (**PLANE4**) and open a new sketch .

- Switch to the TOP view orientation

- Sketch the profile as shown below.

- Add Dimensions 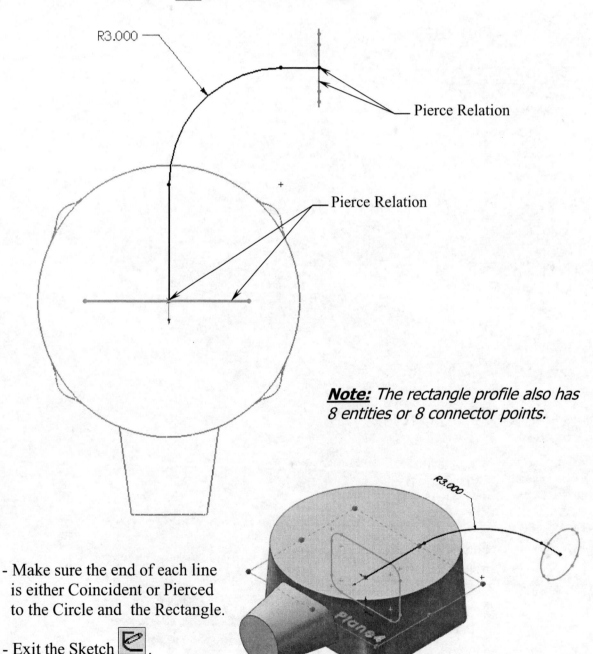 and Sketch Fillet .

R3.000

Pierce Relation

Pierce Relation

Note: *The rectangle profile also has 8 entities or 8 connector points.*

R3.000

Plane4

- Make sure the end of each line is either Coincident or Pierced to the Circle and the Rectangle.

- Exit the Sketch .

14. Creating the Outlet solid feature:

- Click  or select **Insert / Boss / Loft**.

- Select the 2 Sketch Profiles (Rectangle and Circle) from the graphics area.

- Expand the **Centerline Parameters** option and select *Sketch6* from either the graphics area or from the FeatureManager tree.

- The preview appears, check the connector points to make sure a proper loft transition.

- Click **OK** ✅.

> ### 💡 Centerline Parameters
>
> If the number of entities in each sketch is the same, a "Centerline Parameter Sketch" can be used instead of the guide curves.

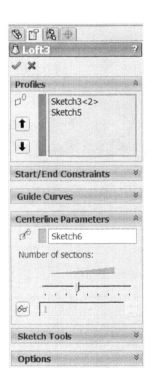

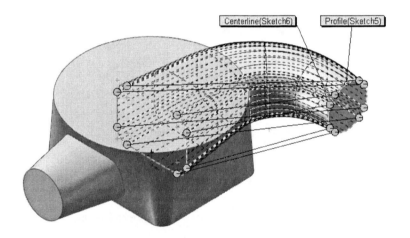

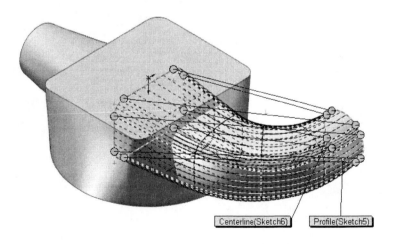

15. Adding .250" fillet to the Bottom:

- Click 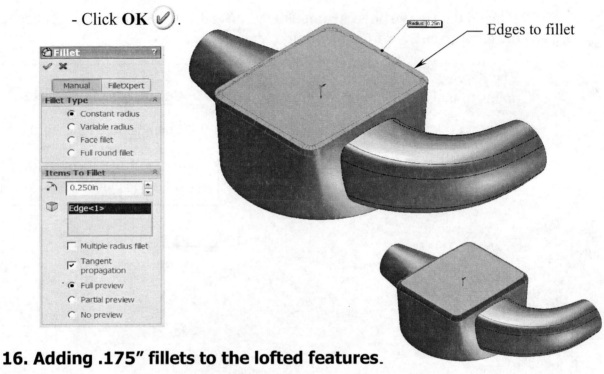 or select **Insert / Features / Fillet-Round**.

- Enter **.250 in**. for Radius and select the **bottom edges** as indicated.

- Click **OK** ✅.

Edges to fillet

16. Adding .175" fillets to the lofted features.

- Click 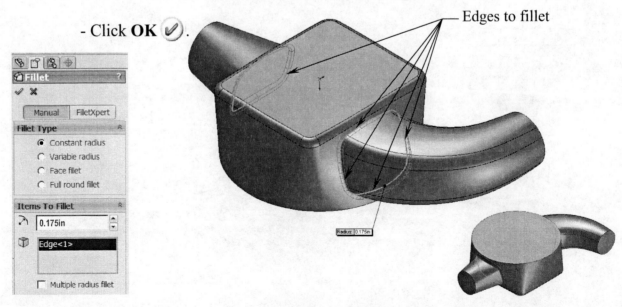 or select **Insert / Features / Fillet-Round**.

- Enter **.175 in**. for Radius and select the **side edges** as noted.

- Click **OK** ✅.

Edges to fillet

17. Shelling the part:

- Click 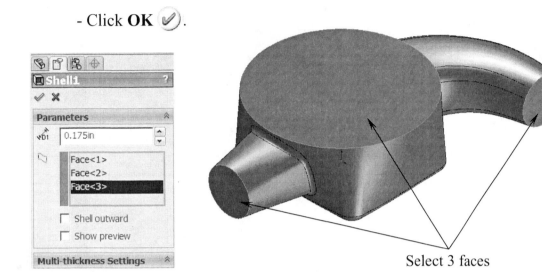 or select **Insert / Features / Shell**.

- Enter **.175** for wall thickness and select the 3 faces as shown.

- Click **OK** ✓.

Select 3 faces

18. Creating the 1st Mounting bracket:

- Select the Face as noted and open a new sketch ✏.

- Sketch the profile as shown below, use Convert Entities where applicable.

- Add Dimensions and Relations needed to fully define the sketch.

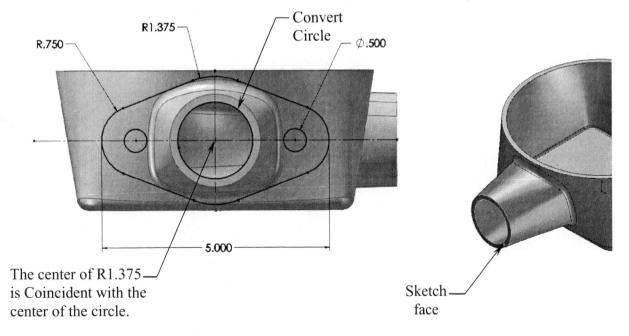

R1.375

R.750

Convert Circle

∅.500

5.000

The center of R1.375 is Coincident with the center of the circle.

Sketch face

19. Extruding the Left bracket:

- Click 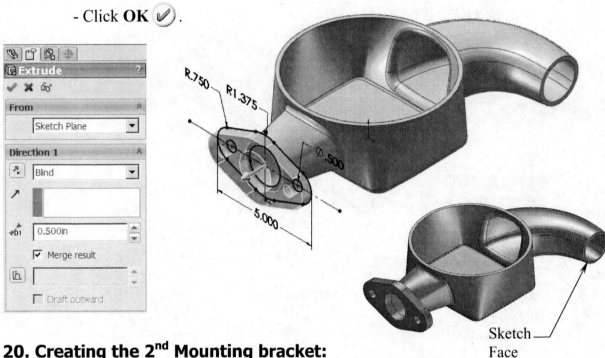 or select **Insert / Boss-Base / Extrude**.

- End Condition: **Blind**   - Depth: **.500 in**.

- Click **OK** ✓.

20. Creating the 2ⁿᵈ Mounting bracket:

- Select the Face as noted and open a new sketch.

- Either copy the previous sketch – or – recreate the same sketch again on the right side of the part.

- Add Dimensions and Relations needed to fully define the sketch.

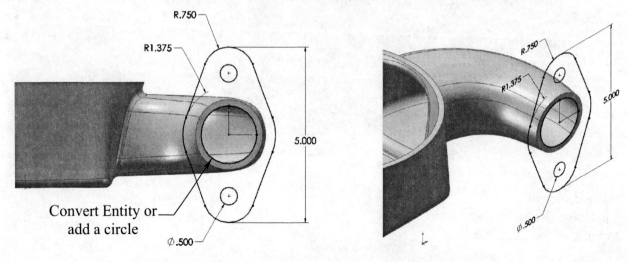

21. Extruding the Right bracket:

- Click [icon] or select **Insert / Boss-Base / Extrude**.

- End Condition: **Blind**   - Depth: **.500 in**.

- Click **OK** ✓.

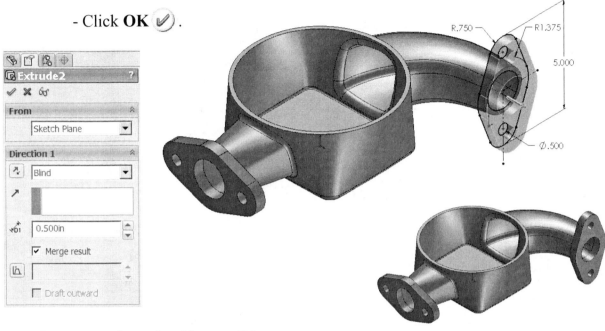

22. Constructing the Upper Ring:

- Select the Face as indicated and open a new sketch [icon].

- Sketch the profile below, use Convert Entities [icon] where needed.

- The centers of the Ø.250 Circles are coincident with the Ø7.375 bolt-circle.

Sketch a circle and convert to Construction

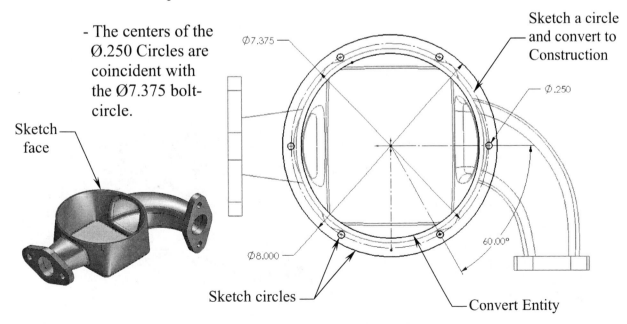

Sketch face

Ø7.375

Ø.250

Ø8.000

60.00°

Sketch circles

Convert Entity

23. Extruding the Upper Ring:

    - Click ⬚ or select **Insert / Boss-Base / Extrude**.

    - End Condition: **Blind**   - Depth: **.400 in**. (upward)

    - Click **OK** ⊘.

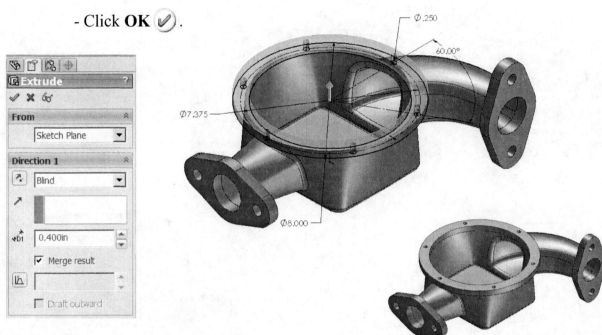

24. Adding a Seal-Ring bore:

    - Select the Face as noted and open a new sketch ✎.

    - Select the Inside Circular Edge and click **Offset Entities** ⬦.

    - Enter **.150 in**. for Offset Value (offset to a larger diameter).

    - Click **OK** ⊘.

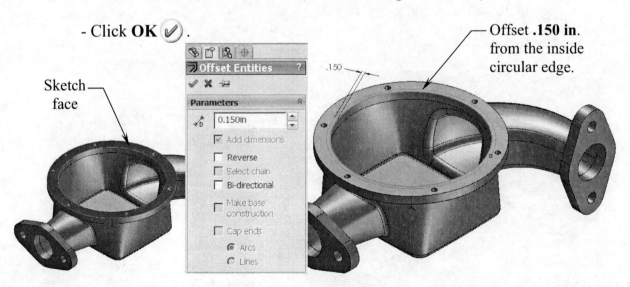

Offset **.150 in**. from the inside circular edge.

Sketch face

25. Cutting the Seal Ring bore:

- Click  or select **Insert / Cut / Extrude**.

- End Condition: **Blind**

- Depth: **.250 in**.

- Click **OK** ✅.

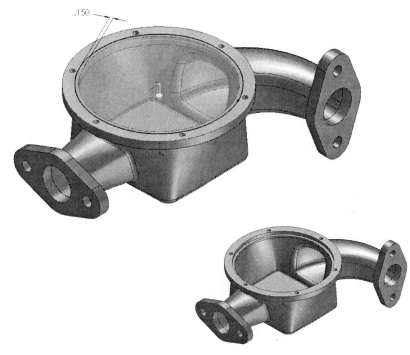

26. Adding more fillets:

- Click 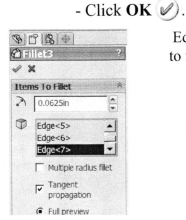 or select **Insert / Features / Fillet-Round**.

- Enter **.0625 in**. for Radius value.

- Select the 7 edges as noted.

- Click **OK** ✅.

Edges to fillet

27. Adding Chamfers:

- Click 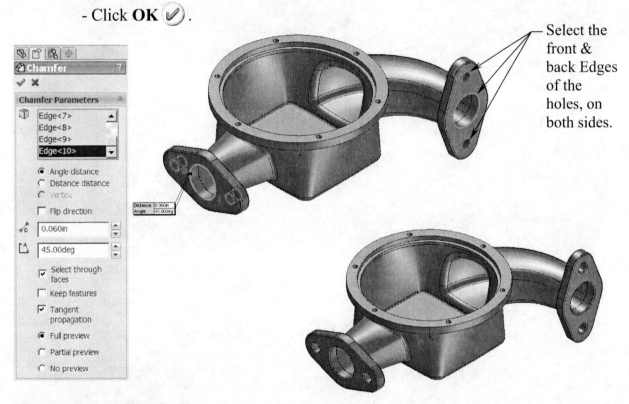 or select **Insert / Features / Chamfer**.

- Enter **.060 in**. for Depth.

- Enter **45 deg**. for Angle.

- Select the edges of the 6 holes.

- Click **OK** .

Select the front & back Edges of the holes, on both sides.

Chamfer

Chamfer Parameters

Edge<7>
Edge<8>
Edge<9>
Edge<10>

- Angle distance
- Distance distance
- Vertex

☐ Flip direction

0.060in

45.00deg

☑ Select through faces

☐ Keep features

☑ Tangent propagation

- Full preview
- Partial preview
- No preview

Distance: 0.060in
Angle: 45.00deg

28. Saving your work:

- Select **File / Save As / Water Meter Housing / Save**.

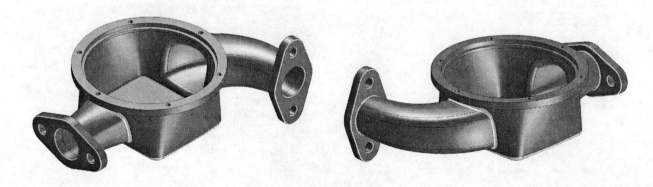

Questions for Review

Loft Vs. Sweep

1. In a new part template, when the Sketch Pencil is selected first, SolidWorks will prompt the user to select a sketch plane.
    a. True
    b. False

2. It is sufficient to create a Parallel-Plane-At-Point with a Reference Plane and a Reference Point.
    a. True
    b. False

3. A loft feature uses multiple sketch profiles to define its shape.
    a. True
    b. False

4. Only one guide curve can be used in each loft feature.
    a. True
    b. False

5. Multiple guide curves can be used to connect and control the loft feature.
    a. True
    b. False

6. The guide curves can be either a 2D sketch or a 3D curve.
    a. True
    b. False

7. The loft profiles and the guide curves should be related with Coincident or Pierce relations.
    a. True
    b. False

8. The loft profiles should be created before the guide curves.
    a. True
    b. False

1. TRUE   2. TRUE
3. TRUE   4. FALSE
5. TRUE   6. TRUE
7. TRUE   8. TRUE

Exercise: Loft

There are several different ways to model this part; this exercise focuses on the **Loft** command.

1. Create the part below, using the Loft and the Circular Pattern features.

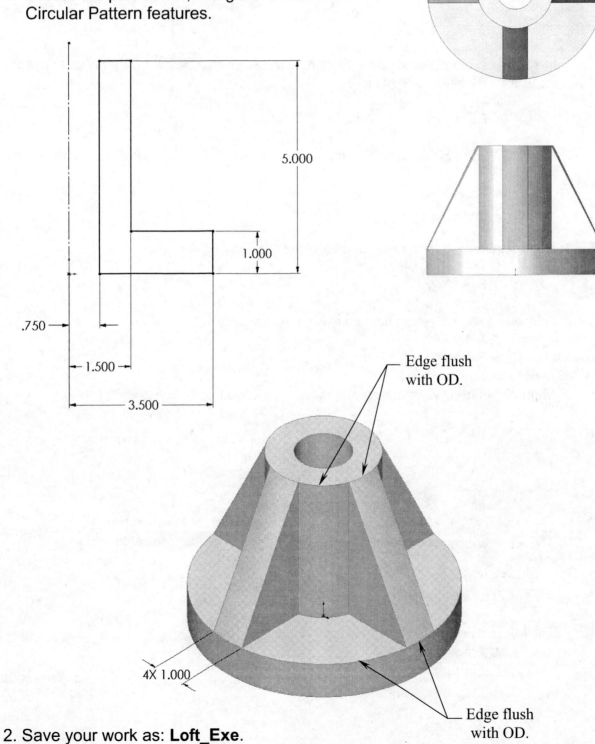

2. Save your work as: **Loft_Exe**.

CHAPTER 7

Loft with Guide Curves

Loft with Guide Curves

This exercise was developed to demonstrate how a loft feature is created using 4 sketch profiles a single 3D guide curve.

A loft feature normally contains several sections and one or more guide curves in it.

* In this exercise, four identical profiles will be used as the loft sections and a single guide curve will be used to connect the sections..

    - Since the sections are identical, the derived-sketch option will be used to show how the sketches can be derived or copied.

    - A derived sketch is driven by the original sketch, it can only be positioned with relations or dimensions but its sketched entities cannot be changed.

    - When the Original sketch is changed, the derived-sketch will be updated automatically. However, the derived sketches can also be <u>Un</u>-derived to break their associations with the Original sketch.

* The loft sections are connected with a 3D curve.

    - The 3D curve will be generated through some defined points called: Curve-Through-Reference-Points, and Pierce to the loft profile.

    - The Curve-Through-Reference-Points will then be used to guide and control the loft sections from twisting .

Waved Washer
Loft with Guide Curves

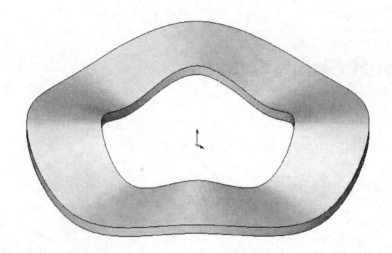

Dimensioning Standards: **ANSI**

Units: **INCHES** – 3 Decimals

Tools Needed:

Insert Sketch	Line	Circle
Sketch Point	Add Geometric Relations	Dimension
Derived Sketch	Curve Through Reference Points	Base/Boss Loft

1. Creating the 1ˢᵗ construction profile:

- Select the TOP plane from the FeatureManager tree.

- Click 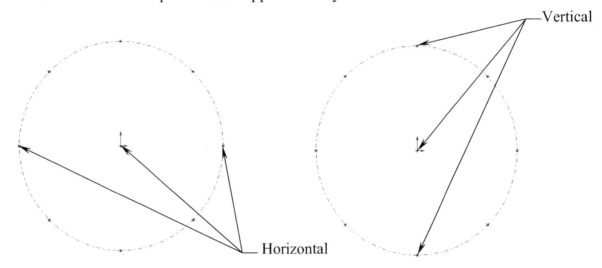 or select **Insert / Sketch**.

- Sketch a Circle ⊕ and convert it into a construction circle ☑ For construction .

- Add **8** sketch points ✳ approximately as shown.

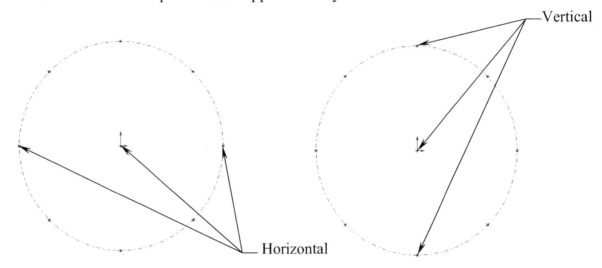

Vertical

Horizontal

2. Fully defining the sketch:

- Select the dimension tool ◇ and add dimensions to the sketch points.

- Add a vertical and a horizontal ⊥ relation as indicated.

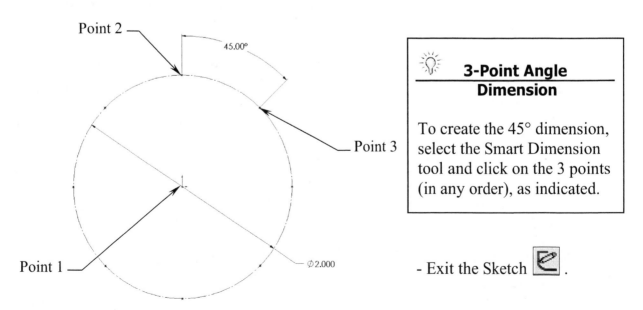

Point 2

45.00°

Point 3

Point 1

⌀2.000

💡 **3-Point Angle Dimension**

To create the 45° dimension, select the Smart Dimension tool and click on the 3 points (in any order), as indicated.

- Exit the Sketch ✏.

3. Creating an Offset Distance plane:

- Click 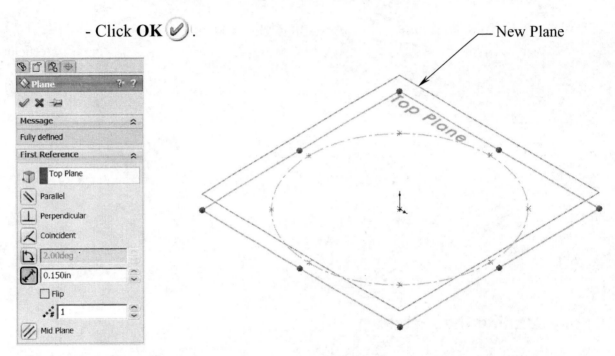 or select **Insert / Reference Geometry / Plane**.

- Select the TOP plane as Reference Entities.

- Select **Offset Distance** option and enter **.150 in**.

- Click **OK** ✓.

New Plane

4. Creating the 2nd construction profile using Derived Sketch:

- Hold the CONTROL key, select the new Plane (*plane1*) and the *Sketch1* from Feature Manager tree.

- Select **Insert / Derived Sketch**.

Derived Sketch

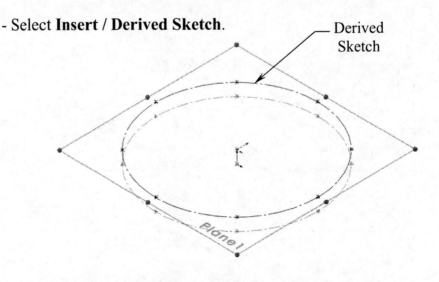

5. Fully defining the Derived Sketch:

- Add a Vertical & Coincident relation 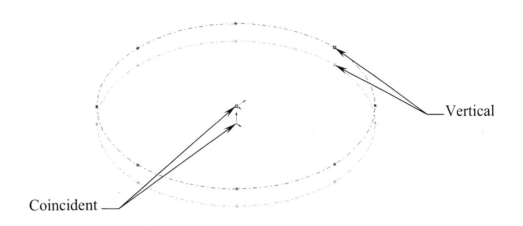 between the indicated points.

Vertical

Coincident

- Exit the Sketch 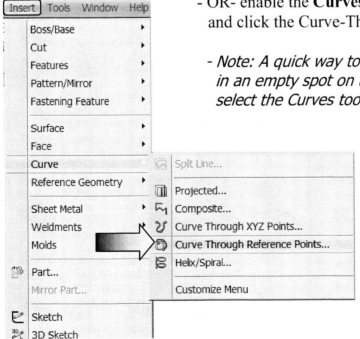 or select **Insert / Sketch**.

6. Creating a 3D Curve: Curve Through Reference Points

- Click [icon] or select **Insert / Curve / Curve-Through-Reference-Points**.

- OR- enable the **Curves** toolbar (View / Tool Bars /Curves), and click the Curve-Through-Reference-Points icon.

- *Note: A quick way to access the toolbars is to right click in an empty spot on the top right area of the screen and select the Curves toolbar from the pop-up list.*

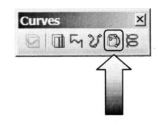

Curve Though Reference Points

- Select the sketch points in the order as shown (Required for this lesson only).

- Click [☑ Closed curve] to close the curve.

- Click **OK** ✅.

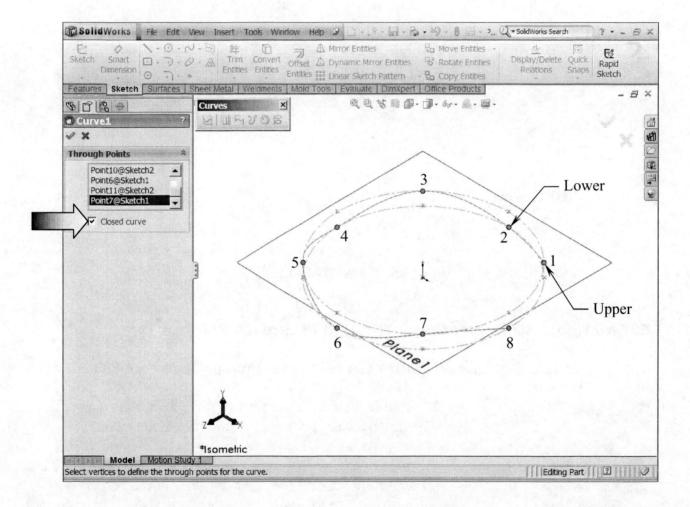

- The resulted 3D curve.

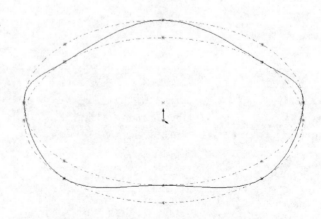

7. Sketching the 1ˢᵗ loft section:

- Select the FRONT plane from the Feature Manager tree.

- Sketch a rectangle 🔲 add Dimensions 🔷 and Relations ⊥ as shown.

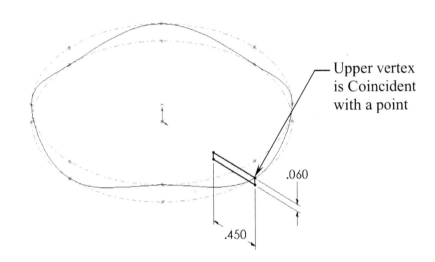

Upper vertex
is Coincident
with a point

.060

.450

- Exit the sketch ✏️ or select **Insert / Sketch**.

8. Creating the 2ⁿᵈ loft section using Derived-Sketch:

- Hold down the CONTROL key, select the FRONT plane

and the sketch of the rectangle from the Feature tree.

- Select **Insert / Derived Sketch**.

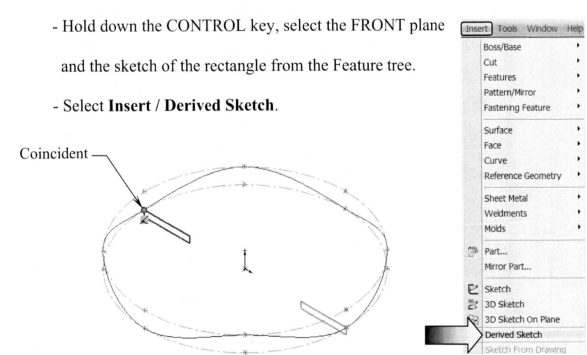

Coincident

Insert Tools Window Help

Boss/Base ▸
Cut ▸
Features ▸
Pattern/Mirror ▸
Fastening Feature ▸

Surface ▸
Face ▸
Curve ▸
Reference Geometry ▸

Sheet Metal ▸
Weldments ▸
Molds ▸

Part...
Mirror Part...

Sketch
3D Sketch
3D Sketch On Plane
Derived Sketch
Sketch From Drawing

9. Fully defining the Derived Sketch:

- Add a Collinear relation 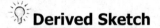 between the 2 lines as indicated.

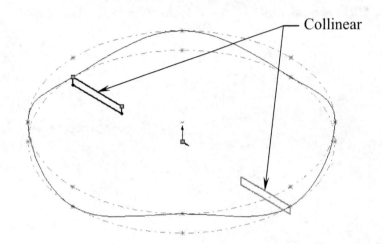

Collinear

> ☀ **Derived Sketch**
>
> A derived sketch is a dependent copy of the original sketch. It can only be moved or positioned on the same or different plane with respect to the same model.

- Exit the Sketch or select **Insert / Sketch**.

10. Sketching the 3rd loft section: (or use the Derived Sketch option).

- Select the RIGHT plane from the FeatureManager tree.

- Sketch a rectangle □ (or copy and paste the previous sketch).

- Add Dimensions ◇ and Relations ⊥ needed to fully define the sketch.

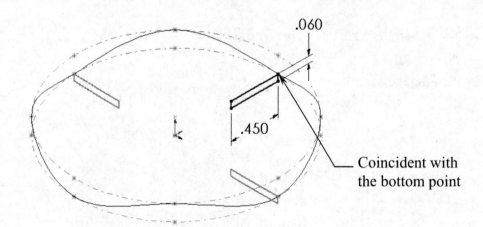

.060

.450

Coincident with the bottom point

- Exit the Sketch or select **Insert / Sketch**.

11. Creating the 4th loft section using Derived-Sketch:

- Hold down the CONTROL key, select the RIGHT plane <u>and</u> the sketch of the 3rd rectangle from the FeatureManager tree.

- Select **Insert / Derived Sketch**.

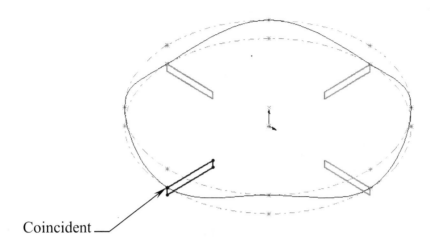

Coincident

12. Fully-defining the Derived sketch:

- Add a Collinear relation 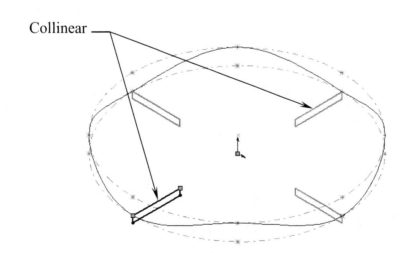 between the 2 lines as shown.

Collinear

- Exit the Sketch or select **Insert / Sketch**.

13. Lofting between the sections and the Guide curve:

- Click 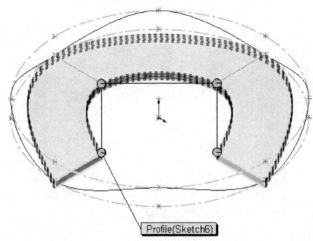 or select **Insert / Boss-Base / Loft**.

- Select the four rectangular sketches as Loft Profiles.

Profile(Sketch6)

- Select the 3D curve as Guide Curve

- Click **Close Loft** ☑ Close loft under Options (arrow).

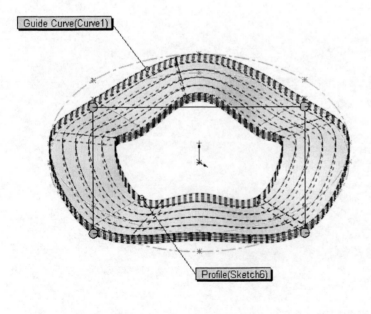

Guide Curve(Curve1)

Profile(Sketch6)

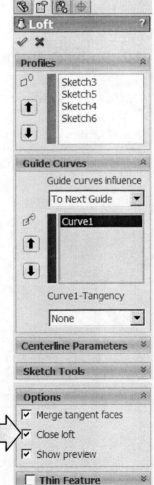

Loft

✓ ✗

Profiles
Sketch3
Sketch5
Sketch4
Sketch6

Guide Curves
Guide curves influence
To Next Guide
Curve1

Curve1-Tangency
None

Centerline Parameters

Sketch Tools

Options
☑ Merge tangent faces
☑ Close loft
☑ Show preview

☐ Thin Feature

- Click **OK** ✓.

- The finished Waved Washer (with the construction sketches still visible).

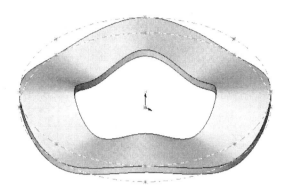

14. Hiding the construction sketches:

- Right-mouse click on the construction sketches and select **Hide** .

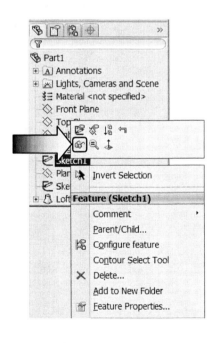

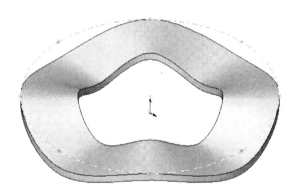

15. Saving your work:

- Select **File / Save As / Waved-**

Washer / Save.

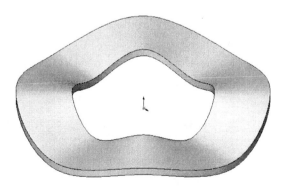

Questions for Review

Loft with Guide Curves

1. A sketch profile can be copied onto another plane or a planar surface.
   a. True
   b. False

2. Sketch points can be added in any sketch to help define the sketch geometries.
   a. True
   b. False

3. If a derived sketch is driven by the original sketch, its entities cannot be changed.
   a. True
   b. False

4. A 3D curve can be created using reference points in the sketches or model's vertices.
   a. True
   b. False

5. The loft sections should either be Pierced or Coincident with the guide curves.
   a. True
   b. False

6. The guide curves can also be used to control the loft sections from twisting.
   a. True
   b. False

7. Only two guide curves can be used in each loft feature.
   a. True
   b. False

8. Up to four sketch profiles can be used in a loft feature.
   a. True
   b. False

9. The construction sketches can be toggled (Show/Hide) at any time.
   a. True
   b. False

9. TRUE
7. FALSE   8. FALSE
5. TRUE   6. TRUE
3. TRUE   4. TRUE
1. TRUE   2. TRUE

CHAPTER 8

Using Surfaces

Advanced Modeling - Using Surfaces

- Surfaces are a type of geometry that can be used to create solid features.

- The surfaces option is used to form complex free-form shapes and to manipulate files imported from other CAD formats.

- Unlike solid models, surfaces can be opened, overlapped, and have no thickness.

- Each surface can be constructed individually and then knitted together. A solid feature is created by thickening the surfaces that have been knit into a closed volume.

- Surfaces can be modeled in any shape and their sketches can either be extruded, revolved, swept, or lofted into a surface; and surfaces can also be replaced and filled with other surfaces.

- The edges of the surfaces can be extended and trimmed.

- Surfaces can be moved, rotated, and made into copies.

- The angle between the faces of a surface can be calculated using the Draft Analysis tool; Positive Drafts, Negative Drafts, and Required Drafts are reported on screen.

- Full Round Fillets are used in this design to create a perfect blend-radius for the whole perimeter of the part.

- This 1st half of the chapter discusses the use of some surfacing tools in SolidWorks.

Advanced Modeling
Using Surfaces

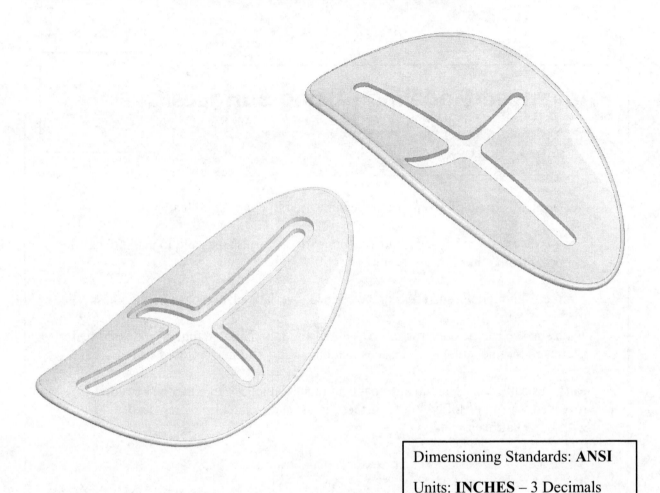

| Dimensioning Standards: **ANSI** |
| Units: **INCHES** – 3 Decimals |

Tools Needed:

	Insert Sketch		3 Point Arc		Ellipse
	Dimension		Add Geometric Relations		Split Line
	Plane		Lofted Surface		Surface Thicken

1. Constructing a new work plane:

- Select the FRONT plane from the FeatureManager tree.

- Click 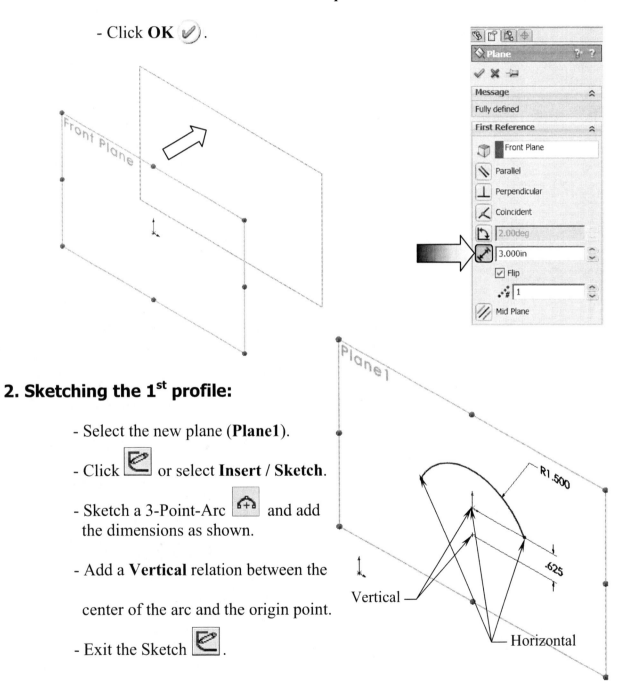 or select **Insert / Reference Geometry / Plane**.

- Select the Front plane and click the **Offset Distance** button.

- Enter **3.000 in**. and enable the **Flip** check box to reverse direction.

- Click **OK** .

2. Sketching the 1st profile:

- Select the new plane (**Plane1**).

- Click or select **Insert / Sketch**.

- Sketch a 3-Point-Arc and add the dimensions as shown.

- Add a **Vertical** relation between the

center of the arc and the origin point.

- Exit the Sketch .

3. Sketching the 2nd profile:

- Select the FRONT plane from the FeatureManager tree.

- Click 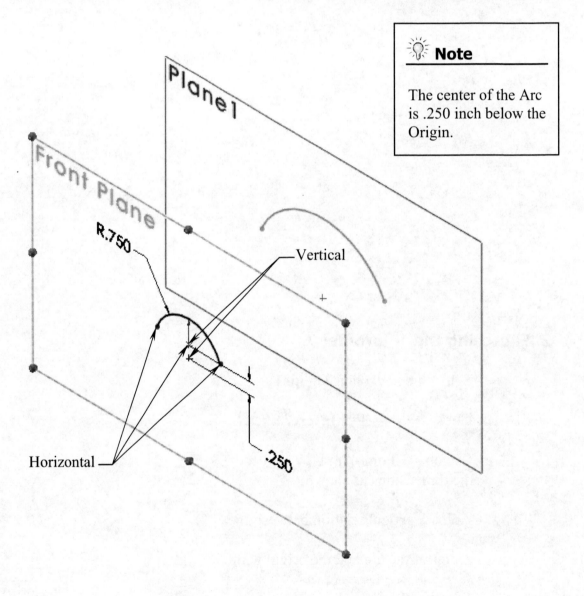 or select **Insert / Sketch**.

- Sketch a 3-Point-Arc as shown.

- Add a **.750** radius dimension to the arc.

- Add a Horizontal and a Vertical relation as indicated.

> ### ☀ Note
>
> The center of the Arc is .250 inch below the Origin.

- Exit the sketch .

4. Sketching the Guide Curve:

- Select the RIGHT plane from the FeatureManager tree and open a new sketch.

- Sketch a 3-Point-Arc and add a **4.00** in. dimension

- Add the Pierce relations as noted

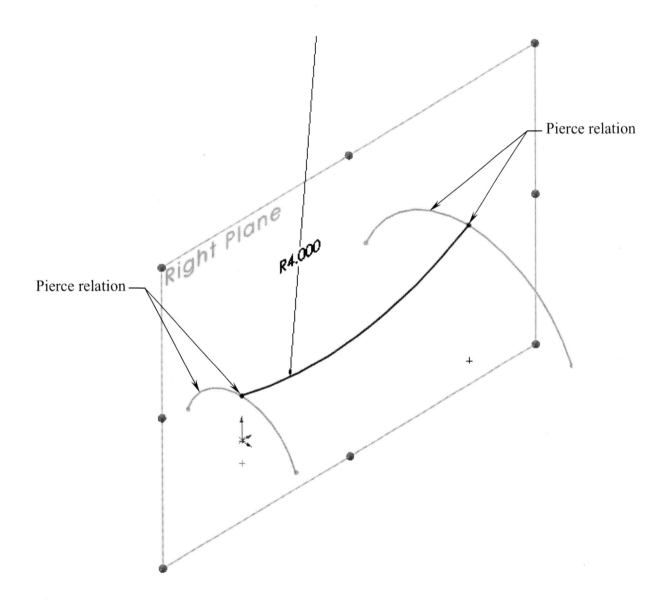

Pierce relation

Right Plane

R4.000

Pierce relation

- Exit the sketch .

5. Creating the Surface-Loft:

- Click  or **Insert / Surface / Loft**.

- Select the 2 Sketched Profiles by clicking on their *right-most end points*.

- Expand the Guide-Curve section and select the sketched Arc as noted.

- Set <u>both</u> *Start/End Constraints* to *Normal-To-Profile*.

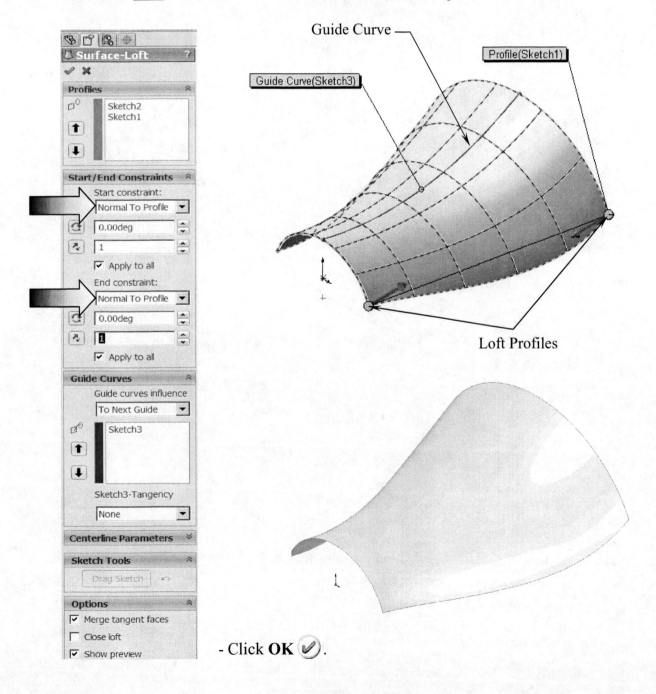

Guide Curve

Profile(Sketch1)

Guide Curve(Sketch3)

Loft Profiles

- Click **OK** ✅.

6. Sketching the Split profile:

- Select the TOP plane from the FeatureManager tree.

- Click [✐] or **Insert / Sketch**.

- Change to Top view orientation [⊡] .

- Sketch an Ellipse [⬭] and add Dimensions/Relations as shown.

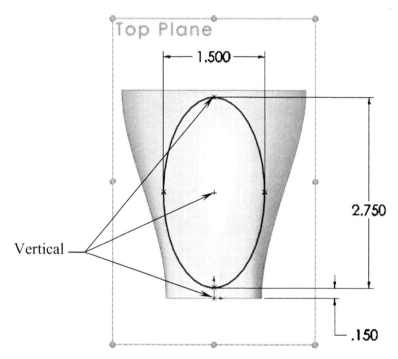

7. Splitting the surface:

- Click [⬭] on the Curves toolbar OR select **Insert / Curve / Split Line**.

- Select the Ellipse as Sketch-to-Project [✐] .

- Select the Surface-Loft1 as Faces-to-Split [⬭] .

- Click **OK** [✓] .

8. Deleting Surfaces:

- Right click on the outer portion of the surface.

- Select **Face** / **Delete** from the menu.

- Click **Delete** under Options (circled).

- Click **OK** .

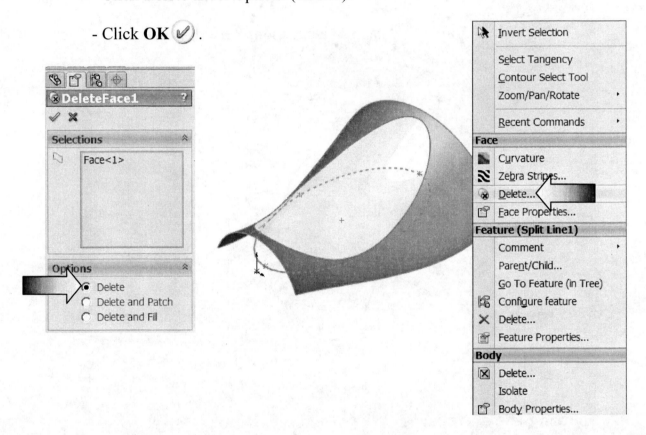

- The resulting surface.

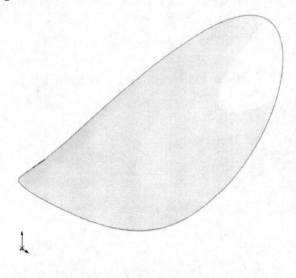

9. Thickening the surface:

- Select **Insert / Boss-Base / Thicken** 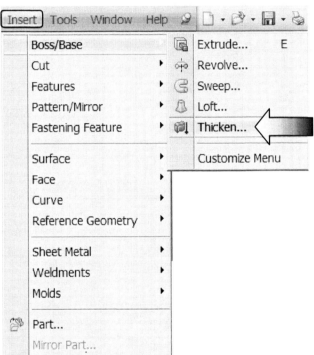 .

- Click on the surface as Surface-To-Thicken .

- Choose **Thicken Both Sides** option .

- Enter **.030** in. as Thickness (.060 Total Thickness)

> **Thicken Surfaces**
>
> In order to create a solid volume, all surfaces have to form a closed shape.
>
> If the shape is open, a wall thickness can be added to the surface instead.

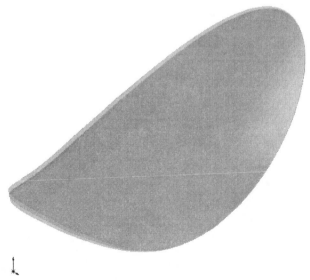

- Click **OK**  .

- The surface turns into a solid model.

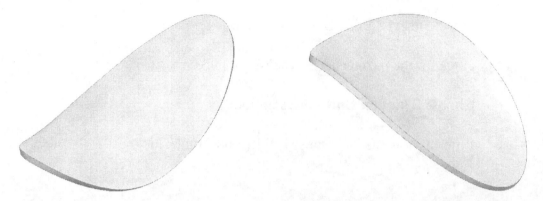

10. Calculating the angles between the faces:

- Click  on the **Mold toolbar** or select **View/Display/ Draft Analysis**.

- Select the **TOP** plane for Direction of Pull.

- Enter **1.00** deg. for Draft Angle.

- Click **Calculate**.

- The **Yellow Surfaces** indicate that drafts are required.

> 💡 **Draft Analysis**
>
> Using the settings in draft analysis, you can verify draft angles on model faces or you can examine angle changes within a face.

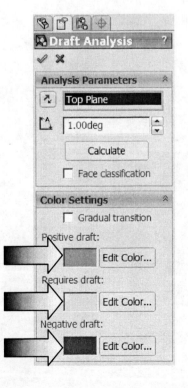

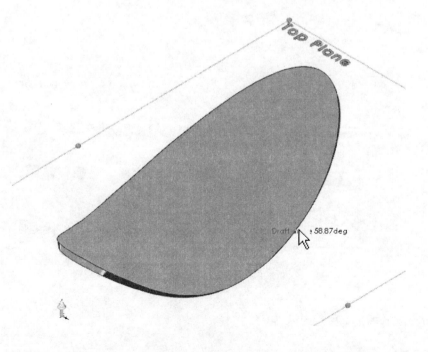

Draft Analysis

The **Draft Analysis** is a tool to check the correct application of draft to the faces of their part. With draft analysis, you can verify draft angles, examine angle changes within a face, as well as locate parting lines, injection, and ejection surfaces in parts.

Draft analysis results listed under Color Settings are grouped into four categories, when you specify Face classification:

Positive draft: Displays any faces with a positive draft based on the reference draft angle you specified. A positive draft means the angle of the face, with respect to the direction of pull, is more than the reference angle.

Negative draft: Displays any faces with a negative draft based on the reference draft angle you specified. A negative draft means the angle of the face, with respect to the direction of the pull, is less than the negative reference angle.

Draft required: Displays any faces that require correction. These are faces with an angle greater than the negative reference angle, and less than the positive reference angle.

Straddle faces: Displays any faces that contain both positive and negative types of draft. Typically, these are faces that require you to create a split line.

*Note: When analyzing the draft for surfaces, an additional **Face classification** criterion is added: **Surface faces with draft**. Since a surface includes an inside and an outside face, surface faces are not added to the numerical part of the classification (**Positive draft** and **Negative draft**). **Surface faces with draft** lists all positive and negative surfaces that include draft.*

- Move the mouse cursor over the upper surface to see the read out draft angle for that area.

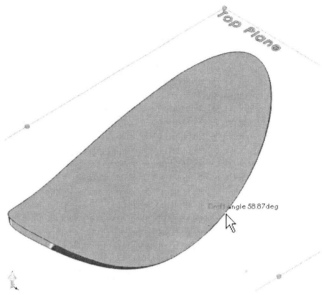

- Position the mouse cursor over the yellow areas (required drafts) and check the draft angles to see if they meet your draft requirements.

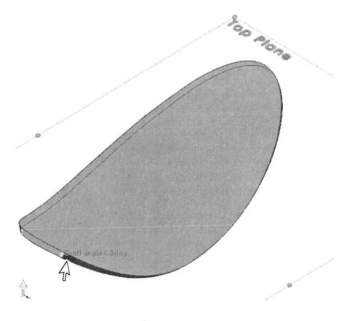

- Click **OK** .

11. Adding a Full Round Fillet:

- Click 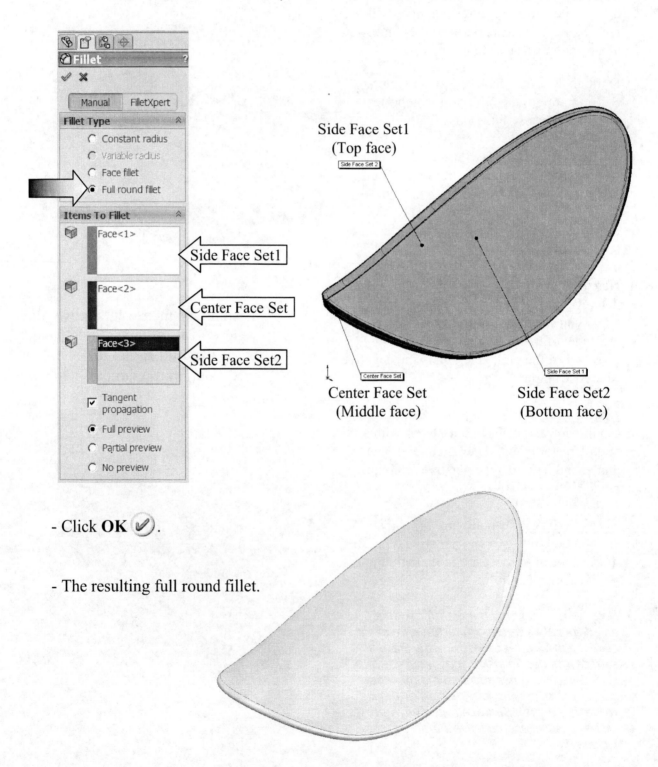 or select **Insert / Features / Fillet-Round**.

- Select the Side-Face-Set1, Center-Face-Set and Side-Face-Set2 as noted.

Side Face Set1
(Top face)

Side Face Set1

Center Face Set
(Middle face)

Side Face Set2
(Bottom face)

- Click **OK** ✅.

- The resulting full round fillet.

12. Creating an Offset Distance plane:

- Select the TOP plane from the FeatureManager tree and click [icon].

- Enter **.850 in**. for Distance and place the new plane ABOVE the Top plane.

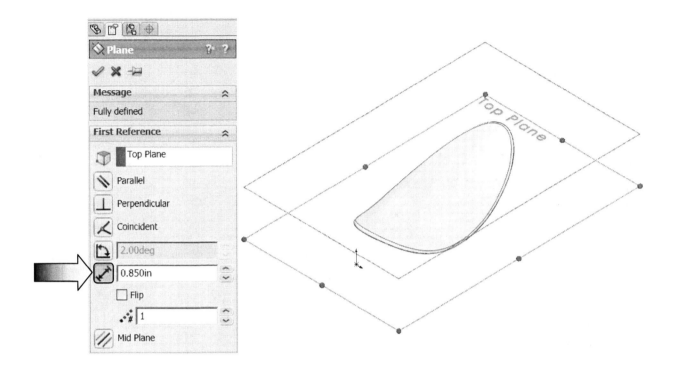

- Click **OK** [icon].

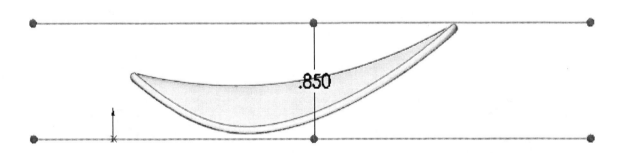

13. Sketching the Slot Contours:

- Select the new plane (**Plane2**) and open a new sketch [icon].

- Create the sketch using EITHER **Mirror** or **Offset** options.

- Sketch the profile as shown, add dimensions to fully position the sketch.

- Create an offset 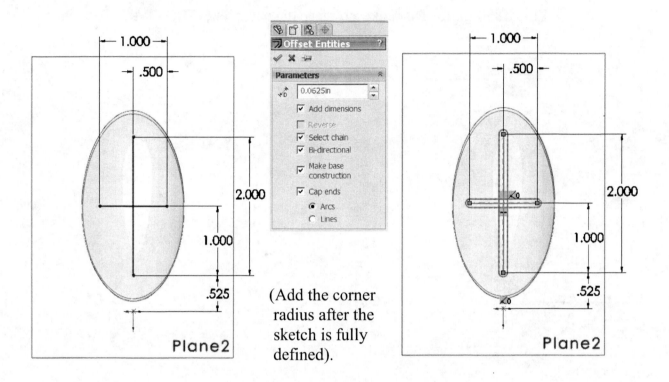 of **.0625** in. from the 2 sketch lines, use the settings below.

(Add the corner radius after the sketch is fully defined).

- Trim the inner intersections and create a second offset as shown.

- Clean up the corners and add the .031 radius as indicated.

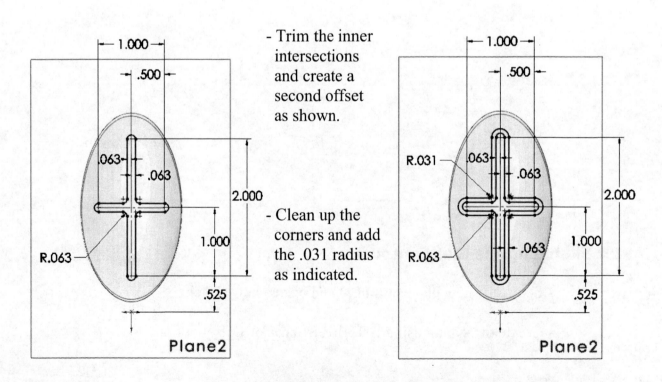

14. Extruding Cut the 1st Contour:

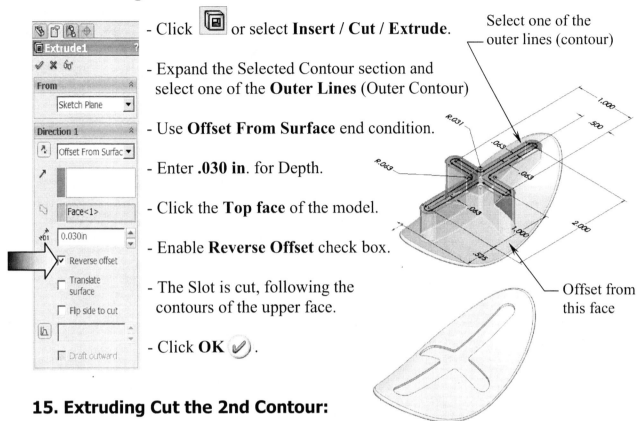

- Click [icon] or select **Insert / Cut / Extrude**.

- Expand the Selected Contour section and select one of the **Outer Lines** (Outer Contour)

- Use **Offset From Surface** end condition.

- Enter **.030 in**. for Depth.

- Click the **Top face** of the model.

- Enable **Reverse Offset** check box.

- The Slot is cut, following the contours of the upper face.

- Click **OK** [icon].

Select one of the outer lines (contour)

Offset from this face

15. Extruding Cut the 2nd Contour:

- Expand the Cut-Extrude1 from the FeatureManager tree, right click on the

Sketch5 and select **SHOW** [icon].

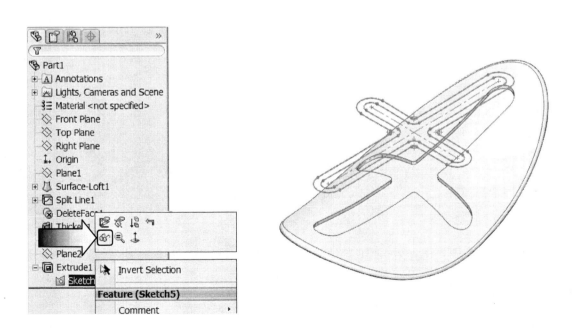

- Right click on one of the *Inner lines* and pick **Select Chain**.

- Click 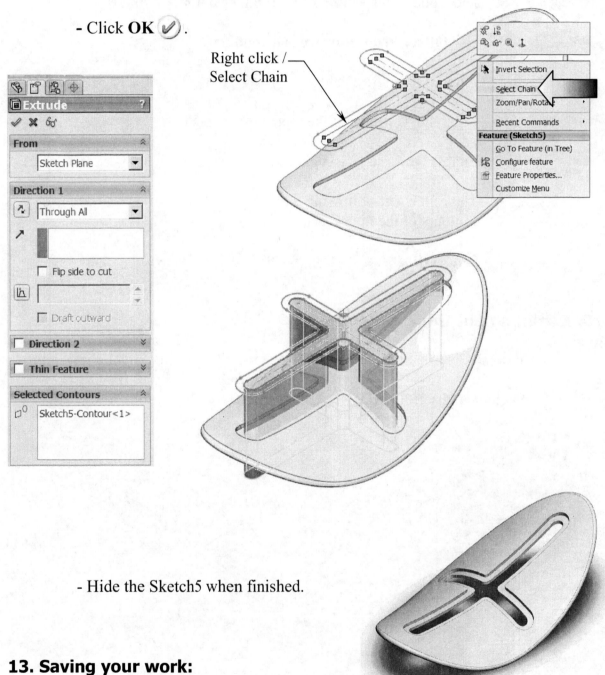 or select **Insert / Cut / Extrude**.

- Select **Though All** for end condition.

- Click **OK** ✓.

Right click /
Select Chain

- Hide the Sketch5 when finished.

13. Saving your work:

- Select **File / Save As / Lofted-Surface / Save**.

Questions for Review

Advanced Modeling – Using Surfaces

1. Surfaces are a type of geometry that can be used to create complex shapes.
    a. True
    b. False

2. Surfaces can be opened, overlapped, and have no thickness.
    a. True
    b. False

3. Surfaces can be modeled into any shape and can be extruded, revolved, swept, or lofted.
    a. True
    b. False

4. The split line option can be used to "divide" a surface into two or more surfaces.
    a. True
    b. False

5. Several surfaces can be lofted together to form a solid feature.
    a. True
    b. False

6. A surface(s) cannot be moved or copied in a part document.
    a. True
    b. False

7. Each surface can be created individually and then knitted together as one surface.
    a. True
    b. False

8. The same Sketched profile can be Re-used to create different extruded contours.
    a. True
    b. False

9. Offset From Surface (extrude option) only work with surfaces, not solid features.
    a. True
    b. False

1. TRUE	2. TRUE
3. TRUE	4. TRUE
5. TRUE	6. FALSE
7. TRUE	8. TRUE
9. FALSE	

CHAPTER 8 (cont.)

Lofted Surface

Advanced Modeling – Lofted Surface

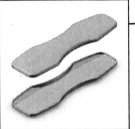

- Surfaces are a type of geometry that can be used to create solid features.

- The surfaces option is used to form complex free-form shapes and to manipulate filesimported from other CAD formats.

- Unlike solid models, surfaces can be opened, overlapped, and have no thickness.

- Each surface can be constructed individually and then knitted together. A solid feature is created by thickening the surfaces that have been knit into a closed volume.

- Surfaces can be modeled in any shape and their sketches can either be extruded, revolved, swept, or lofted into a surface; and surfaces can also be replaced and filled with other surfaces.

- The edges of the surfaces can be extended and trimmed.

- Surfaces can be moved, rotated, and made into copies.

- The angle between the faces of a surface can be calculated using the Draft Analysis tool; Positive Drafts, Negative Drafts, and Required Drafts are reported on screen.

- This 2nd half of the chapter discusses some other surfacing techniques in SolidWorks such as: loft surface, revolve surface, extrude, trim, move, planar / non-planar, knit and thicken surface.

Advanced Modeling
Lofted Surface

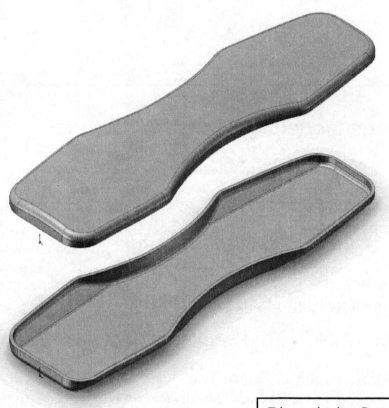

Dimensioning Standards: **ANSI**

Units: **INCHES** – 3 Decimals

Tools Needed:

 Insert Sketch

 Plane

 Dimension

 Add Geometric Relations

 Lofted surface

 Revolved Surface

Surface Move/Copy

 Trimmed Surface

 Planar Surface

 Knit Surface

 Surface Thicken

 Extruded Cut

1. Creating a new work plane:

- Select the FRONT plane from the FeatureManager tree.

- Click 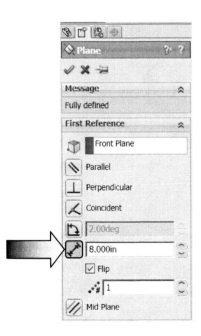 or select **Insert / Reference Geometry / Plane**.

- Choose **Offset Distance** and enter **4.00 in**.

- Use **Flip** direction if needed to place the new plane on the *right side*.

- Click **OK** ✅.

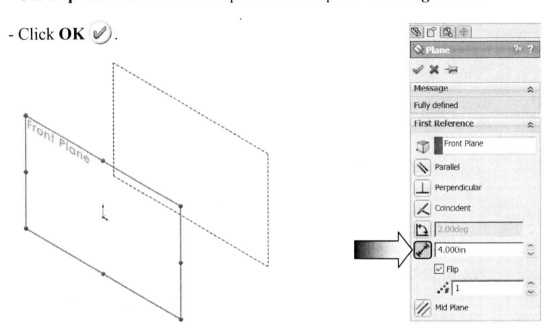

2. Creating another Offset Distance plane:

- Offset from FRONT plane.

- Offset Distance: **8.00 in**.

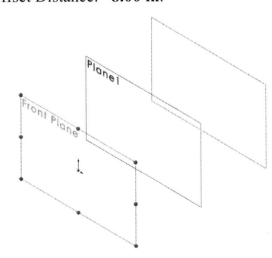

3. Sketch the first profile: the front section

- Select the FRONT plane from the FeatureManager tree.

- Click 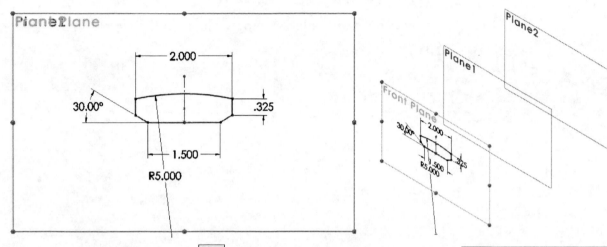 or select **Insert / Sketch**.

- Sketch the profile and add dimensions as shown.

- Exit the Sketch or select **Insert / Sketch**.

4. Sketching the second profile: the middle section

- Select the PLANE1 from FeatureManager tree.

- Click or select **Insert / Sketch**.

- Sketch the profile and add dimensions as shown.

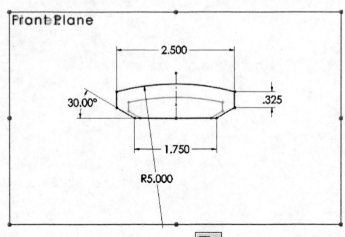
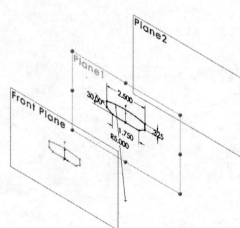

- Exit the Sketch or select **Insert / Sketch**.

💡 Copy & Paste

The 1st profile can be copied and pasted to make the next 2 sketches. The dimensions will then be adjusted to size.

5. Sketching the third profile: the end section.

- Select the PLANE2 from the FeatureManager tree.

- Click 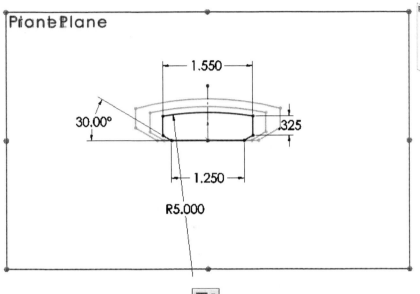 or select **Insert / Sketch**.

- Sketch the profile and add dimensions as shown.

Front Plane

1.550

30.00°

.325

1.250

R5.000

- Exit the Sketch or select **Insert / Sketch**.

6. Selecting the loft profiles:

> 💡 **Lofted Surface**
>
> Lofted Surface creates a surface by making transitions between the sketch profiles.
>
> Two or more profiles are needed to create a loft.

- To prevent the loft feature from being twisted, it is

recommended that each sketch profiles should be selected from the same sides.

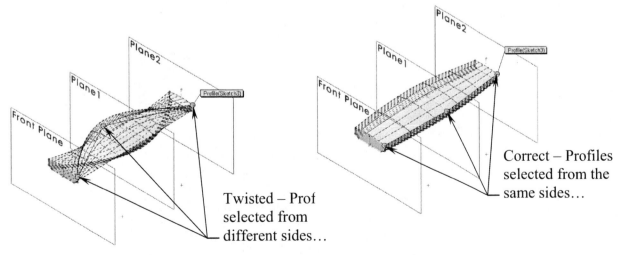

Twisted – Prof selected from different sides…

Correct – Profiles selected from the same sides…

7. Lofting between the profiles:

- Click  or select **Insert / Surface / Loft**.

- Select the upper-right-most vertex of each profile  .

- Expand **Centerline Parameters** option and select Sketch5 ⬜⁰ .

- Enable **Merge Tangent Faces**.

- Click **OK** ✓.

> ### Merge Tangent Faces
>
> Select Merge tangent faces to cause the corresponding surfaces in the resulting loft to be tangent if the corresponding lofting segments are tangent.

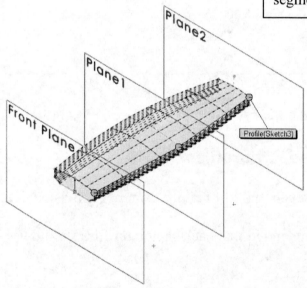

- The resulting Surface-Loft.

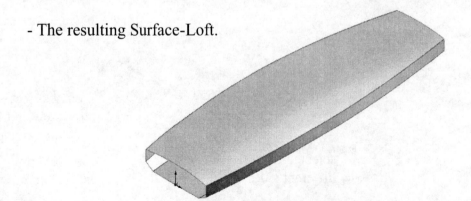

8. Creating a Revolved sketch:

- Select the TOP plane from the FeatureManager tree.

- Click ![icon] or select **Insert / Sketch**.

- Sketch the revolve profile and add dimensions as shown.

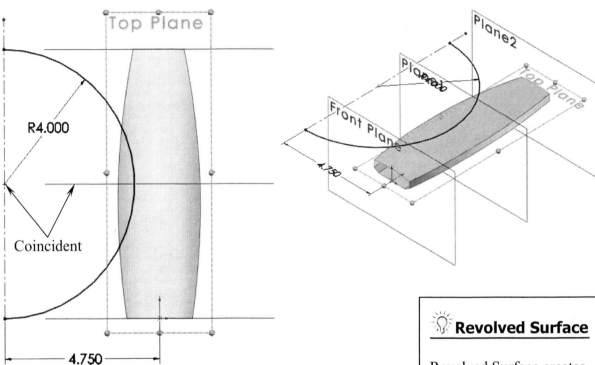

9. Revolving the Spherical surface:

- Click ![icon] or select **Insert / Surface / Revolve**.

- Revolve Type: **One Direction** ![icon].

- Revolve Angle: **360 deg**. ![icon].

- Click **OK** ![icon].

> ### ☀ Revolved Surface
>
> Revolved Surface creates a surface by rotating a sketch profile around a centerline (or the Axis of Revolution).

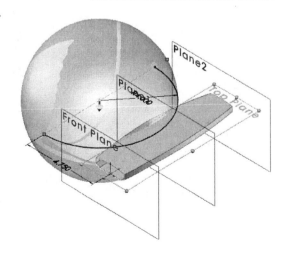

- The Revolved Surface.

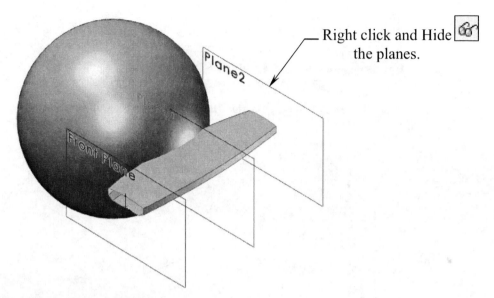

Right click and Hide the planes.

10. Mirroring the Revolved Surface:

- Click 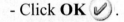 or select **Insert / Surface / Move/Copy**.

- Under Surfaces to Move/Copy, select the Surface-Revolve1 ▢ .

- Enable the **Copy** check box ▢ Copy .

- Enter **1** for Number of Copies .

- Enter **9.500** in the **Delta X** distance box Δx [9.500in] .

- Click **OK** ✓ .

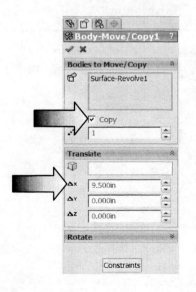

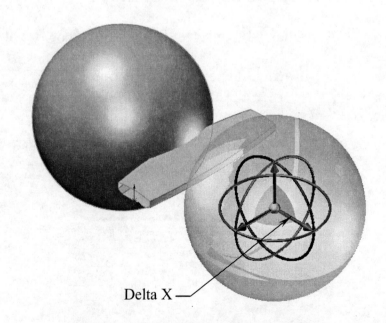

Delta X

11. Trimming the Base part:

- Click 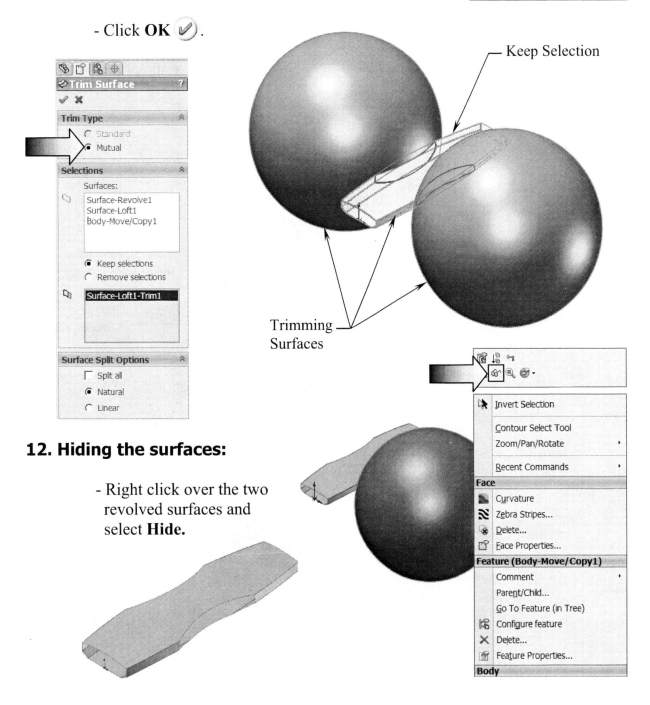 or select **Insert / Surface / Trim**.

- For Trim-Type, click **Mutual Trim** .

- For **Trimming-Surfaces**, select all **3 surfaces** .

- For **Keep Selection**, select the Surface-Loft1 .

- Click **OK** .

> **Trim Surface**
>
> A surface or a sketch can be used as a trim tool to trim the intersecting surfaces.

Keep Selection

Trimming Surfaces

12. Hiding the surfaces:

- Right click over the two revolved surfaces and select **Hide.**

13. Filling the openings with Surface-Fill:

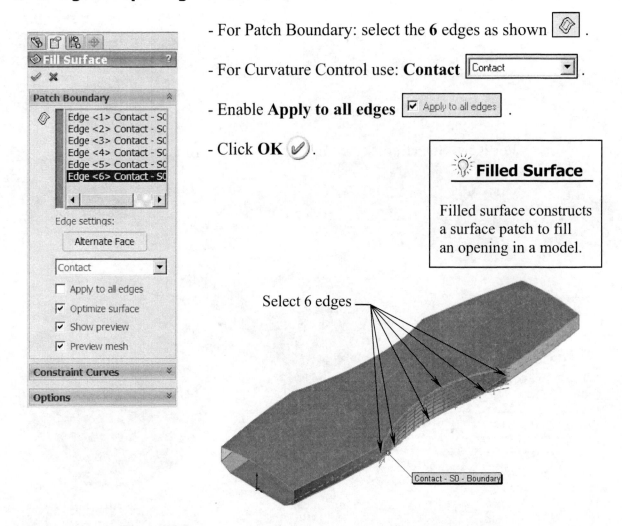

- For Patch Boundary: select the **6** edges as shown .

- For Curvature Control use: **Contact** Contact .

- Enable **Apply to all edges** ☑ Apply to all edges .

- Click **OK** .

> **Filled Surface**
>
> Filled surface constructs
> a surface patch to fill
> an opening in a model.

Select 6 edges

Contact - S0 - Boundary

- The right side cutout is filled with a new surface (Surface-Fill1).

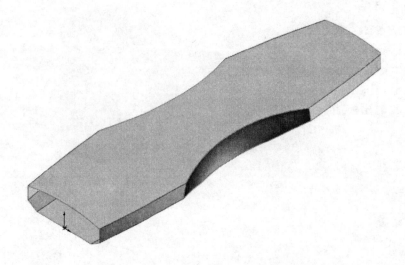

14. Filling the left side cutout:

- Rotate the view 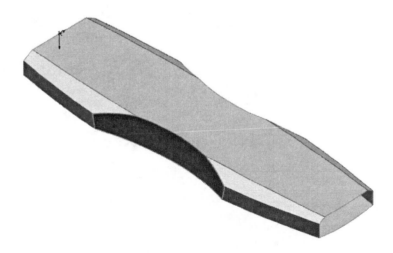 to the other side (or Hold the Shift key and press the Up arrow key twice (rotate 90° per key stroke).

- Repeat step 13 to fill the left side cutout with a new surface.

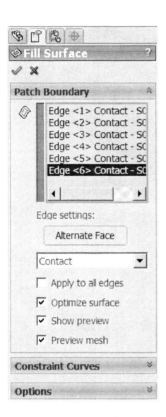

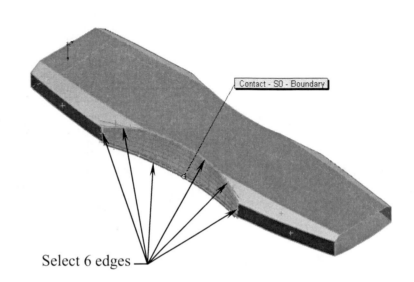

Select 6 edges

- The left side cutout is filled with a new surface (Surface-Fill2)

15. Filling the front opening using Planar Surface:

- Click 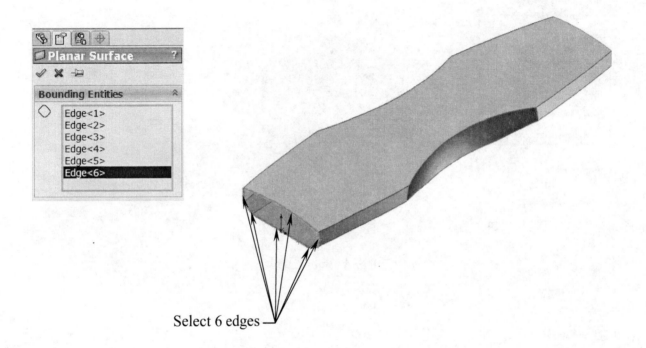 or select **Insert / Surface / Planar**.

- For Boundary Entities: select all **6** edges on the front opening .

- Click **OK** .

Select 6 edges —

- The front opening is filled with a planar surface (Surface-Plane1).

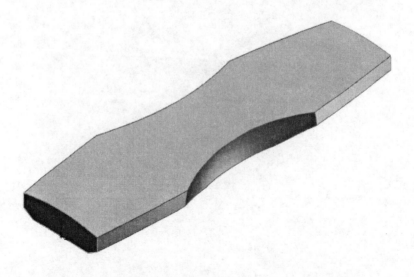

16. Filling the rear opening using Planar Surface:

- Click or select **Insert / Surface / Planar**.

- For Boundary Entities: select all **6** edges on the rear opening .

- Click **OK** .

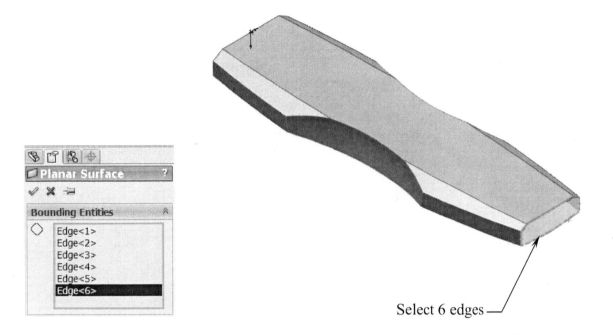

Select 6 edges

- The rear opening is filled with a planar surface (Surface-Plane2).

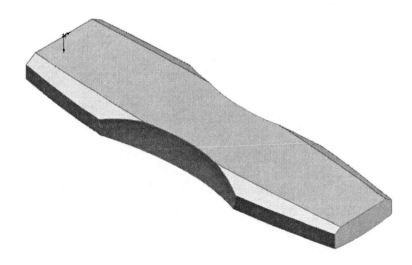

17. Combining all surfaces with Surface-Knit:

- Click 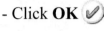 or select **Insert** / **Surface** / **Knit**.

- For Surfaces/Faces-To-Knit, select all **5** surfaces .

- Click **OK** .

> ### Knit Surface
>
> Combines two or more faces and surfaces into one

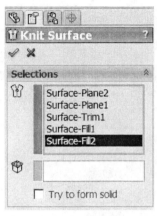

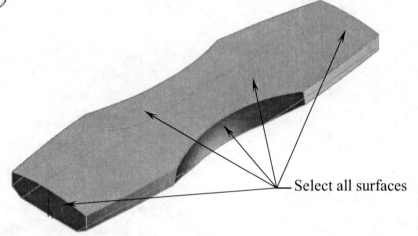

Select all surfaces

- All 5 surfaces are knitted and combined into one (Surface-Knit1).

18. Adding .500" fillets:

- Click  or select **Insert** / **Features** / **Fillet/Round**.

- Type **.500 in**. for Radius .

- Select **8** vertical edges as shown .

- Click **OK** .

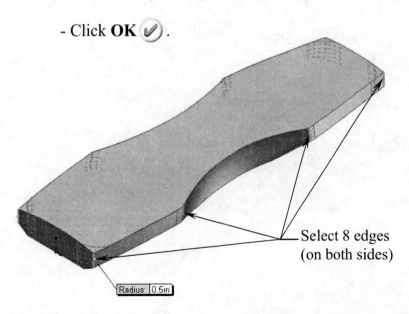

Select 8 edges
(on both sides)

Radius: 0.5in

19. Adding .125" fillets:

- Click  or select **Insert / Features / Fillet/ Round**.

- Type **.125 in**. for Radius .

- Select **all edges** as shown for Edges/ Faces to fillet .

- Tangent Propagation: **Enabled** .

- Click **OK** .

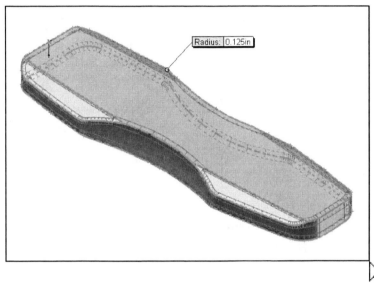

Box-Select to
group all edges
(on both sides)

- Compare your model with this image. Rotate the model to make sure that all edges are filleted.

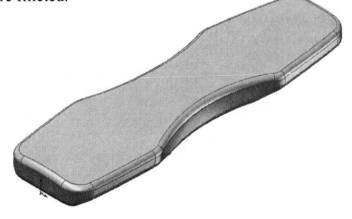

20. Creating a solid from the surface model:

- Click 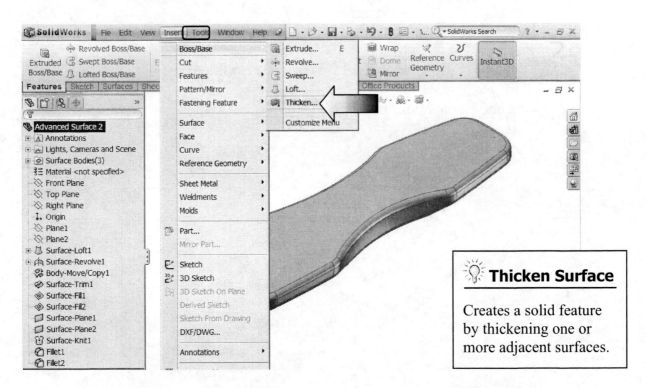 or select **Thicken** from the **Insert / Boss-Base** menu.

Thicken Surface

Creates a solid feature by thickening one or more adjacent surfaces.

- For **Surface-To-Thicken**: Select the face indicated ⬛ or select the **Surface-Knit1** from the Feature Tree.

- For thickness Direction: Select **Thicken Side 2** ⬛ (Inside).

- For Thickness: Enter **.060 in**. `0.060in` .

- Click **OK** ✅.

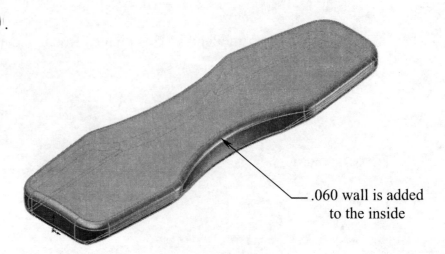

.060 wall is added to the inside

21. Sketching the cut profile: (to split the part into 2 halves)

- Select the RIGHT plane from the FeatureManager tree.

- Click or select **Insert / Sketch**.

- Sketch a 3-Point-Arc and add dimension as shown.

- Add a **Mid-point** relation between the end points of the arc and the

outer-most edges.

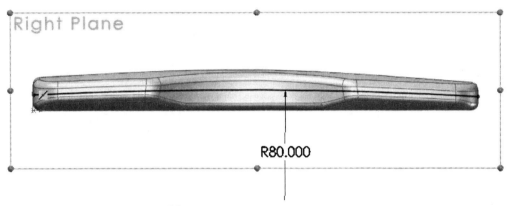

R80.000

22. Removing the Upper Half:

- Click or select **Insert / Cut / Extrude**.

- Extrude Type: **Through All** (default)

- Direction 2:   **Through All** (default)

- Click **OK** . (use Flip-side-to-Cut if needed)

The direction of the
middle arrow indicates
which half is being
removed…

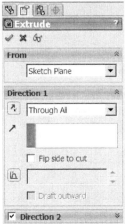

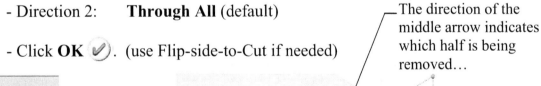

- The Upper Half of the part is removed.

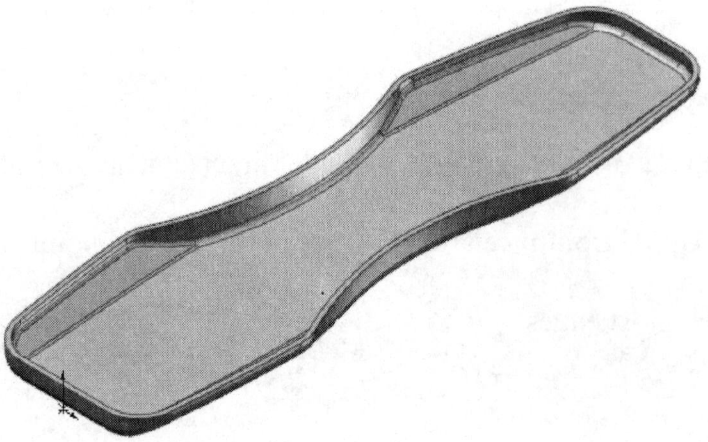

- Rotate the part around 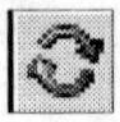 to see the other side.

23. Saving the lower half of the part: Original

- Select **File / Save As / Lower-Half / Save**.

---

24. Saving the upper half of the part: Copy

- Select **File / Save As / Upper Half**

- Enable the **Save As Copy** check box and click **Save**.

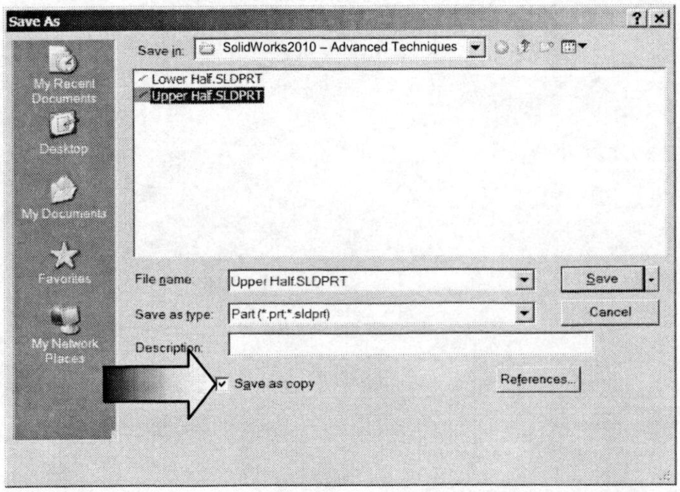

- This saves an exact copy of the same part with a different name, so that we can modify it and make the other half.

25. Modifying the copied file:

- Select **File / Open**.

- Select the document **Upper-Half** and click **Open**.

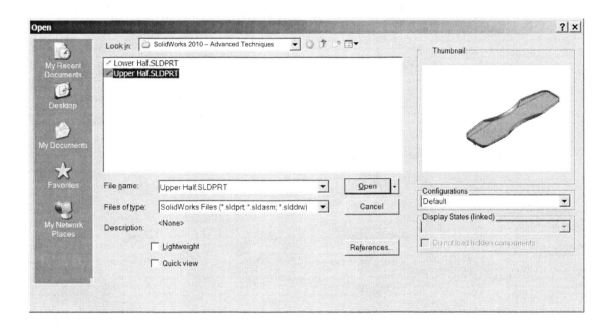

26. Changing the direction of the cut using the Flip-Side option:

- Right click on the **Cut-Extrude1** (the last feature on the tree) and select

Edit Feature .

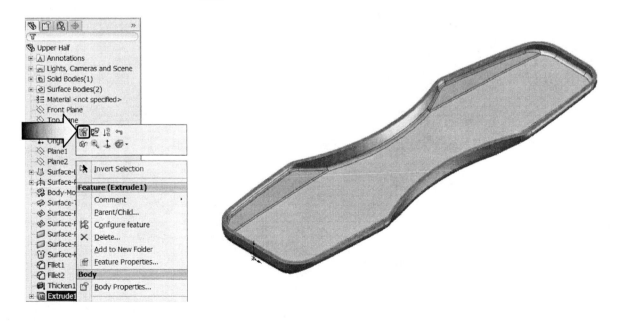

- Select **Flip Side To Cut** option ☑ Flip side to cut .

- Click **OK** ✅.

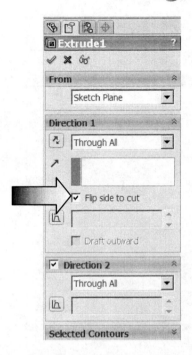

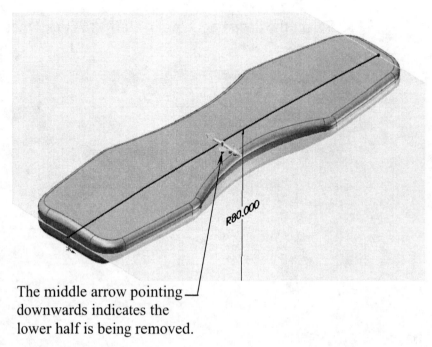

The middle arrow pointing downwards indicates the lower half is being removed.

- The Lower Half of the part is removed, leaving the Upper-Half as the result of the Flip-Side cut.

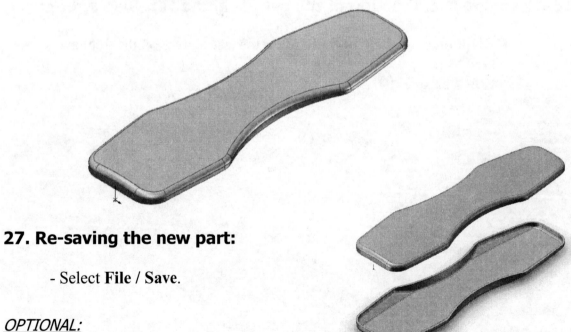

27. Re-saving the new part:

- Select **File / Save**.

OPTIONAL:

- Insert the 2 halves into an assembly document and assemble them as shown.

Questions for Review

Advanced Modeling with Surfaces

1. There are no limits on how many sections you can have in a loft feature.
   a. True
   b. False

2. Each loft section should be modeled onto a different plane.
   a. True
   b. False

3. The guide curves for use in a loft feature must be Coincident or Pierce to the sections.
   a. True
   b. False

4. Surfaces cannot be mirrored as solid features.
   a. True
   b. False

5. Only two surfaces can be used for knitting at a time.
   a. True
   b. False

6. Fillets cannot be used with surfaces, only in solid models.
   a. True
   b. False

7. Surfaces can be thickened after they are knitted together.
   a. True
   b. False

8. Mass properties options such as volume, surface area, etc., are available for all surfaces.
   a. True
   b. False

9. Surfaces can be knitted into a closed volume and thickened into a solid.
   a. True
   b. False

1. TRUE   2. TRUE
3. TRUE   4. FALSE
5. FALSE   6. FALSE
7. TRUE   8. FALSE
            9. TRUE

Exercise: Loft

1. Create 2 new Planes offset from Top plane

2. Sketch the 1st Profile

3. Sketch the 2nd Profile

4. Sketch the 3rd Profile

5. **Solid-Loft** the Profiles

6. Shell to .020" thick, remove 3 Faces, & add the Raised features.

CHAPTER 9

Advanced Surfaces

Using Offset Surface 🗐 & Ruled Surface 🖎

- The Offset Surface command creates a new surface from a *single face* or a *set of faces*, with a distance of zero or greater. The offset surface can be created inward or outward.

Offset Surface

Offset from a single face   *Offset from a set of faces*

- The Ruled Surface command creates a new surface from a single edge or a set of edges. The ruled surface can either be perpendicular or tapered from the selected edges.

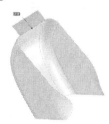

Ruled Surface

Ruled surface from a single edge   *Ruled surface from a set of edges*

- The Offset Surface and the Ruled Surface are used to create reference surfaces that help to define the solid features in a part. In most cases, these surfaces should be knitted together before the next operation like extruded cut, fillets etc., can be performed.

Advanced Surfaces Using
Surface Offset & Ruled

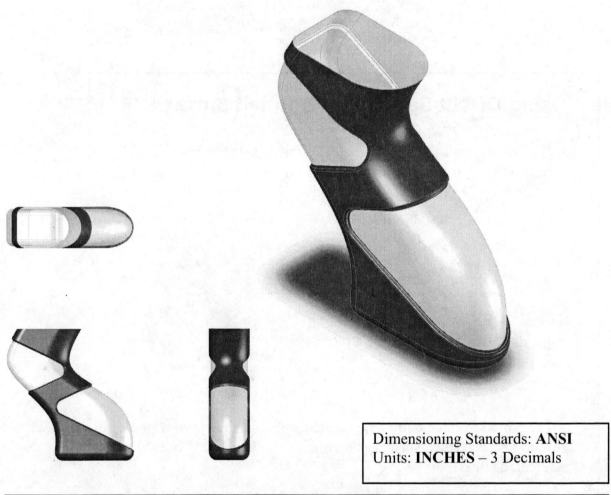

Dimensioning Standards: **ANSI**
Units: **INCHES** – 3 Decimals

Tools Needed:

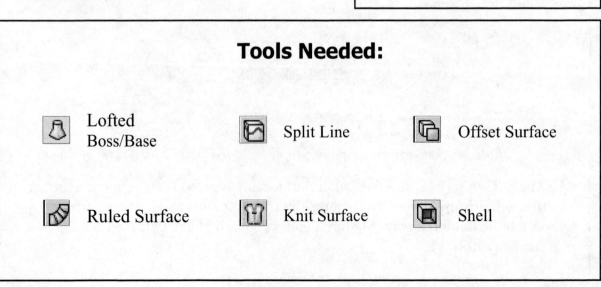

Lofted Boss/Base

Split Line

Offset Surface

Ruled Surface

Knit Surface

Shell

Advanced Surface Modeling
Using Offset & Ruled Surface options

1. Opening the existing file:

- Go to: Training CD – OR – The Web link
Class Files folder
and open a copy:
Surface_Offset_Ruled.sldprt

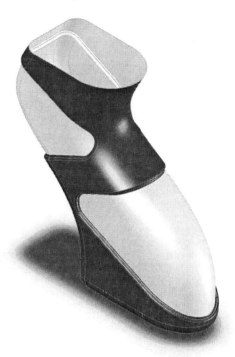

- This document contains several sketches for use
as the Loft Profiles, and 2 other sketches for use
as the Guide Curves to help control the transition
between each profile.

- This lesson focuses on the use of the Offset and
Ruled Surface commands.

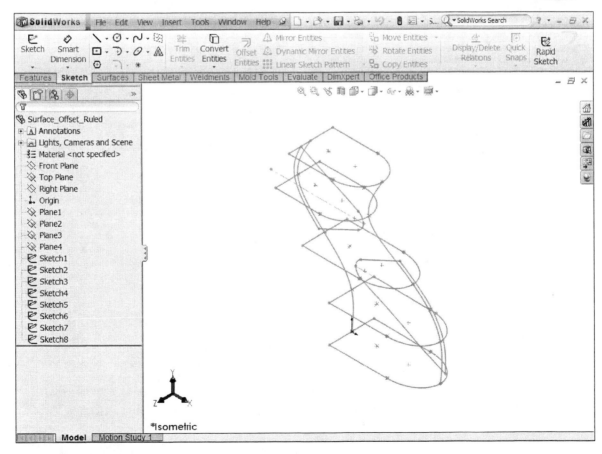

2. Creating the Base Loft:

- Click  or select **Insert / Boss-Base / Loft**.

- Select the 5 Loft Profiles and the 2 Guide Curves as noted below.

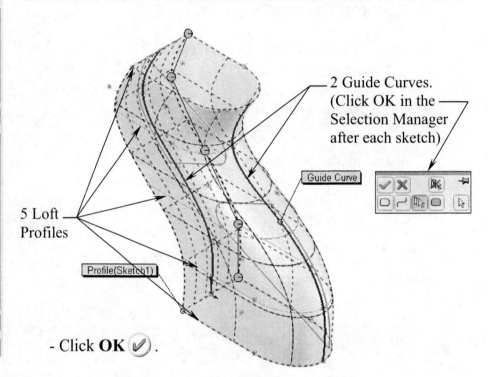

2 Guide Curves.
(Click OK in the
Selection Manager
after each sketch)

Guide Curve

5 Loft
Profiles

Profile(Sketch1)

- Click **OK** .

3. Adding .250" fillets:

- Click  or select **Insert / Features / Fillet-Round**.

- Enter **.250 in**. for Radius value.

- Select the edges as Shown, to add the fillets.

- Click **OK** .

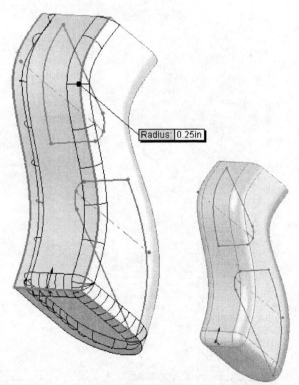

Radius: 0.25in

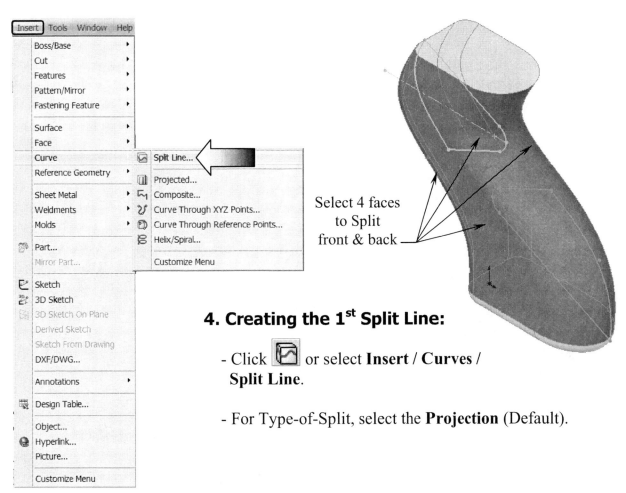

Select 4 faces
to Split
front & back

4. Creating the 1ˢᵗ Split Line:

- Click 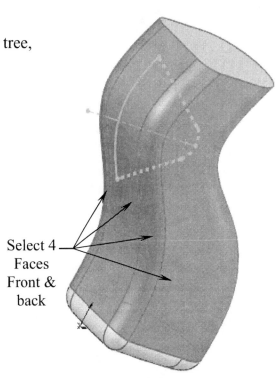 or select **Insert / Curves / Split Line**.

- For Type-of-Split, select the **Projection** (Default).

- Select the **Sketch7** from the FeatureManager tree, for Sketch-To-Project.

- Select the 4 faces as indicated to split.

- Click **OK** ✅.

- The Handle body now has a new set of surfaces, which will help define the next steps: The recessed area.

Select 4
Faces
Front &
back

5. Creating the 2nd Split Line:

- Using the **Sketch8**, repeat step number 3 to create the 2nd Split Line.

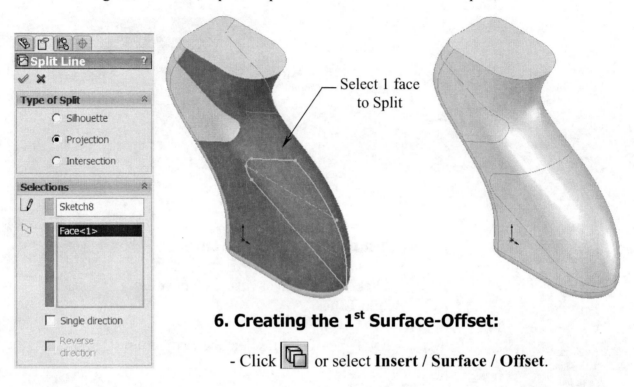

Select 1 face
to Split

6. Creating the 1st Surface-Offset:

- Click or select **Insert / Surface / Offset**.

- Select the 5 Split-Faces to offset from.

- Enter **.050 in**. for Offset Distance **(Inside).**

- Click **OK**.

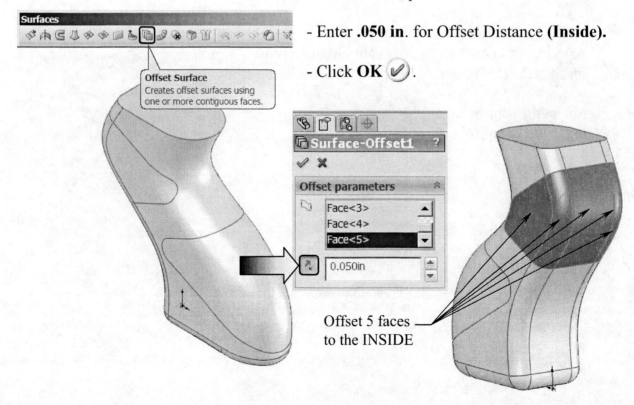

Offset 5 faces
to the INSIDE

7. Hiding the Solid Body:

- Right click on the upper surface of the solid body and select **HIDE**.

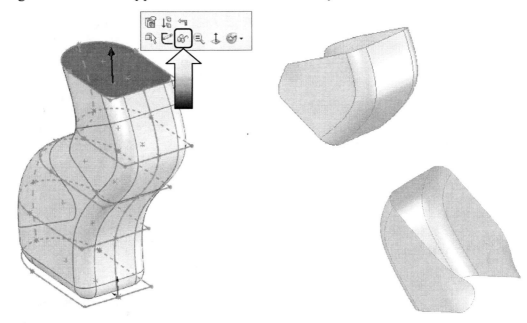

8. Creating the 1st Ruled Surface:

- Click the Ruled-Surface icon or select: **Insert / Surface / Ruled Surface**

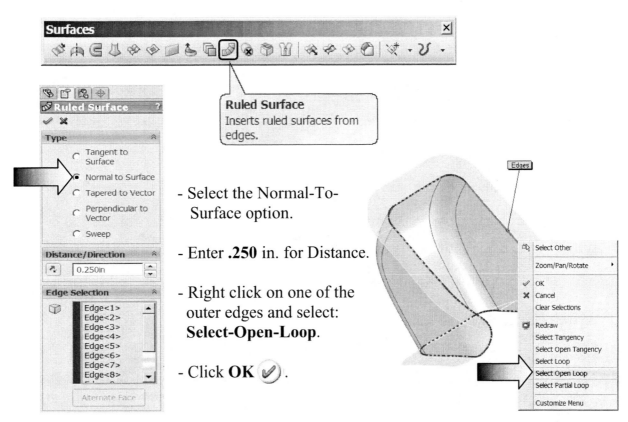

Ruled Surface
Inserts ruled surfaces from edges.

- Select the Normal-To-Surface option.

- Enter **.250** in. for Distance.

- Right click on one of the outer edges and select: **Select-Open-Loop**.

- Click **OK**.

- The resulted Ruled Surfaces.

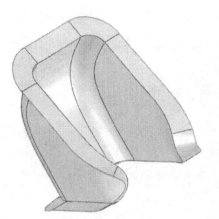

Ruled Surfaces

The Ruled Surface creates a set of surfaces that are either perpendicular or tapered from the selected edges.
These surfaces can also be used as the Interlock Surfaces in molded parts.

9. Knitting the 2 surfaces:

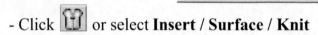

- Click 🔲 or select **Insert / Surface / Knit**

Knit Surface
Combines two or more adjacent, non-intersecting surfaces together.

- Select the Surface-Offset and the Ruled-Surface to knit.

- Disable the **GAP CONTROL** check box.

- Click **OK** .

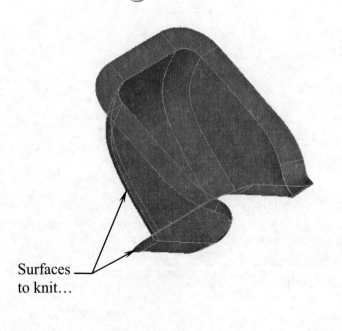

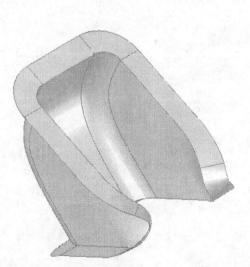

Surfaces to knit…

10. Adding .020" Fillets:

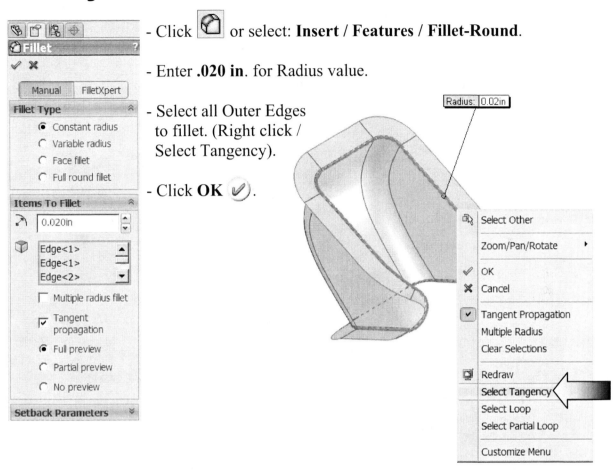

- Click 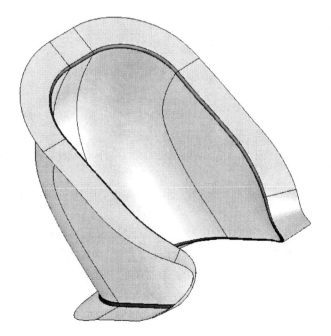 or select: **Insert / Features / Fillet-Round**.

- Enter **.020 in**. for Radius value.

- Select all Outer Edges to fillet. (Right click / Select Tangency).

- Click **OK**.

- The resulting fillets.

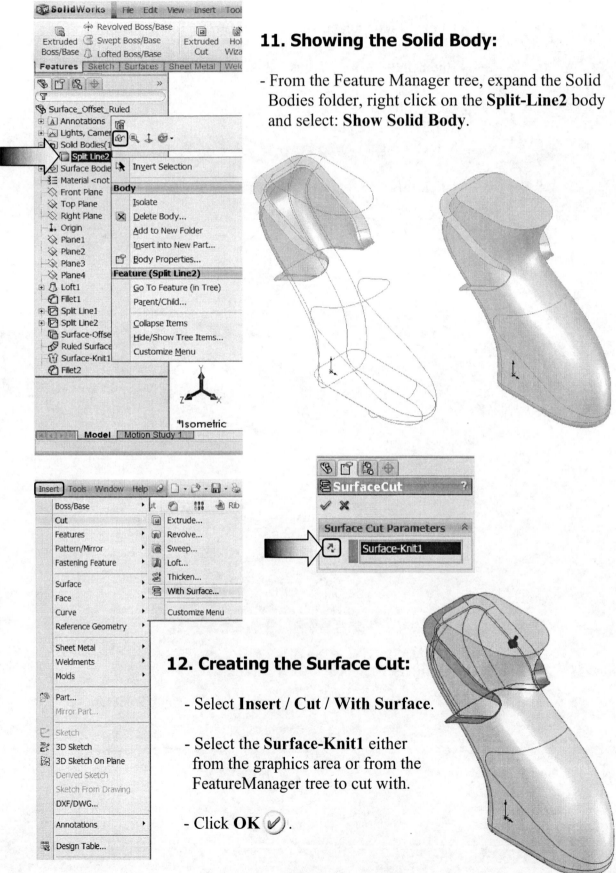

11. Showing the Solid Body:

- From the Feature Manager tree, expand the Solid Bodies folder, right click on the **Split-Line2** body and select: **Show Solid Body**.

12. Creating the Surface Cut:

- Select **Insert / Cut / With Surface**.

- Select the **Surface-Knit1** either from the graphics area or from the FeatureManager tree to cut with.

- Click **OK** ✔.

13. Hiding the Knit Surface:

- Right click on the Knit Surface and Select **Hide**.

R/C
and
Hide

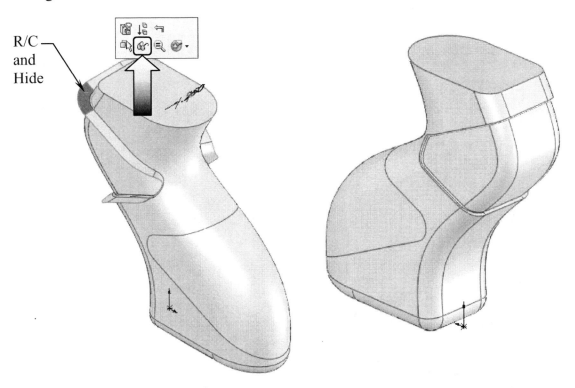

14. Creating the 2nd Ruled Surface:

- Repeat from step number 8 to create the 2nd Ruled Surface.

- Create the Surface Cut as instructed in step 12.
  (If the cut failed, change the OFFSET VALUE to .325in).

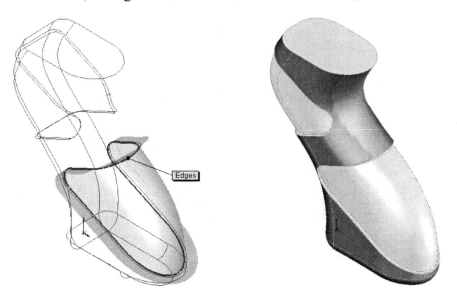

15. Adding more Fillets:

- Click 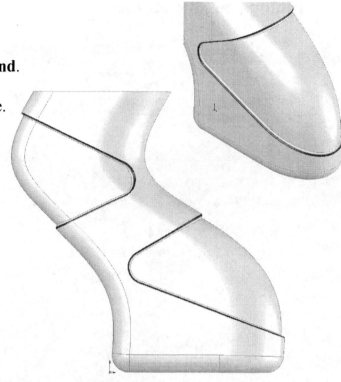 or select:
  Insert / Features / Fillet-Round.

- Enter **.020 in**. for Radius value.

- Select all Outer Edges of both
  upper and lower cuts, to fillet.

- Click **OK** .

16. Shelling the part:

- Select the uppermost face as shown.

- Click 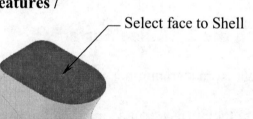 or select **Insert / Features /
  Shell**.

— Select face to Shell

- Enter **.020 in.** for thickness.

- Click **OK** .

17. Saving your work:

- Click **File / Save As**.

- Enter: **Surface_Offset_Ruled** for file name.

- Click **Save**.

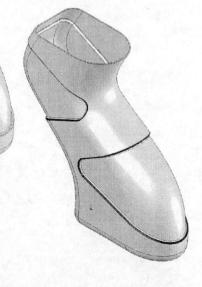

Exercise: Advanced Modeling

1. Opening an Existing file:

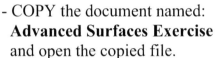

- Go to the Training CD or the Web link.

- Training Files folder.

- COPY the document named: **Advanced Surfaces Exercise** and open the copied file.

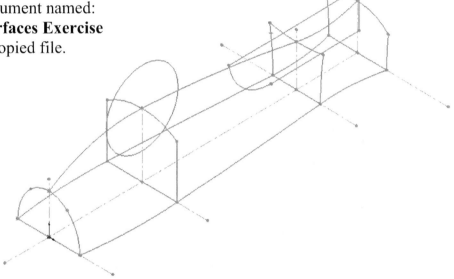

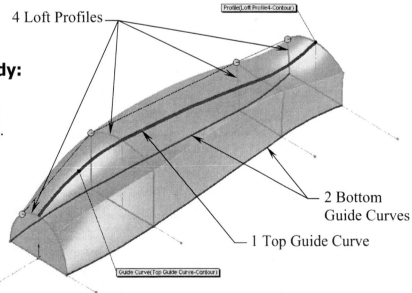

4 Loft Profiles

Profile(Loft Profile4-Contour)

2 Bottom Guide Curves

1 Top Guide Curve

Guide Curve(Top Guide Curve-Contour)

2. Creating the Loft body:

- Create a *SOLID* loft from the 4 profiles as indicated.

- Use the 2 Bottom Guide Curves to control the sides.

- Use the Top Guide-Curve to control the Upper curvatures.

3. Adding Fillets:

- Add a **.500 in**. fillet to the upper edges, and a .250 in. fillet to the edges on the end, as shown.

(By adding the fillets in the sketches the tangent lines can be eliminated using the Merge Tangent Faces option).

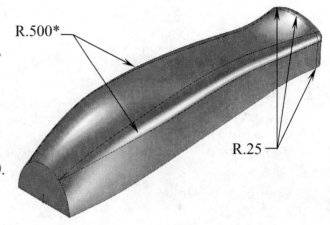

4. Creating the Split Lines & Lofted-Cuts:

- Use the 2 sketches named: Circular-Split and Side-Split to create 2 split surfaces.

- Create 2 lofted-cuts at **.093** in. deep, using the **Offset** or **Ruled** surface options.

5. Adding the Nose and Fillets:

- Add the Nose feature that measured **1.250 in**. from the front face.

- Remove all sharp edges with **.040 in**. Fillets.

4. Saving your work:

- Save the exercise as: **Advanced Surfaces Exe**.

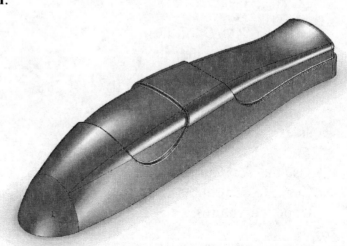

Exercise: Advanced Surfacing Techniques

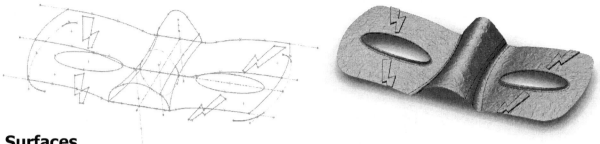

Surfaces

- Surfaces are a type of geometry that can be used to create solid features. Surfaces can be created in a variety of different ways; from a sketch or multiple sketches, a surface can be made by extruding, revolving, sweeping or lofting.
- Surfaces are normally created individually and knitted together so that an enclosed volume, or a solid feature, can be generated afterwards.
- This exercise discusses some advanced techniques on surfacing, to create the mask as pictured above.

1. Opening the existing document named:

Advanced Surfacing from the network drive (or CD).

2. Creating the 1st Lofted Surface:

- Click [ ] or select:

   Insert / Surface / Loft.

- Select the **2 Loft Profiles** and the **2 Guide Curves** as indicated.

- Click **OK** .

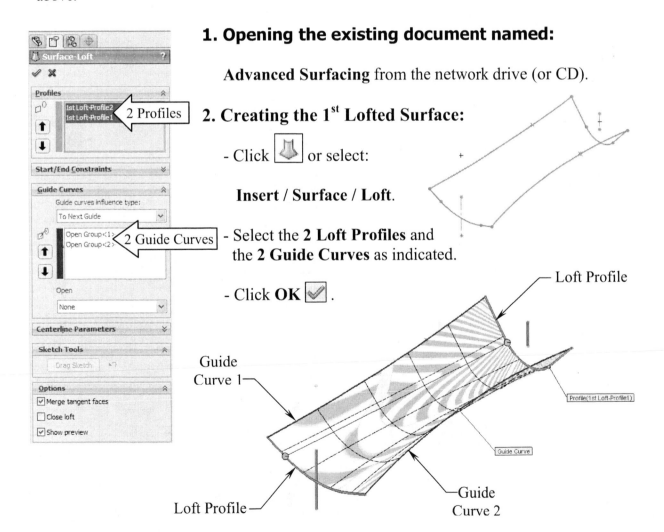

Lofted-Surface creates a feature by making transitions between two or more profiles. A loft Can either be a surface or a solid and one or more Guide Curves can be used to guide the transitions between the profiles.

3. Creating the 2nd Lofted Surface:

- Click 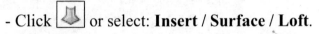 or select: **Insert / Surface / Loft**.

- Select the **3 Loft Profiles** and the **4 Guide Curves** as indicated.

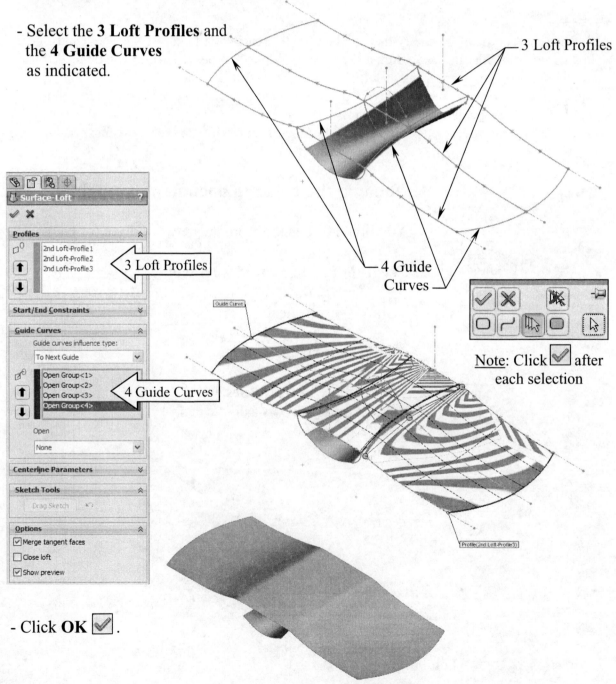

3 Loft Profiles

4 Guide Curves

Note: Click ☑ after each selection

- Click **OK** ☑.

4. Creating the Boundary-Surfaces:

- Click [icon] or select **Insert / Surface / Boundary-Surface**.

- For **Direction 1**, select the **2 edges** as shown (Blue tags).

> **Boundary-Surface**
> creates a new surface from a set of 2D or 3D sketch entities.
> The Boundary Surface can be tangent or curvature-continuous in both directions (all sides of the surface).
> This option offers a higher quality result than the Loft.

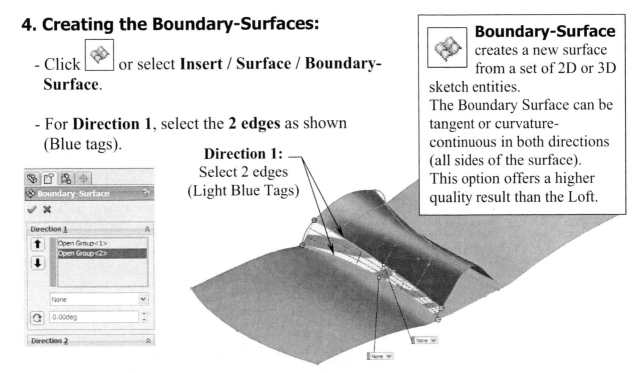

Direction 1:
Select 2 edges
(Light Blue Tags)

- For **Direction 2**, select the **3 Arcs** in the Boundary Sketch as shown (Purple tags).

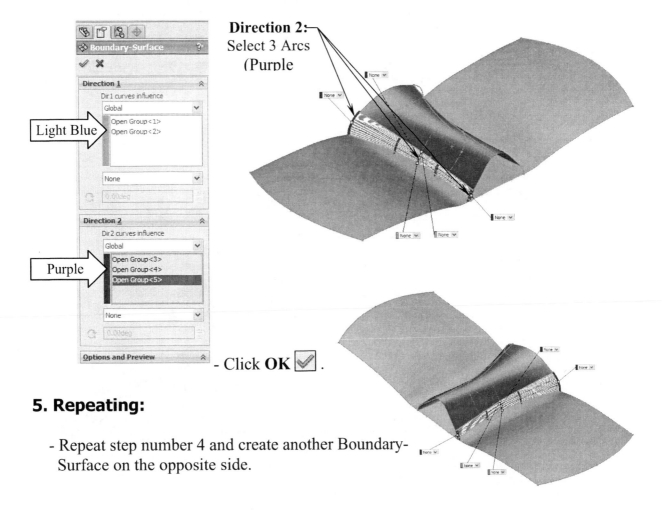

Direction 2:
Select 3 Arcs
(Purple

Light Blue

Purple

- Click **OK** [icon].

5. Repeating:

- Repeat step number 4 and create another Boundary-Surface on the opposite side.

6. Creating an Extruded-Surface:

- Select the **Eyes Sketch** from the FeatureManager tree and Click [icon] or select:
  Insert / Surface / Extrude.

- Change the option **Extrude From** to **Surface/Face/Plane** (Arrow)

- Select the surface as indicated, to extrude from.

> **Extruded-Surface**
> creates a new surface
> from a 2D or 3D sketch,
> which protrudes normal to the
> sketch plane.

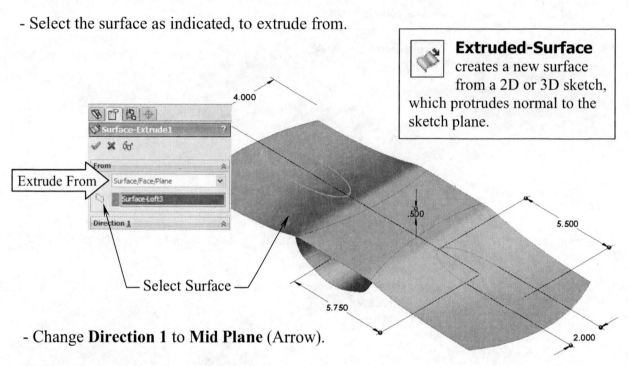

- Change **Direction 1** to **Mid Plane** (Arrow).

- Enter **.410in**. for Extrude Depth.

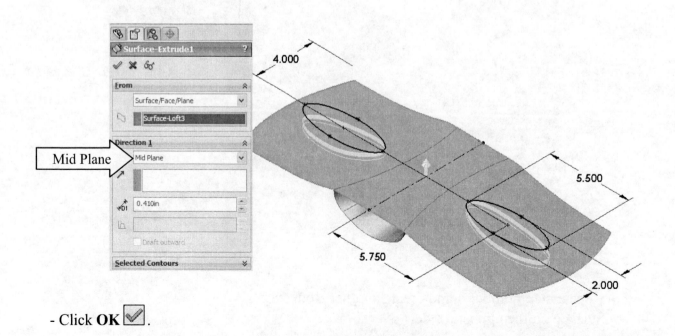

- Click **OK** [icon].

7. Creating a Trimmed Surface:

- Click 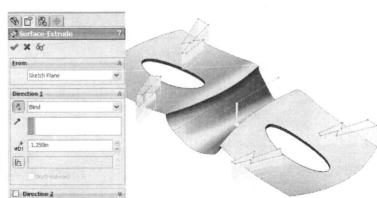 or select **Insert / Surface / Trim**.

- Select **Mutual** under Trim Type (Arrow).

- For **Trimming Surfaces**, select **all surfaces** of the model.

- For **Pieces To Remove**, select the **5 Faces** as shown (Arrow).

> **Trimmed-Surface**
> Uses a plane, a surface,
> or a sketch as a trim tool
> to trim the intersecting surfaces.

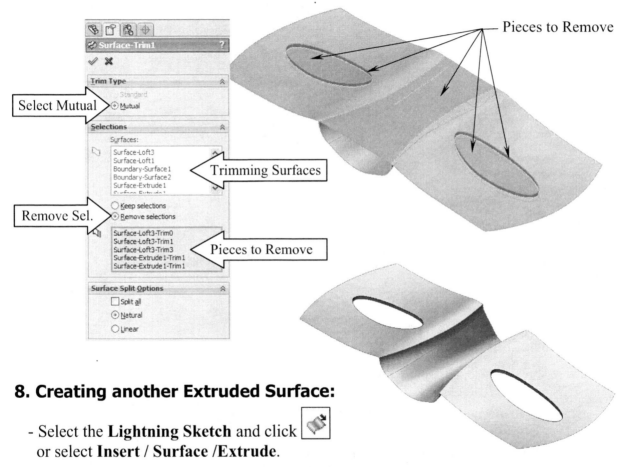

Pieces to Remove

Select Mutual

Trimming Surfaces

Remove Sel.

Pieces to Remove

8. Creating another Extruded Surface:

- Select the **Lightning Sketch** and click
  or select **Insert / Surface /Extrude**.

- Set the **Direction 1** to **Blind**

and click **Reverse Direction**.

- Set **Extrude Depth** to:
  1.250in.

- Click **OK**.

9. Creating an Offset-Surface:

- Click 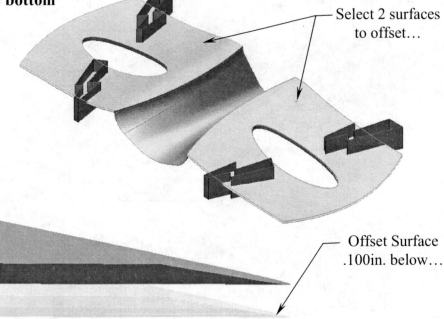 or select **Insert / Surface / Offset**.

- Select the **2 surfaces** as shown (Arrow).

- Enter **.100in**. for **Offset Distance**.

- Place the copy on the **bottom** of the original.

- Click **OK** ✓.

> **Offset-Surface** creates a copy of a surface in either directions, and is parallel to the selected surface(s). The offset distance can be Zero or any other value.

Select 2 surfaces to offset…

Offset Surface .100in. below…

10. Creating a Mutual Trimmed Surface:

- Click or select **Insert / Surface / Trim**.

- Select **Mutual** under Trim Type (Arrow).

- For **Trimming Surfaces**, select **all surfaces** of the Thunder Sketch and the Offset Surfaces.

Trimming Surfaces

Trimming Surfaces

Select Mutual

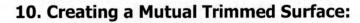

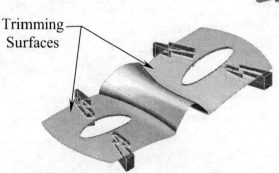

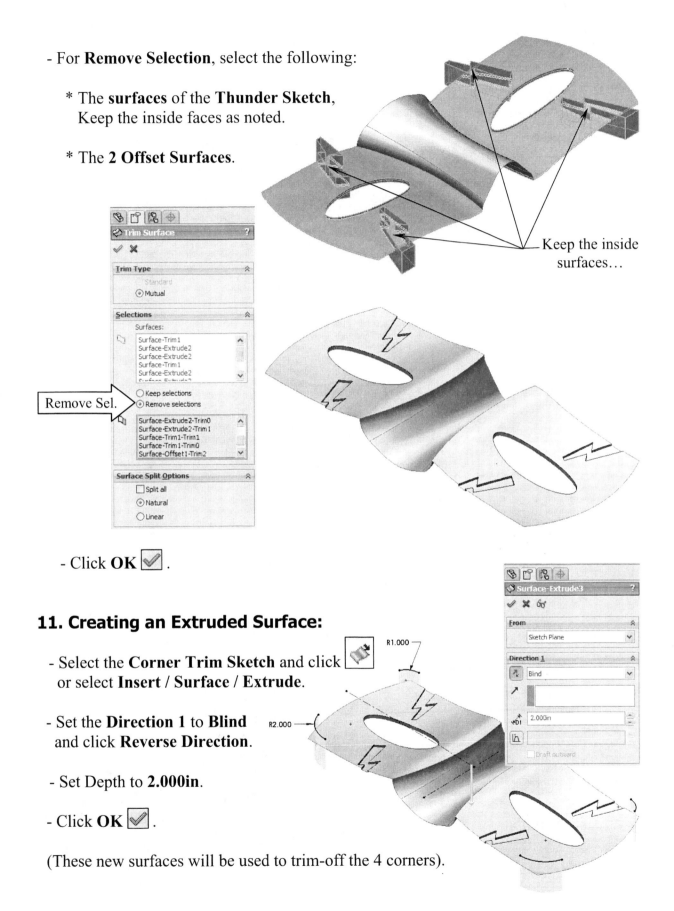

- For **Remove Selection**, select the following:

  * The **surfaces** of the **Thunder Sketch**,
    Keep the inside faces as noted.

  * The **2 Offset Surfaces**.

Keep the inside
surfaces...

Remove Sel.

- Click **OK** .

11. Creating an Extruded Surface:

- Select the **Corner Trim Sketch** and click
  or select **Insert / Surface / Extrude**.

- Set the **Direction 1** to **Blind**
  and click **Reverse Direction**.

- Set Depth to **2.000in**.

- Click **OK** .

(These new surfaces will be used to trim-off the 4 corners).

12. Creating a corner Trimmed Surface:

- Click ⬚ or select **Insert / Surface / Trim**.

- Select **Mutual** under Trim Type (Arrow).

- For **Trimming Surfaces**, select the following:

   * The **4 extruded faces** and the **4 corner pieces**.

   * The **2 left/right faces** of the model.

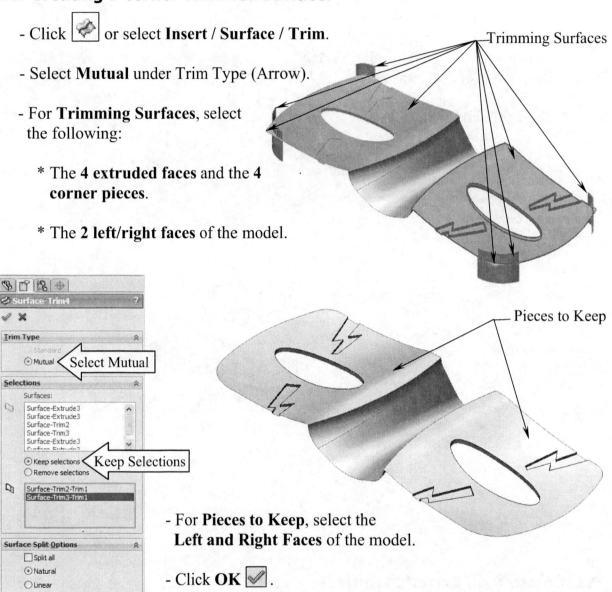

Trimming Surfaces

Pieces to Keep

- For **Pieces to Keep**, select the **Left and Right Faces** of the model.

- Click **OK** ✓.

13. Creating a Knit-Surface:

- Click 🧵 or select **Insert / Surface / Knit**.

- Select **all surfaces** either from the FeatureManager tree, or from the graphics area.

- Enable Minimum Adjustment.

- Click **OK** ✓.

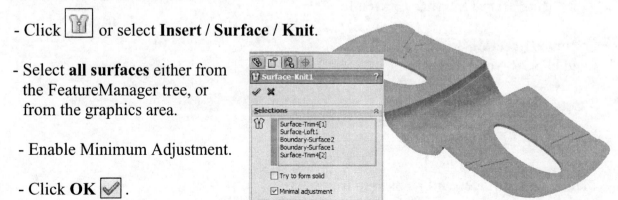

14. Adding a Variable Fillet:

- Click 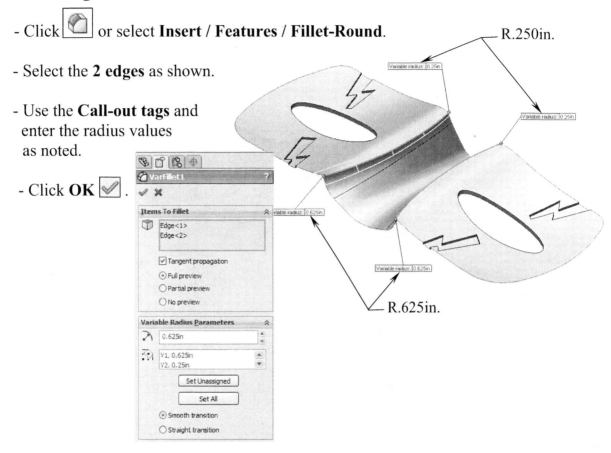 or select **Insert / Features / Fillet-Round**.

- Select the **2 edges** as shown.

- Use the **Call-out tags** and enter the radius values as noted.

- Click **OK**.

15. Adding a Constant Fillet:

- Click 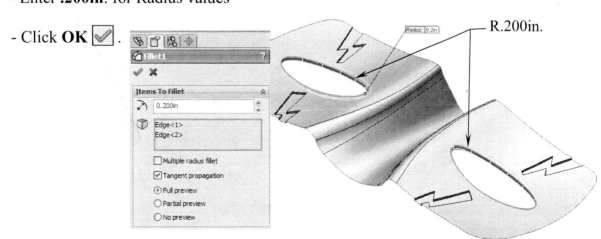 or select **Insert / Features / Fillet-Round**.

- Select the **2 edges** as shown.

- Enter **.200in**. for Radius values

- Click **OK**.

16. Optional: Adding texture

- From the **Appearances** folder, select the **Rubber/Texture** folder.

- Drag & Drop the **Textured Rubber** onto the part, select the Apply to Part option

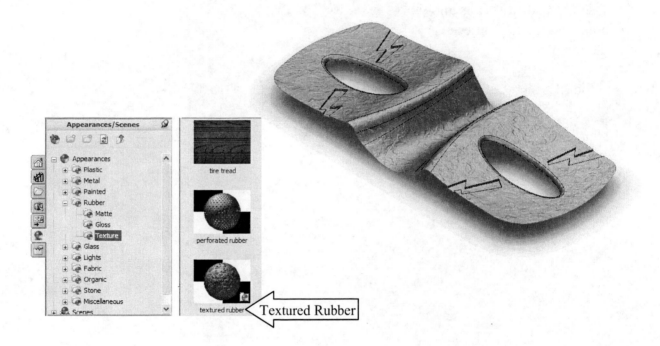

Textured Rubber

17. Saving your work:

- Click **File / Save As**.

- Enter **Advanced Surfacing Techniques** as file name.

- Click **Save**.

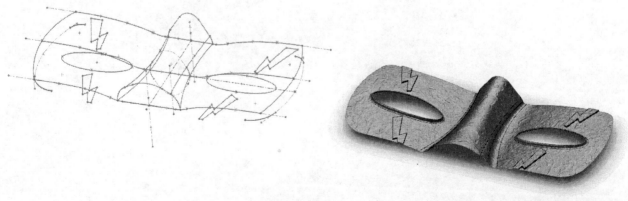

CHAPTER 10

Surfaces vs. Solid Modeling

Surfaces Vs. Solid Modeling

Surfaces are a type of geometry that can be used to create solid features. Surface tools are available on the Surfaces toolbar. You can <u>create surfaces</u> by these methods:

- Insert a planar surface from a sketch or from a set of closed edges that lie on a plane
- Extrude, revolve, sweep, or loft, from sketches
- Offset from existing faces or surfaces
- Import a file
- Create mid-surfaces
- Radiate surfaces

You can <u>modify surfaces</u> in the following ways:

- Extend
- Trim existing surfaces
- Un-trim surfaces
- Fillet surfaces
- Repair surfaces using Filled Surface
- Move/Copy surfaces
- Delete and patch a face
- Knit surfaces

You can <u>use surfaces</u> in the following ways:

- Select surface edges and vertices to use as a sweep guide curve and path.
- Create a solid or cut feature by thickening a surface.
- Extrude a solid or cut feature with the end condition Up to Surface or Offset from Surface.
- Create a solid feature by thickening surfaces that have been knit into a closed volume.
- Replace a face with a surface

Safety Helmet
Hybrid Modeling with Solid & Surfaces

| Dimensioning Standards: **ANSI** |
| Units: **INCHES** – 3 Decimals |

Tools Needed:

Insert Sketch	Plane	Lofted Surface
Swept Surface	Planar Surface	Knit Surface
Revolved Cut	Swept Cut	Surface Thicken

1. Opening the Existing file:

- From the Training CD,

(or the Web-link), open

the document named:

Helmet.

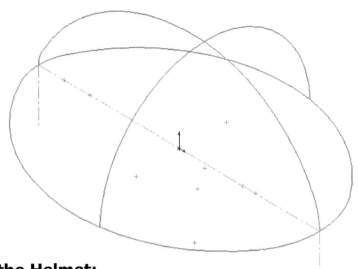

2. Constructing the Body of the Helmet:

- Click **Lofted Surface** 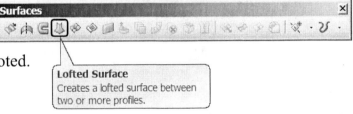 OR – select **Insert / Surface / Loft**.

- Select the 3 Sketch Profiles.

- Select the 3 Guide Curves as noted.

- Click **OK** ✅.

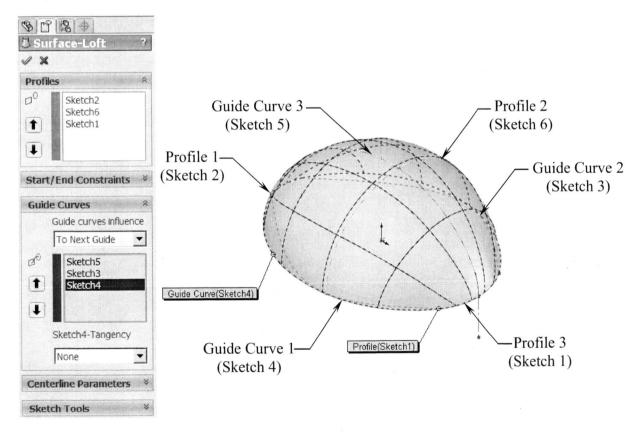

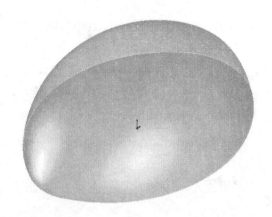

- The resulted Surface-Loft.

3. Creating a new work plane

- Create a plane **Normal To Curve** as illustrated.

- **(Insert / Reference Geometry / Plane)**.

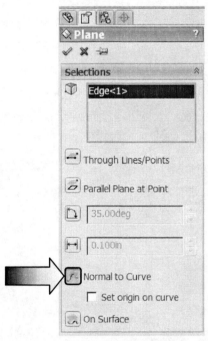

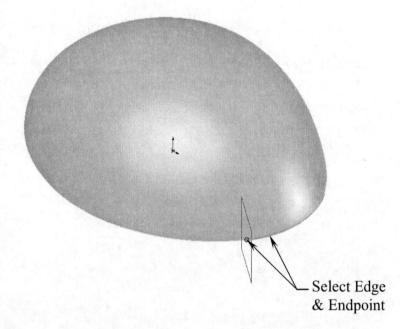

Select Edge
& Endpoint

4. Sketching the Sweep-Profile:

- Open a new sketch on the
New plane and sketch a
Vertical Line as shown.

- Add a **3.00 in**. dimension to
Fully define the sketch.

- **Exit the Sketch** .

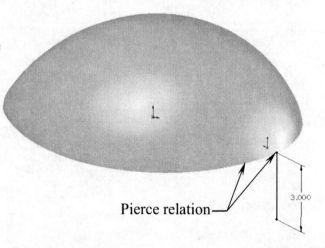

Pierce relation

3.000

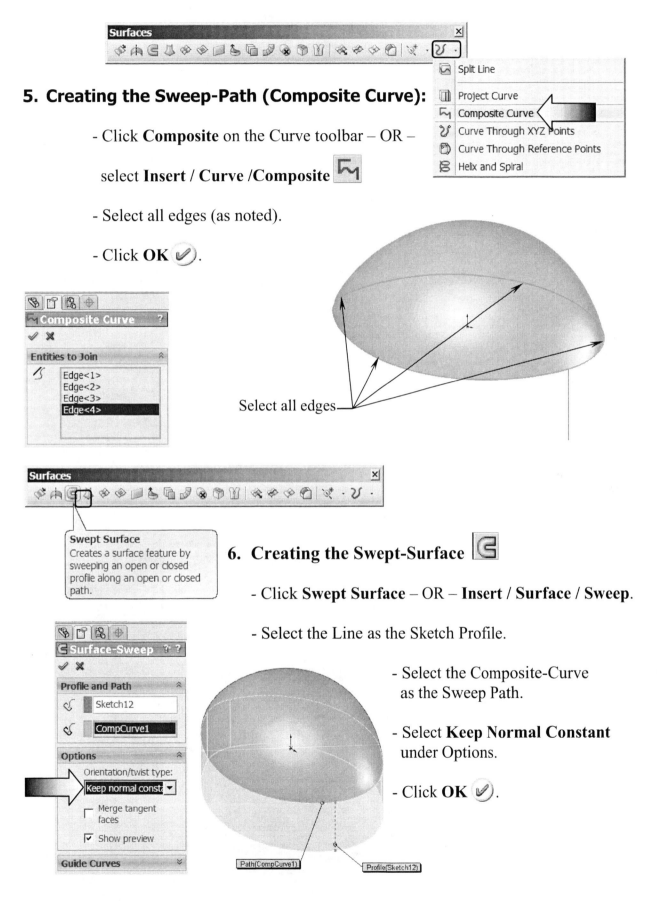

5. Creating the Sweep-Path (Composite Curve):

- Click **Composite** on the Curve toolbar – OR –

select **Insert / Curve /Composite**

- Select all edges (as noted).

- Click **OK**.

Split Line
Project Curve
Composite Curve
Curve Through XYZ Points
Curve Through Reference Points
Helix and Spiral

Composite Curve

Entities to Join

Edge<1>
Edge<2>
Edge<3>
Edge<4>

Select all edges

Swept Surface
Creates a surface feature by sweeping an open or closed profile along an open or closed path.

6. Creating the Swept-Surface

- Click **Swept Surface** – OR – **Insert / Surface / Sweep**.

- Select the Line as the Sketch Profile.

- Select the Composite-Curve as the Sweep Path.

- Select **Keep Normal Constant** under Options.

- Click **OK**.

Surface-Sweep

Profile and Path

Sketch12

CompCurve1

Options

Orientation/twist type:

Keep normal consta

Merge tangent faces

Show preview

Guide Curves

Path(CompCurve1)   Profile(Sketch12)

7. Adding a Planar Surface:

- Click **Planar Surface** – OR –
Insert / Surface / Planar.

- Select **all edges** on the bottom
as the Bounding Entities.

- Click **OK** 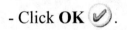.

- The new surface covers
the bottom of the part.

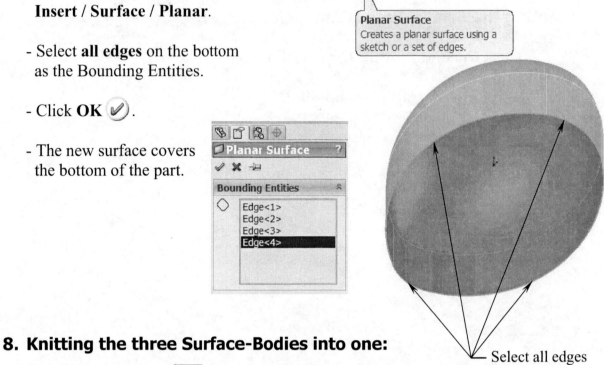

Planar Surface
Creates a planar surface using a
sketch or a set of edges.

Select all edges

8. Knitting the three Surface-Bodies into one:

- Click **Knit Surface** OR – select **Insert / Surface / Knit**.

- Select the Lofted-Surface, the Swept-Surface and the Planar-Surface either from the
FeatureManager tree or from the graphics area.

- Click **OK** 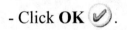.

- The three surfaces are
knitted into one.

Knit Surface
Combines two or more
adjacent, non-intersecting
surfaces together.

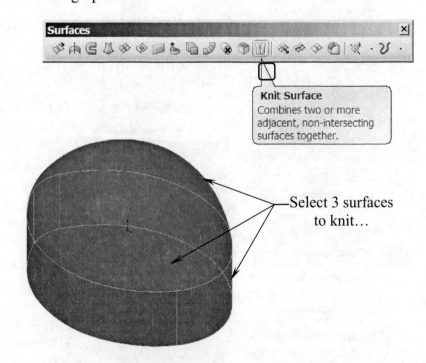

Select 3 surfaces
to knit...

9. Thickening the Surface-Knit (Closed Volume):

- Click 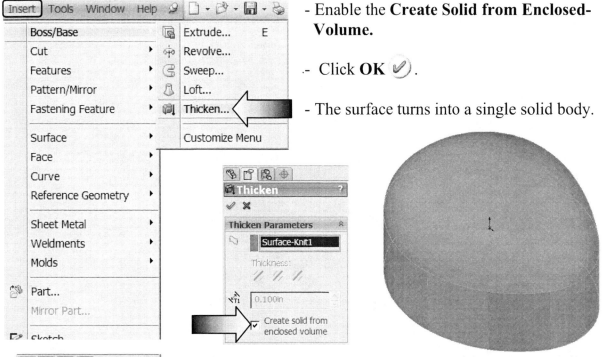 or select **Insert / Boss-Base / Thicken**.

- Select the Surface-Knit either from the FeatureManager tree or from the Graphics area.

- Enable the **Create Solid from Enclosed-Volume.**

- Click **OK** ✅ .

- The surface turns into a single solid body.

10. Adding an Extruded Cut feature:

- Show and edit the **Sketch8** from the Feature Manager Tree.

- This sketch will be used to shape the *outside* of the Helmet.

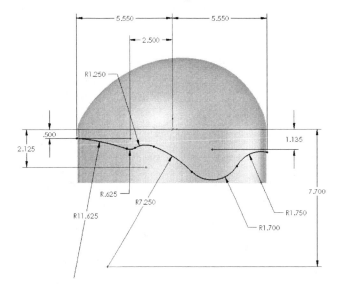

- Click **Extruded-Cut**  OR – **Insert / Cut / Extrude**.

- Use **Through-All** end conditions for both **Direction 1** and **Direction 2**.

- Enable **Flip-Side-To-Cut** if needed to remove the lower portion of the part.

- Click **OK** ✅.

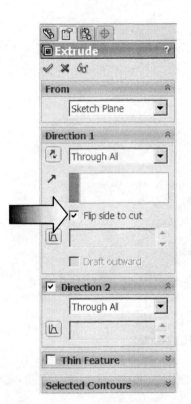

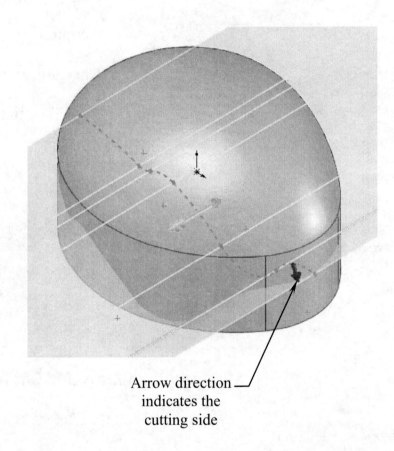

Arrow direction indicates the cutting side

- The resulted cut.

- Hide the Sketch8.

- Compare your model with this illustration before moving to the next step.

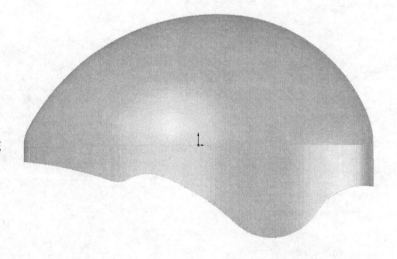

11. Adding a Revolve-Cut feature:

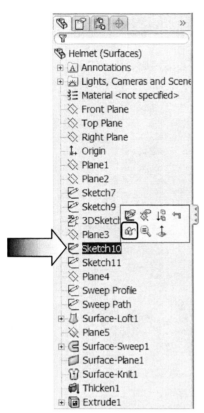

- Show and edit the **Sketch10** from the Feature Manager Tree.

- This sketch will be used to shape the *inside* of the Helmet.

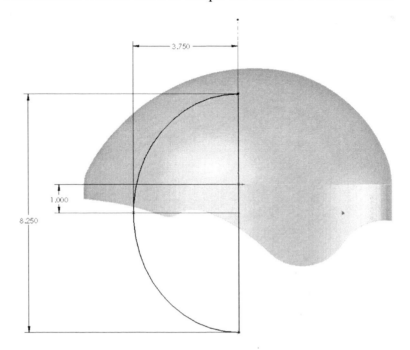

- Click **Revolve-Cut**  OR – select **Insert / Cut / Revolve**.

- Select the Vertical Centerline as Revolve-Direction.

- Revolve Angle: **360.00deg**.

- Click **OK** ✅.

- Hide the Sketch10.

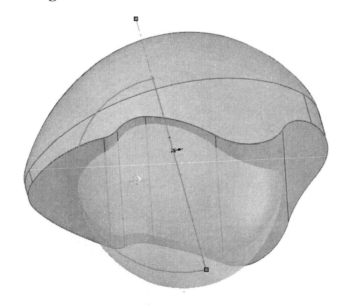

12. Adding the side cut features:

- Show and edit the **Sketch9** from the Feature Manager Tree.

- This sketch will be used to cut from the *inside* with a **1.00deg**. draft angle.

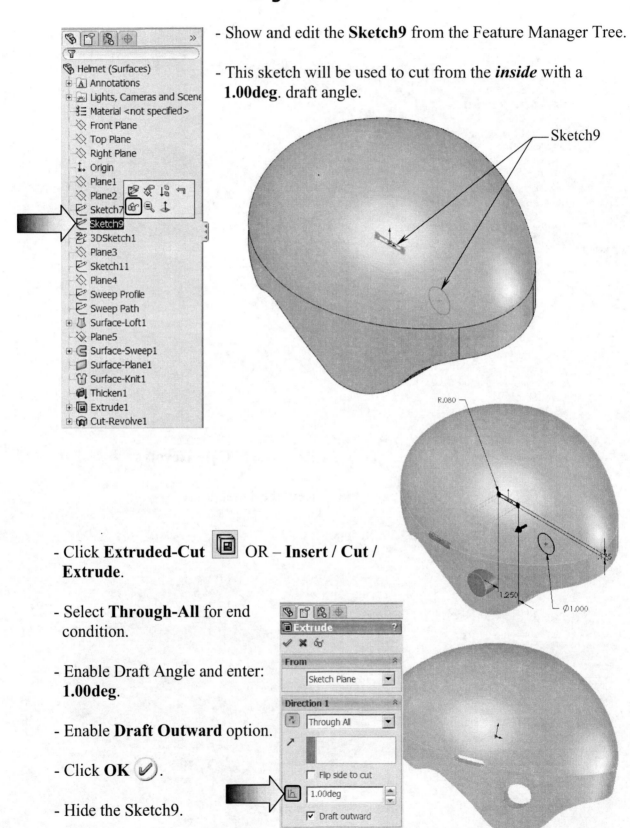

Sketch9

- Click **Extruded-Cut** OR – **Insert / Cut / Extrude**.

- Select **Through-All** for end condition.

- Enable Draft Angle and enter: **1.00deg**.

- Enable **Draft Outward** option.

- Click **OK**.

- Hide the Sketch9.

13. Creating the cut-out slot:

- Show and edit the **Sketch11** from the Feature Manager Tree.

- This sketch will be used to cut a slot from the *outside* with a **10.00deg.** draft angle.

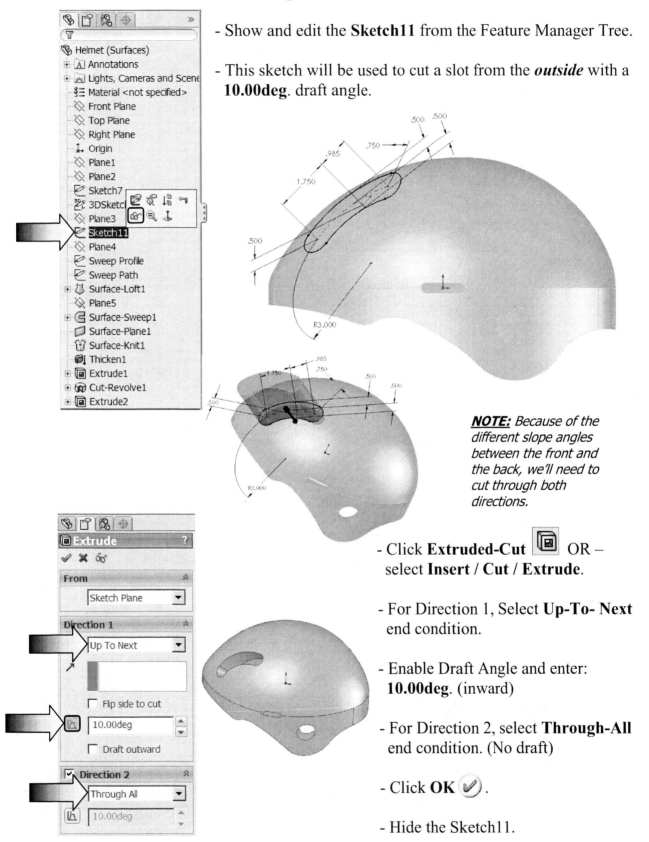

NOTE: *Because of the different slope angles between the front and the back, we'll need to cut through both directions.*

- Click **Extruded-Cut** OR – select **Insert / Cut / Extrude**.

- For Direction 1, Select **Up-To- Next** end condition.

- Enable Draft Angle and enter: **10.00deg.** (inward)

- For Direction 2, select **Through-All** end condition. (No draft)

- Click **OK**.

- Hide the Sketch11.

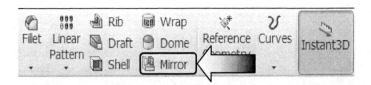

14. Mirroring the slot:

- Click **Mirror** – OR – select **Insert / Pattern-Mirror /**

  Mirror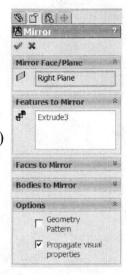

- For Mirror Plane, select the **RIGHT** plane.

- Under Features to Mirror, select the cut-out (Cut Extrude3)

- Click **OK** ✅.

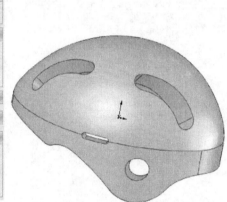

15. Mirroring the Cut Features:

- Click **Mirror** – OR – select **Insert / Pattern-Mirror / Mirror** 📇

- Select the **FRONT** plane as the Mirror Face/Plane.

- Select **both Slots** and the **Side-Holes** as Features to Mirror.

  - Click **OK** ✅.

  - Check your model with the one shown here.

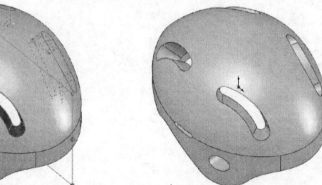

16. Creating the Sweep-Cut

- Click **Insert / Cut / Sweep**.

- Select the sketch **Sweep-Profile** and the sketch **Sweep Path** from the FeatureManager tree.

- The Preview graphics shows the proper transition of the sweep feature.

- Click **OK** ✓.

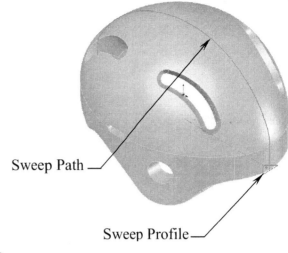

Sweep Path

Sweep Profile

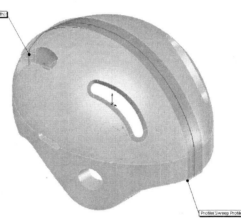

17. Adding the .500" fillets:

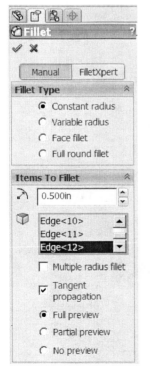

- Click Fillet – OR – select **Insert / Features / Fillet-Round**

- Enter **.500"** for size.

- Select the edges of the Swept feature.

- Click **OK** ✓.

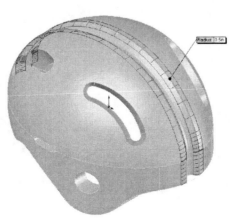

18. Adding the .250" fillets:

- Click Fillet – OR – select: **Insert / Features / Fillet-Round**.

- Enter **.250"** for radius size.

- Select **all edges** of the part (Box Select).

- Click **OK** ✅.

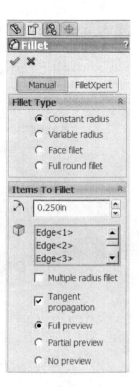

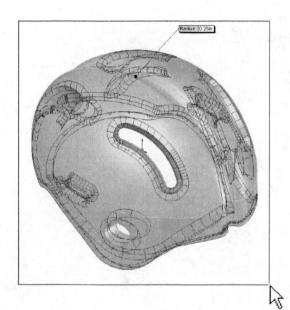

19. Saving your work:

- Click **File / Save As / Helmet / Save**. (Save on the Desktop).

Front Isometric

Back Isometric

<u>Exercise</u>: Advanced Loft

1. Open the existing document:

<u>Go to:</u>
- The Training CD – or –
  the web-link.
- Training Files folder.
- **Turbine (Loft)**.

2. Create the 1st loft:
- Select the 3 Tall Blade
  sketches for Profiles.
- Select the Tall Guide Curve
  sketches for Guide Curves.

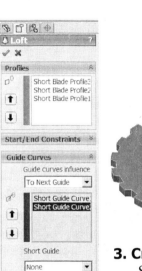

3. Create the 2nd loft:
- Select the 3 Short Blade sketches
  for Profiles.
- Select the Short Guide Curve
  sketches for Guide Curves.

The resulted Lofts.

5. Create a Revolve Cut:
- Use the Blade Trim Sketch
  and create a Revolve-Cut.

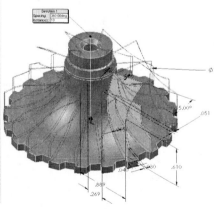

4. Circular pattern the Blades:
- Create a circular pattern for the
  Lofted Blades.
- Enter **10** for number of instances.

6. Save your work as:
- Turbine Blades.

Exercise: Advanced Sweep

1. Create the main profile:

- Using the **Spline** tool  create the profile as shown.

- Add Ordinate dimensions and add the Relations needed to fully define the sketch.

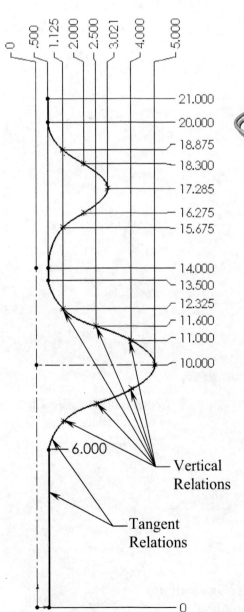

Vertical Relations

Tangent Relations

2. Revolve the sketch profile

as a **SURFACE**

- Click **OK**.

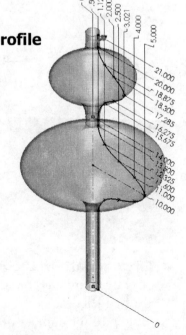

Surface-Revolve1

Revolve Parameters

Line2

One-Direction

360.00deg

Selected Contours

3. Open a new sketch on the TOP plane:

- Sketch a **10.00"** Circle.

- Convert the Circle into a Helix using the settings as shown in the dialog box.

- **Exit the Sketch**.

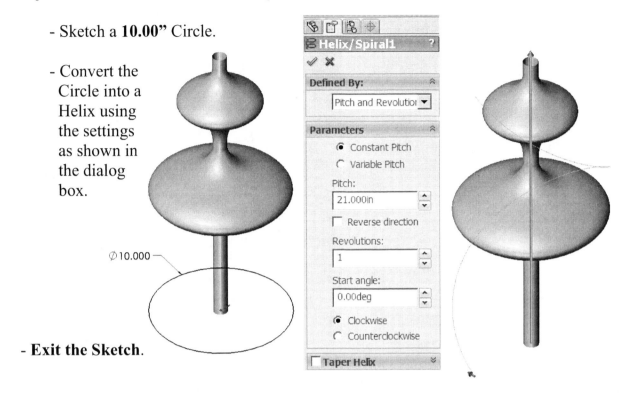

4. Select the TOP plane and open a new sketch.

- Sketch a Line from the Origin and **Pierce** the other end of the line to the Helix.

- Click and Sweep the Line along the Helix using the **Swept-Surface** option.

- Click **OK**.

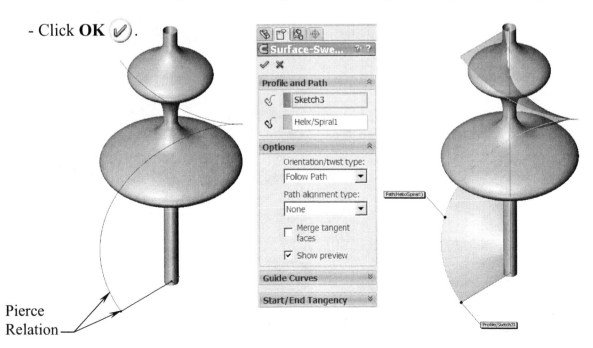

Pierce Relation

5. Create a new Axis: (for use in step 9)

- Select **Insert / Reference Geometry / Axis** 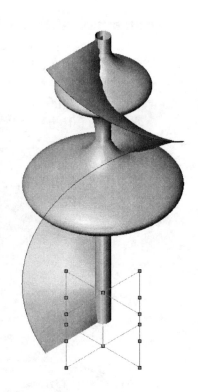.

- Click the **Two-Planes** option.

- Select the FRONT and the RIGHT planes from the FeatureManager tree.

- Click **OK** ✅.

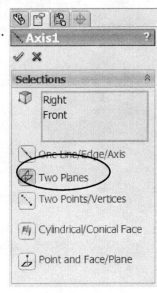

6. Create the Intersection Curve:

- Hold down the CONTROL key and select the **Surface-Revolve1** and the **Surface-Sweep1** from the FeatureManager tree.

- Click ▨ or select **Tools / Sketch Tools / Intersection Curve**.

- A 3D-Sketch is created from the intersection of the two surfaces.

- **Exit the 3D Sketch**.

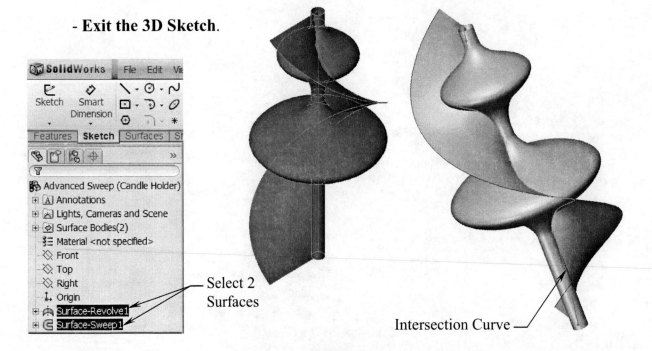

Select 2 Surfaces

Intersection Curve —

7. Hide the 2 Surface Bodies:

- From the Feature Manager tree, right click on each Surface and select **Hide**.

- Select the TOP plane and open a new Sketch.

- Sketch a **Ø.260** circle Centered on the endpoint of the 3D Sketch.

- Click **OK** 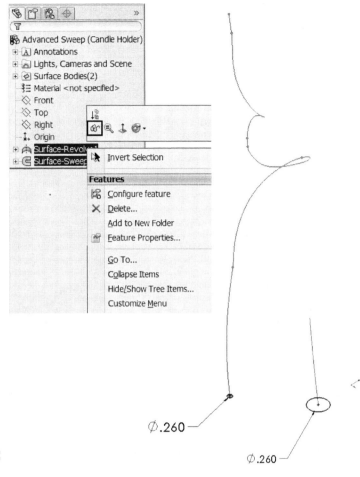.

8. Create a solid sweep feature:

- Click or select **Insert / Boss-Base/ Sweep**.

- Select the Circle for Sweep Profile.

- Select the 3D Sketch for Sweep Path.

- Click OK .

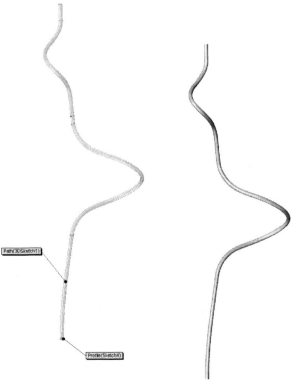

9. Create the Circular Pattern

- Using the Axis created earlier as the Center of the Pattern, repeat the Swept feature **12** times.

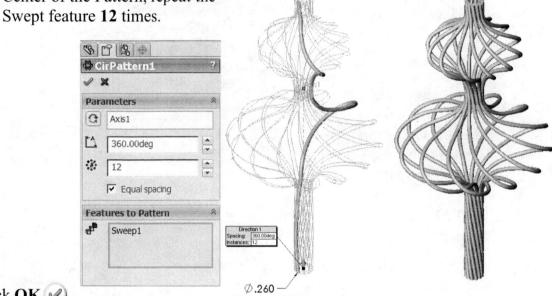

- Click **OK** ✓.

10. OPTIONAL:

- Create the **Base** and the **Candle Holder** solid features as shown below.

- Modify or design your own shapes if needed.

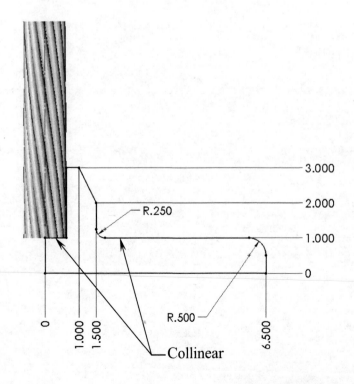

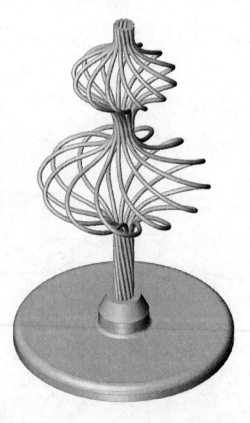

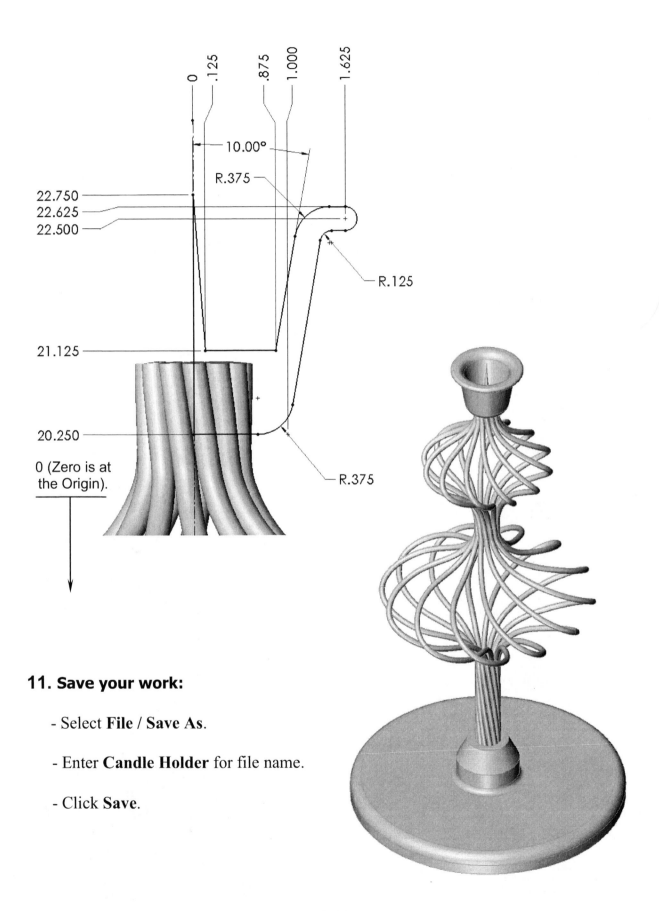

0
.125
.875
1.000
1.625

10.00°

R.375

22.750
22.625
22.500

R.125

21.125

20.250

0 (Zero is at the Origin).

R.375

11. Save your work:

- Select **File / Save As**.

- Enter **Candle Holder** for file name.

- Click **Save**.

Level 3: Final Exam

- Create the part Bottle using the LOFT and SWEEP options where noted.

- All sketch profiles must be fully defined.

- The part must have no errors when finished.

1. Creating an Offset plane:

- From the TOP reference plane, create a new plane at **4.000 in**. offset distance.

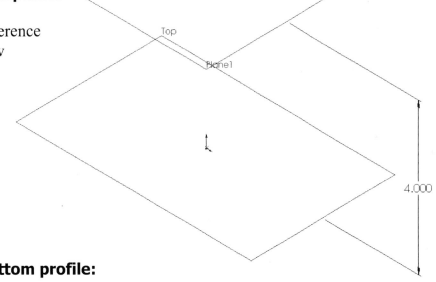

2. Sketching the bottom profile:

- Select the TOP plane and sketch the profile as shown.

- Use the Mirror option to create the **Symmetric** relations between entities.

- **Exit the Sketch** when finished.

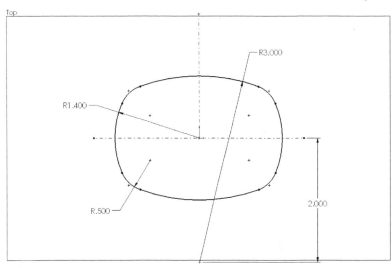

3. Creating the top profile:

- From the PLANE1 reference, sketch a Circle at the Origin.

- Add a diameter dimension to fully define the sketch.

- **Exit the sketch** when finished.

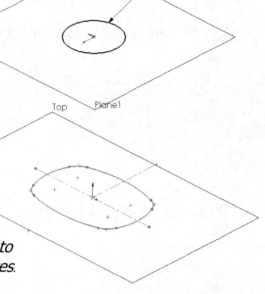

4. Creating the 1st Guide Curve:

- Select the FRONT plane and sketch the profile as shown.

- _Note:_ _The construction lines will be used later to create the Derived-Sketch and the Guide Curves._

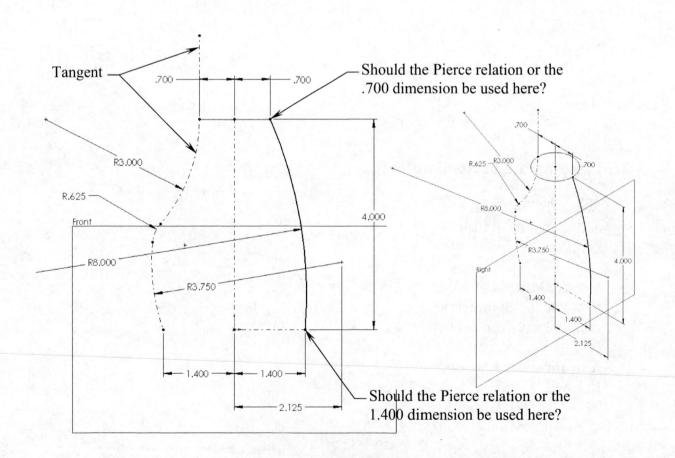

5. Creating the 2ⁿᵈ Guide Curve:

- From the RIGHT plane, sketch a 3-Point-Arc and add dimensions.

Should the Pierce relation or the .700 dimension be used here?

- **Exit the sketch** when finished.

Should the Pierce relation or the 1.000 dimension be used here?

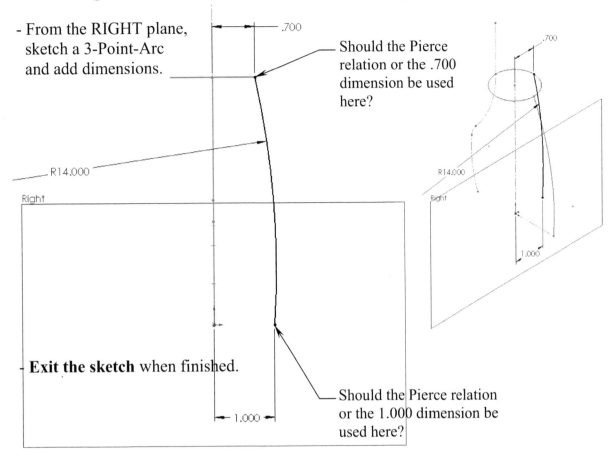

6. Creating the 3ʳᵈ Guide Curve:

- From the RIGHT plane, sketch a 3-Point-Arc and add the same dimensions as step 5.

Should the Pierce relation or the .700 dimension be used here?

- The same arc from step 5 can be Derived to create this sketch.

- **Exit the sketch** when finished.

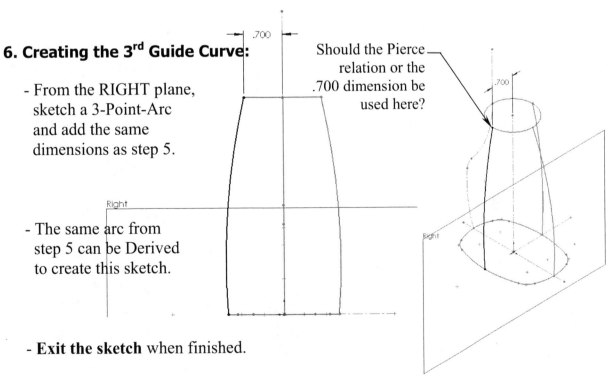

7. Creating the 4th Guide Curve:

- From the FRONT plane, open a new sketch and convert the 3 entities as noted.

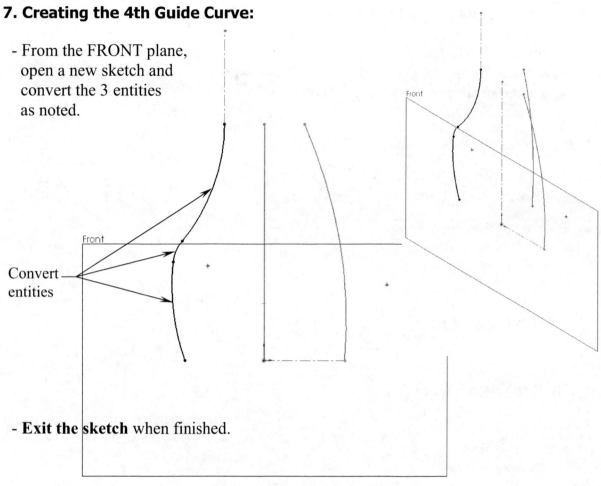

Convert entities

- **Exit the sketch** when finished.

8. Creating the Lofted Surface:

- Use the Top and Bottom sketches as Loft Profiles.

- For Guide Curves, select the next 4 sketches.

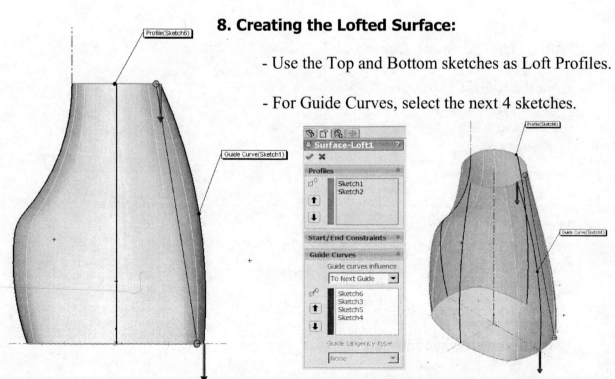

9. Filling the bottom surface:

- Select **Insert / Surface / Planar**.

- Select all of the bottom edges for this operation.

- When finished, the bottom surface should be completely covered.

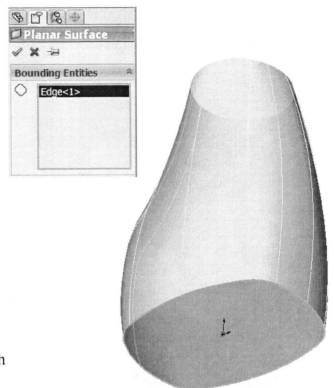

10. Sketching the Neck profile:

- Select the FRONT plane and sketch the profile below.

- Revolve the sketch profile as a <u>SURFACE</u>.

- Revolve One Direction.

- Revolve a complete 360°.

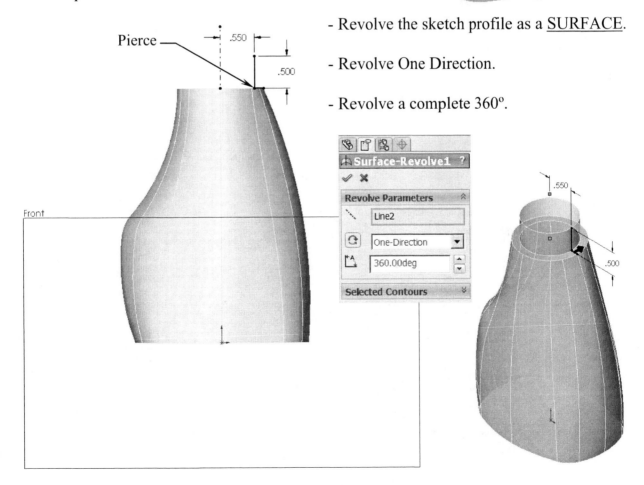

11. Knitting all surfaces into one:

- Select **Insert / Surface / Knit**.

- Select all three surfaces: the body, the Neck and the Bottom surface.

- When finished, all 3 surfaces should now be combined as one continuous surface.

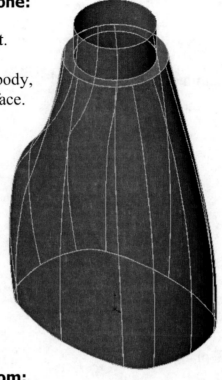

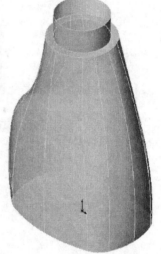

12. Adding a fillet to the bottom:

- Add a **.250 in**. fillet to the bottom edges as shown.

Tips:

- *Right click on one of the edges and pick Select Tangency; this is the fastest way to select all edges at the same time.*

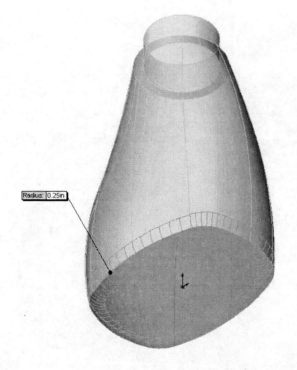

Radius: 0.25in

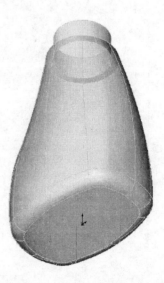

13. Adding a fillet to the shoulder:

- Add a **.093 in**. fillet to the upper edge as indicated.

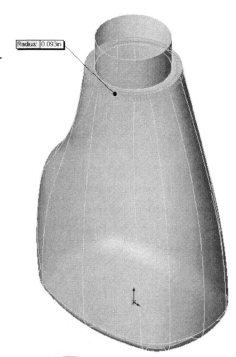

14. Thickening the surfaces:

- Select **Insert / Boss-Base / Thicken**.

- Enter a wall thickness of **.080 in**. to the **INSIDE** of the bottle.

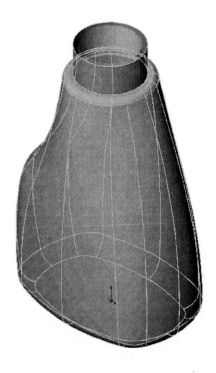

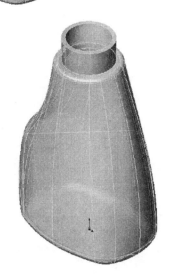

15. Creating a new Offset plane:

- Select the Top face of the neck and create an Offset Distance plane at **.100 in**. <u>BELOW</u> it.

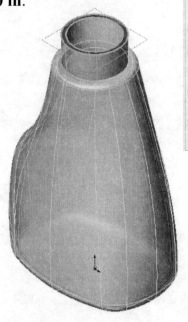

16. Creating the Sweep Path of the Thread (the Helix):

- Select **Insert / Curves / Helix-Spiral**.

- Pitch = **.125 in**.

- Revolution = **2.5**

- Starting Angle = **0 deg**.

- Click **OK** ✓.

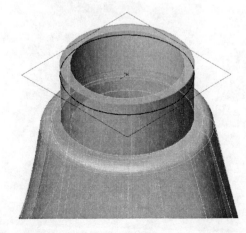

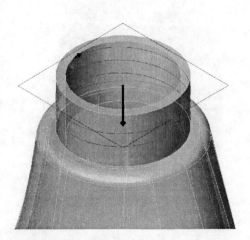

17. Creating the Sweep Profile of the Thread:

- Select the RIGHT plane and sketch the thread profile as shown.

- Add Dimensions and Relations needed to fully define the sketch.

- Exit the sketch when finished.

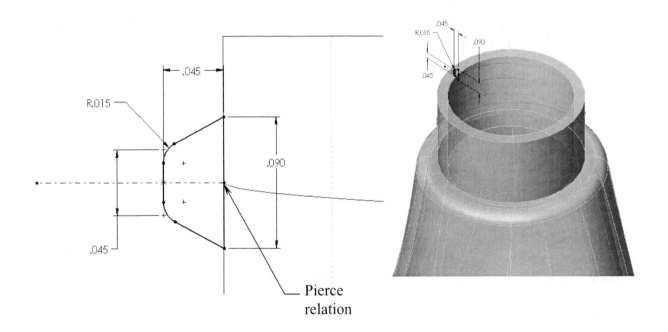

Pierce relation

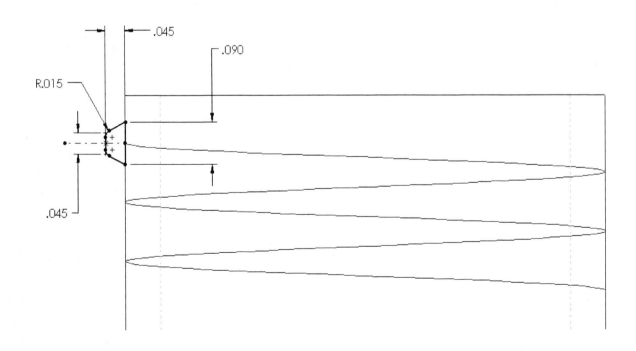

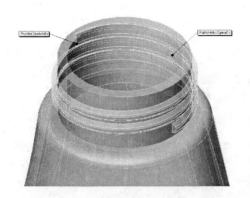

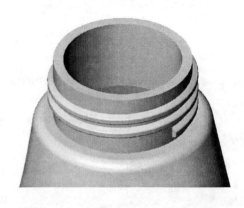

18. Sweeping:

- Sweep the thread profile along the path to create the external threads.

19. Revolving:

- Convert the faces at the end of the thread and revolve them about the vertical centerlines, to round off the ends.

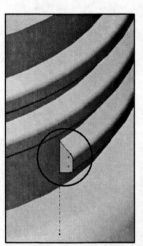

20. Applying dimension changes:

- Change the dimension **R1.400** in the Sketch1 to **R1.500**.

- Change the Ø**1.400** in the Sketch2 to Ø**1.500**.

- Repair any errors caused by the changes.

21. Saving your work:

- Save your work as: **Level 3 – Final Exam**.

CHAPTER 11

SimulationXpress

SimulationXpress

SimulationXpress is a design analysis technology that allows SolidWorks users to perform first-pass stress analysis. SimulationXpress can help you reduce cost and time-to-market by testing your 3D designs within the SolidWorks program, instead of expensive and time-consuming field tests.

There are five basic steps to complete the analysis using SimulationXpress:

1. Apply restraints (Fixture)

Users can define restraints. Each restraint can contain multiple faces. The restrained faces are constrained in all directions due to rigid body motion; you must at least restrain one face of the part to avoid analysis failure.

2. Apply loads

The User inputs of force and pressure loads to the faces of the model.

3. Define material of the part

* EX (Modulus of elasticity).
* NUXY (Poisson's ratio). If users do not define NUXY, SimulationXpress assumes a value of 0.
* SIGYLD (Yield Strength). Used only to calculate the factors of safety (FOS).
* DENS (Mass density). Used only to include mass properties of the part in the report file.

4. Analyze the part

SimulationXpress prepares the model for analysis, then calculates displacements, strains, and stresses.

5. View the results

After completing the analysis, users can view results. A check mark on the Results tab indicates that results exist and are available to view for the current geometry, material, restraints, and loads.

SimulationXpress
Using the Analysis Wizard

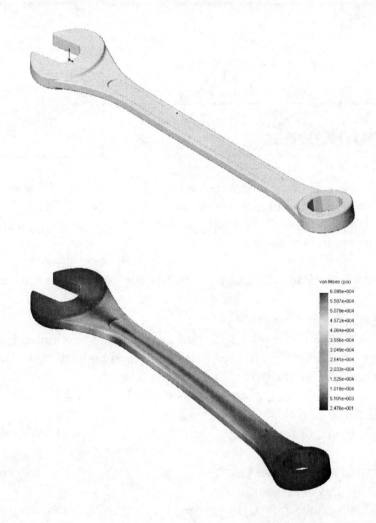

Dimensioning Standards: **ANSI**
Units: **INCHES** – 3 Decimals

Tools Needed:

SimulationXpress is part of
SolidWorks 2010 Basic,
SolidWorks Office Professional
and SolidWorks Premium.

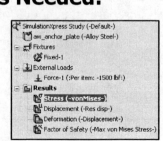

1. Starting SimulationXpress:

- Open the part that was created earlier: **Spanner**.

- **Suppress** the Extruded Text (The 5/8" and the Spanner text).

- From the **Tools** drop down menu, select **SimulationXpress** (Arrow).

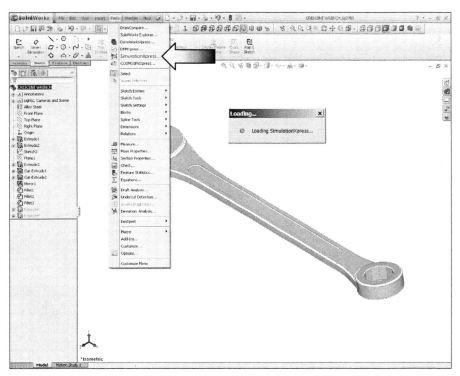

2. Setting up the Units:

- Click **Options** (arrow), to set the system of units for the analysis.

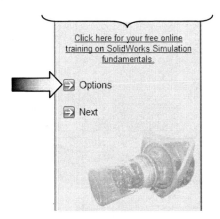

Click here for your free online training on SolidWorks Simulation fundamentals.

→ Options

→ Next

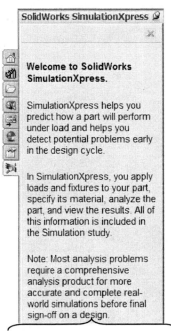

SolidWorks SimulationXpress

Welcome to SolidWorks SimulationXpress.

SimulationXpress helps you predict how a part will perform under load and helps you detect potential problems early in the design cycle.

In SimulationXpress, you apply loads and fixtures to your part, specify its material, analyze the part, and view the results. All of this information is included in the Simulation study.

Note: Most analysis problems require a comprehensive analysis product for more accurate and complete real-world simulations before final sign-off on a design.

- Select **English (IPS)** for System Of Units (Inch, Pound, Second).

- Select the folder and the location to save the analysis results.

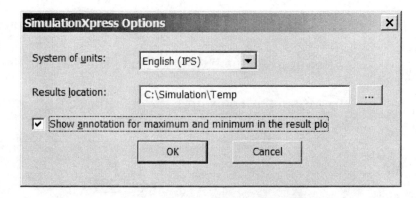

- Enable the option:

Show Annotation for Maximum and Minimum in the Result Plot.

- Create a new folder for each study is recommended.

- Click **OK**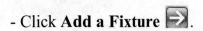

- Click **Next** .

3. Adding a Fixture (restraint):

- The next step is to create the restraint area(s).

- Each restraint can contain one or multiple faces. The restrained faces are constrained in all directions. There must at least one fixed face of the part to avoid analysis failure due to rigid body motion.

- Click **Add a Fixture** .

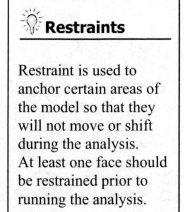

Restraints

Restraint is used to anchor certain areas of the model so that they will not move or shift during the analysis.
At least one face should be restrained prior to running the analysis.

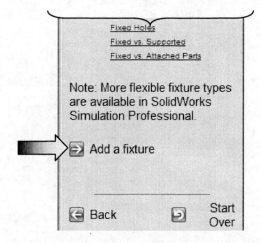

- Select the 3 faces as indicated, for use as restraint faces.

- The Restraint faces are locked in all directions to avoid failure due to rigid body motion.

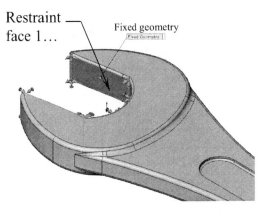

Restraint face 1...

Fixed geometry

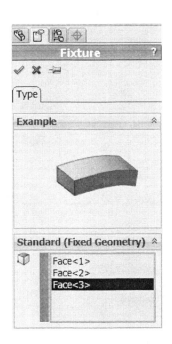

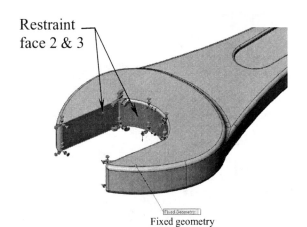

Restraint face 2 & 3

- Click **OK** .

Fixed geometry

- When the restraint faces are selected, more faces can be added to create different restraint sets. They can also be edited or deleted at anytime.

- The information regarding the settings for this study is recorded on the lower half of the Feature-Manager tree (arrows).

- These settings can be modified at anytime.

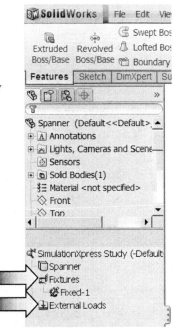

4. Applying a Force:

- Click **Add a Force** →.

- The **Forces** and **Pressures** options allow the SolidWorks users to apply force or pressure loads to faces of the model. Multiple forces can be applied to a single face or to multiple faces.

- Select the 2 faces from the back side of the closed end as shown below.

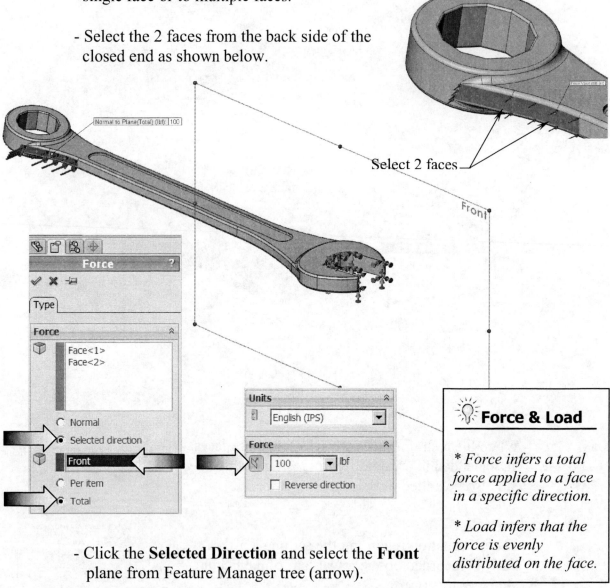

- Click the **Selected Direction** and select the **Front** plane from Feature Manager tree (arrow).

- Click the **Total** option (arrow). Enter **100** lbs. for Total Force value (arrow).

- Check the direction arrows and click Reverse Direction if necessary.

- Click OK ✓.

Force & Load

* Force infers a total force applied to a face in a specific direction.

* Load infers that the force is evenly distributed on the face.

- At this point we will need to specify a material so that SimulationXpress can predict how it will respond to the loads.

5. Selecting the material**:

- Click **Next** ⇥.

- Select **Choose Material** ⇥.

- Expand the **Steel** option (click the + symbol).

- Choose **Alloy Steel** from the list (arrow).

> ### 💡 Material Editor
>
> Material can be assigned to the part using the **Material Editor** PropertyManager, the material will then appears in SimulationXpress.

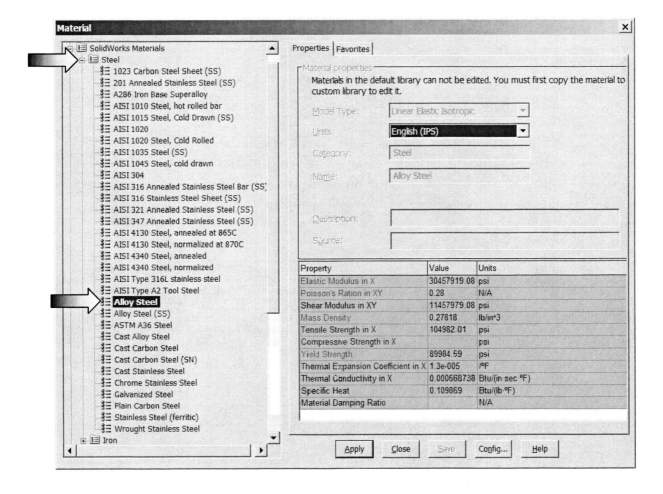

- The analysis results are dependent on the material it is made of. Simulation-Xpress needs to know the Visual and the Physical properties to run the analysis.

- Click **Apply** [Apply] and **Close** [Close].

- The material **Alloy Steel** is now assigned to the part.

- The Modulus of Elasticity and the Yield Strength for the selected material are reported on the right.

- Click **Next** .

- SimulationXpress is ready to analyze the model based on the information provided. Displacements, Strains, and Stresses will then be calculated.

6. Analyzing the model:

- Click **Run Simulation** .

- SimulationXpress automatically tries to mesh the model using the default element size. The smaller the element size the more accurate the results, but more time is needed to analyze the model.

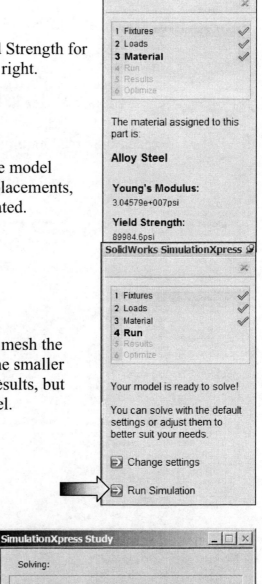

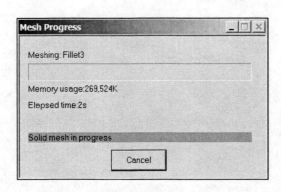

- To change mesh settings: First click **Change settings** then click **Change mesh density**.

* Drag the slider to the right for a finer mesh (more accurate, but takes longer).

* Drag the slider to the left for a coarser mesh (quicker).

- Select **Yes, continue** 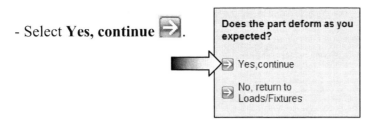.

7. Viewing the Results:

- Click **Show Von Mises stress** →.

- SimulationXpress plots stresses on the deformed shape of the part.

- In most cases, the actual deformation is very small that the deformed shape almost coincides with the un-deformed shape if plotted to scale.

- SimulationXpress exaggerates the deformation to demonstrate it more clearly.

- The Deformation Scale shown on the stress and deformed shape plots is the scale used to rescale the maximum deformation to **8.7928%** of the bounding box of the part.

- The **Stress Distribution Plot** is displayed below.

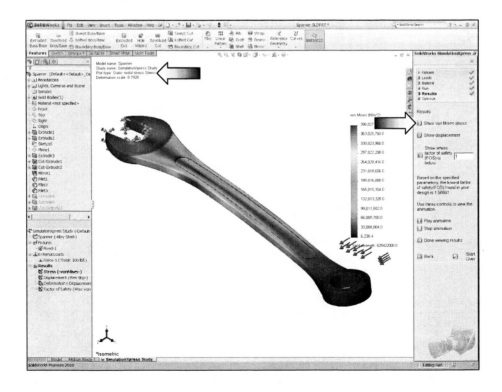

- To see the static displacement plot click **Show Displacement** ⬛.

- Click **Play Animation** ⬛ or **Stop Animation** ⬛ when finished viewing.

Displacement Plot

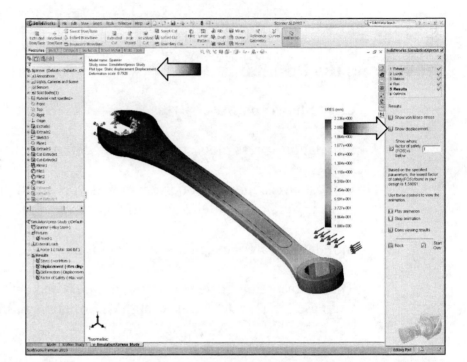

- To view regions of the model with a factor of safety less than a given value (1), click: **Show Where Factor Of Safety (FOS) Is Below: 1** (or enter any value).

- SimulationXpress displays regions of the model with factors of safety less than the specified value in red (unsafe regions) and regions with higher factors of safety in blue (safe regions).

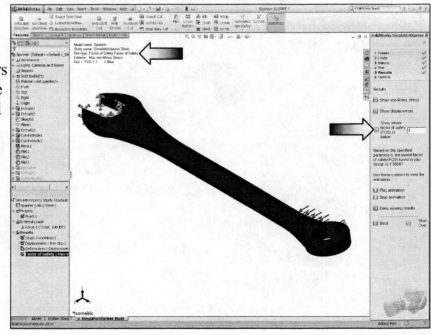

- When finished viewing click: **Done Viewing Results**.

8. Creating the HTML report: (Hyper Text Markup Language)

- Click **Generate HTML Report** →.

- SimulationXpress cycles through the results, generates a report in HTML, and displays the report in your default browser.

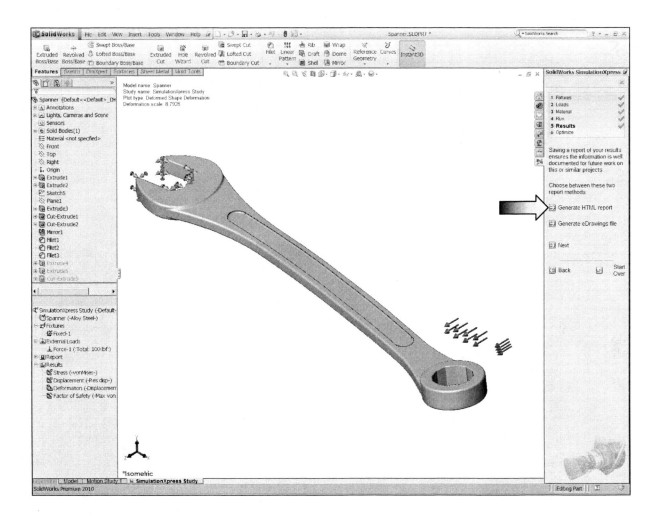

- The HTML report includes:

1. File Information	2. Materials
3. Load Information	4. Study Property
5. Stress Results	6. Deformation Results
7. Design Check Results	8. Appendix.

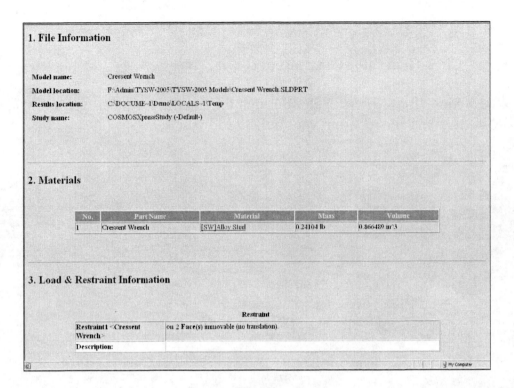

1. File Information

Model name:	Cressent Wrench
Model location:	F:\Admin\TYSW-2005\TYSW-2005 Models\Cressent Wrench.SLDPRT
Results location:	C:\DOCUME~1\Demo\LOCALS~1\Temp
Study name:	COSMOSXpressStudy (-Default-)

2. Materials

No.	Part Name	Material	Mass	Volume
1	Cressent Wrench	[SW]Alloy Steel	0.24104 lb	0.866489 in^3

3. Load & Restraint Information

	Restraint
Restraint1 <Cressent Wrench>	on 2 Face(s) immovable (no translation).
Description:	

File Information Report

	Load
Load1 <Cressent Wrench>	on 2 Face(s) apply force 100lb normal to reference plane with respect to selected reference **Front** using uniform distribution
Description:	

4. Study Property

Mesh Information	
Mesh Type:	Solid mesh
Mesher Used:	Standard
Automatic Transition:	Off
Smooth Surface:	On
Jacobian Check:	4 Points
Element Size:	0.095371 in
Tolerance:	0.0047685 in
Quality:	High
Number of elements:	15730
Number of nodes:	27467

Solver Information	
Quality:	High
Solver Type:	FFE

Study Property Report

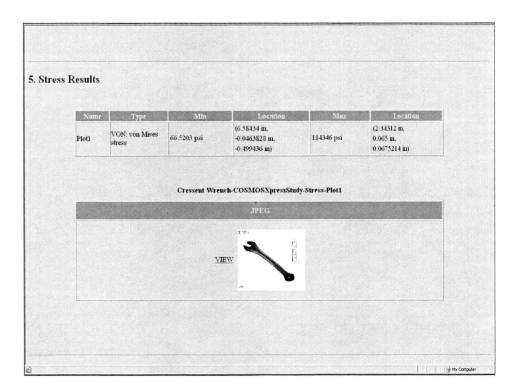

Stress Results

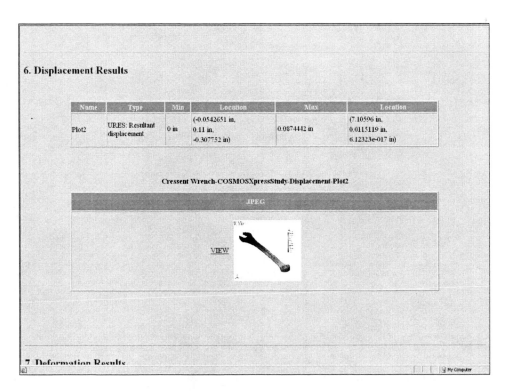

Displacement Results

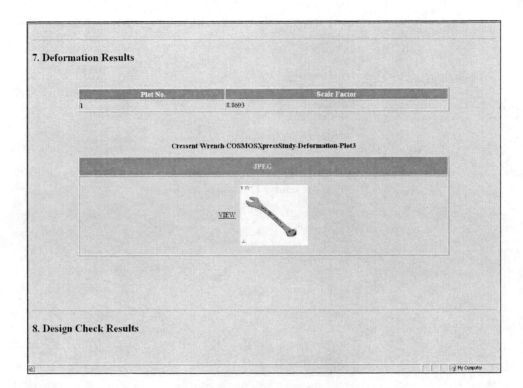

Deformation results

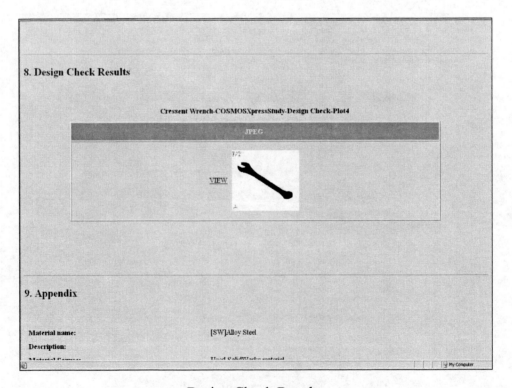

Design Check Results

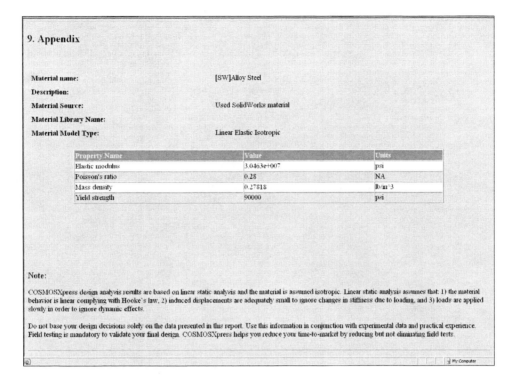

Appendix

- When finished with viewing the HTML Report, click:

Generate eDrawings File →.

- The eDrawings program is launched automatically.

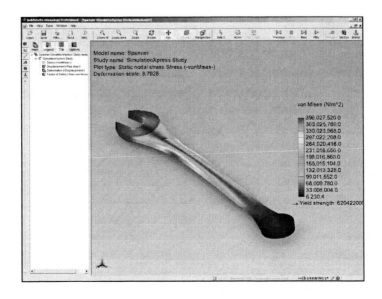

9. Generating the eDrawings file:

- An eDrawings file can be created for the SimulationXpress result plots.

- The eDrawings file allows you to view, animate and print your analysis results.

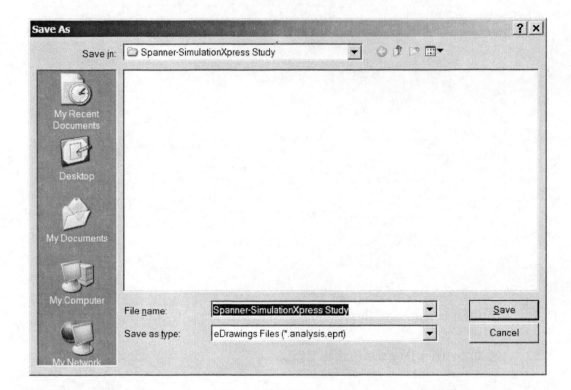

- When prompted, **Save** the analysis study in the default folder.

- SimulationXpress creates an eDrawing file with the **.eprt** extension. The file contains von Mises stress, displacement, deformation, and Factor of Safety plots. By default, the von Mises stress plot is displayed.

- Click the Play button 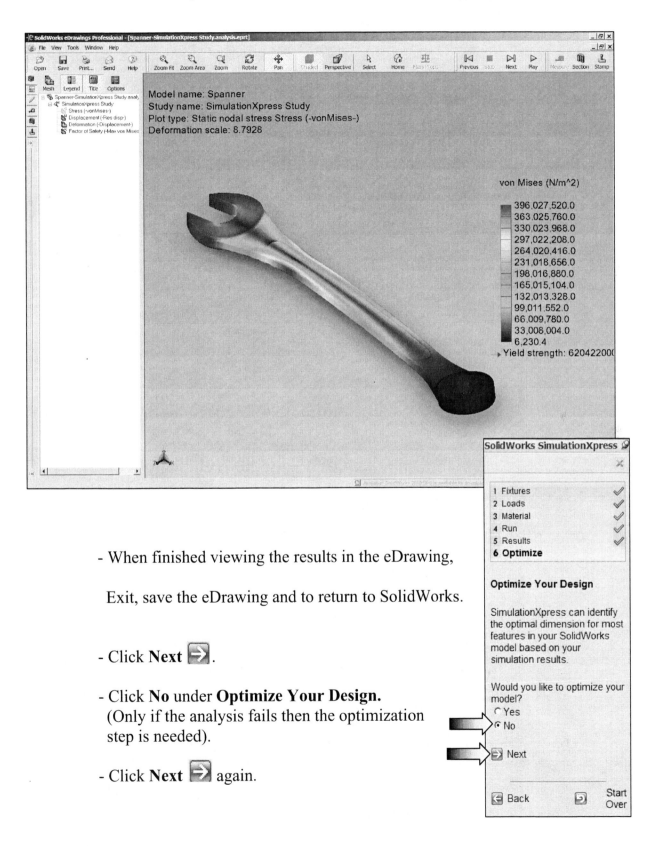 to see the animated results.

- When finished viewing the results in the eDrawing,

  Exit, save the eDrawing and to return to SolidWorks.

- Click **Next**.

- Click **No** under **Optimize Your Design.**
  (Only if the analysis fails then the optimization
  step is needed).

- Click **Next** again.

- At this point, you are prompted that the analysis has been completed.

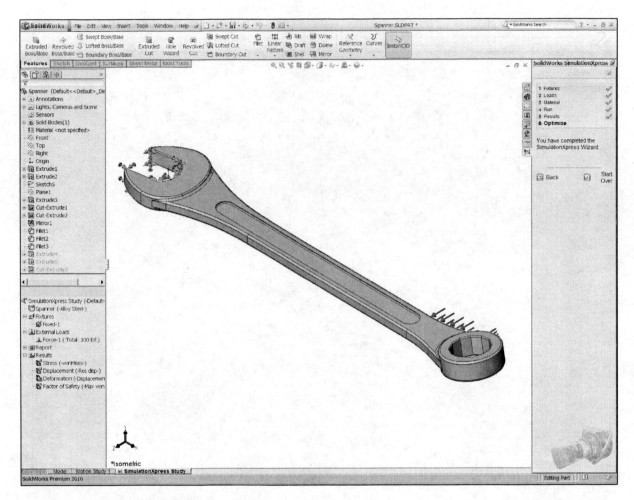

10. Saving your work:

- Click **File / Save As**.

- Enter **Spanner Study** for file name and click **Save**.

Isotropic, Orthotropic & Anisotropic Materials:

Isotropic Material: If its mechanical properties are the same in all directions. The elastic properties of an Isotropic material are defined by the Modulus of Elasticity (EX) and Poisson's Ratio (NUXY).

Orthotropic Material: If its mechanical properties are unique and independent in the directions of three mutually perpendicular axes.

Anisotropic Material: If its mechanical properties are different in different directions. In general, the Mechanical properties of the anisotropic materials are not symmetrical with respect to any plane or axis.

SimulationXpress supports Isotropic materials only.

Questions for Review

SimulationXpress

1. SimulationXpress can be accessed from the Tools pull down menu.
   - a. True
   - b. False

2. System Of Units "SI" is the only type that is supported in SimulationXpress.
   - a. True
   - b. False

3. The material of the part can be selected from the built-in library or input directly by the user.
   - a. True
   - b. False

4. SimulationXpress supports Isotropic, Orthotropic and Anisotropic materials:
   - a. True
   - b. False

5. Restraints/Fixture are used to anchor certain areas of the part so that it will not move during the analysis.
   - a. True
   - b. False

6. Only one surface/face should be use for restraint for each study.
   - a. True
   - b. False

7. The elements size (mesh) can be adjusted to a smaller size for more accurate results.
   - a. True
   - b. False

8. The types of results reported are:
   - a. Stress Distribution
   - b. Deformed Shape
   - c. HTML Report
   - d. eDrawing
   - e. All of the above

1. TRUE
2. FALSE
3. TRUE
4. FALSE
5. TRUE
6. FALSE
7. TRUE
8. E

Exercise 1: SimulationXpress / Force

1. Open the existing part: **Exe_4** (Level 1).

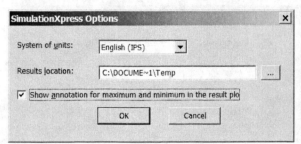

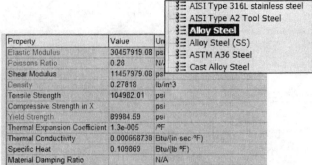

2. Set Unit to: **English (IPS)**

5. Select Material: **Alloy Steel**

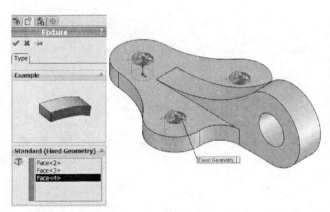

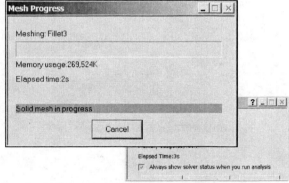

3. Apply Restraint: **to 3 Holes.**

6. Run the Analysis.

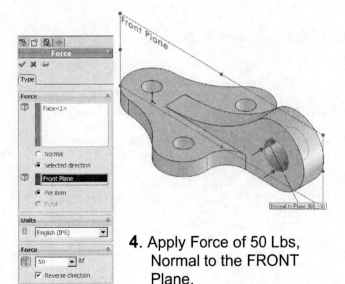

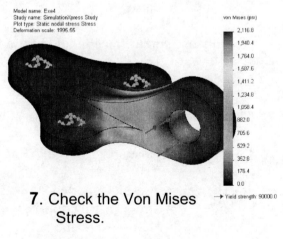

7. Check the Von Mises Stress.

4. Apply Force of 50 Lbs, Normal to the FRONT Plane.

8. Save a copy as: **Simulation_Force**

Exercise 2: SimulationXpress / Pressure

1. Open the existing part: **Bottle-CosmosXpress** (Level 3).

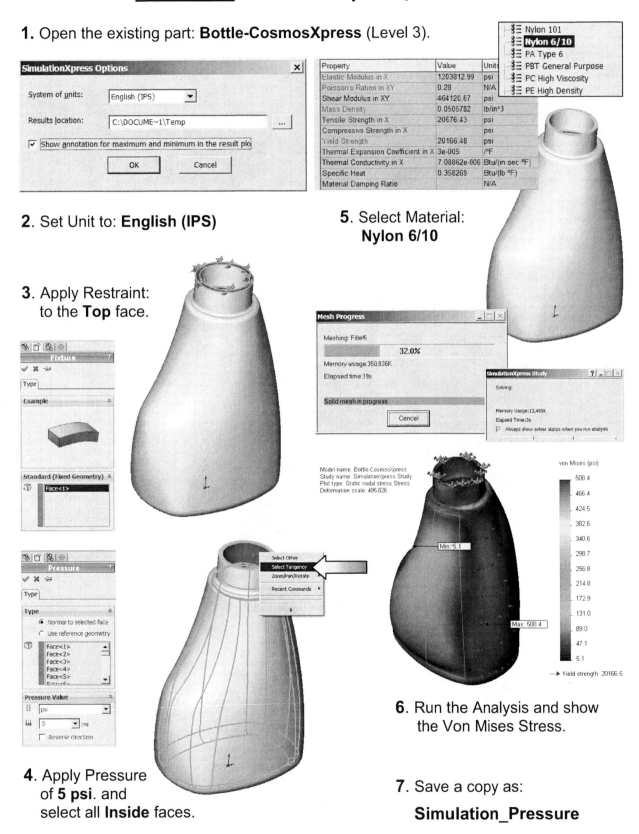

2. Set Unit to: **English (IPS)**

3. Apply Restraint:
to the **Top** face.

4. Apply Pressure
of **5 psi**. and
select all **Inside** faces.

5. Select Material:
Nylon 6/10

6. Run the Analysis and show
the Von Mises Stress.

7. Save a copy as:

Simulation_Pressure

Free SolidWorks SimulationXpress Online Tutorial:
http://www.solidworksmedia.com/SimulationXpress/index.html

CHAPTER 12

Sheet Metal Parts

Sheet Metal Parts

- This chapter discusses the introduction to designing the sheet metal parts.

  * Create a sheet metal part in the folded stage.
  * Add the sheet metal part specific flange features such as:

    • Base Flange.
    • Edge Flanges.
    • Sketch Bends.
    • Cut with Link to Thickness.
    • Normal Cuts.

- There are 3 options for specifying the setback allowance (which is the different in length when the sheet metal part is folded vs. flattened).

  * **Bend Table:** You can specify the bend allowance or bend deduction values for a sheet metal part in a bend table. The bend table also contains values for bend radius, bend angle, and part thickness.

  * **K-Factor:** Is a ratio that represents the location of the neutral sheet with respect to the thickness of the sheet metal part.
  Bend allowance using a K-Factor is calculated as follows: $BA = \Pi(R + KT) A/180$

  * **Use Bend Allowance:** Enter your own bend value base on your shop experience.

Bend allowance Calculations: The following equation is used to determine the total flat length when bend allowance values are used: $L_t = A + B + BA$

Bend Deduction Calculations: The following equation is used to determine the total flat length when bend deduction values are used: $L_t = A + B - BD$

Post Cap
Sheet Metal Parts

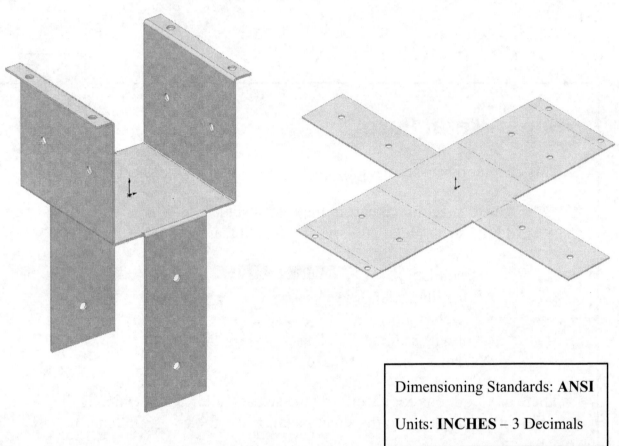

Dimensioning Standards: **ANSI**

Units: **INCHES** – 3 Decimals

Tools Needed:

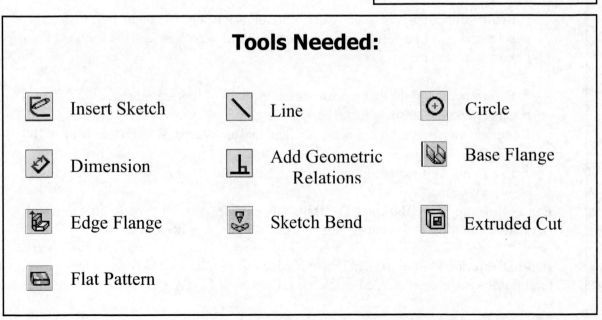

Insert Sketch	Line	Circle
Dimension	Add Geometric Relations	Base Flange
Edge Flange	Sketch Bend	Extruded Cut
Flat Pattern		

1. Starting with the base profile:

- Select RIGHT plane from Feature Manager tree and insert a new sketch .

- Sketch the profile below using the Line tool ◣ .

- Add dimensions ◈ and relations ⊥ needed, fully define the sketch.

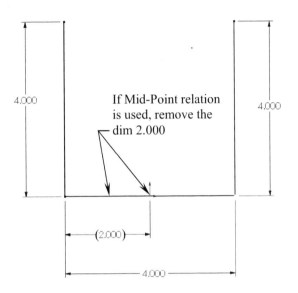

If Mid-Point relation is used, remove the dim 2.000

> 💡 **Gauge Tables**
>
> To enable the Gauge-Tables, while in the Base Flange mode, go to: **Browse / SolidWorks / Lang / English / Sheet Metal Gauge Tables**.

2. Extruding the Base Flange:

- Click 🔲 or select **Insert / Sheet Metal / Base Flange**.

- Direction 1: **Mid-Plane**

- Extrude Depth: **4.00 in**.

- Use Gauge Table: **Sample Table - Steel**

- Mat'l Thickness: **16 Gauge (.0598)** 🔲

- Bend Radius: **.030 in**. (Override Radius) ◣

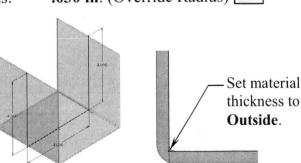

Set material thickness to **Outside**.

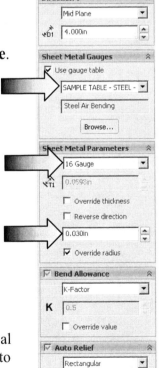

- Click **OK** ✔ .

3. Creating an Edge-Flange:

- Select the model edge as indicated.

- Click 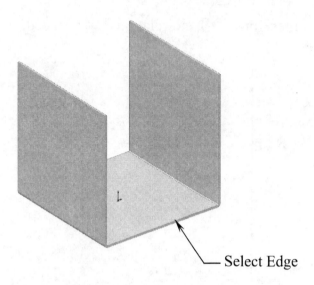 or select **Insert / Sheet Metal / Edge Flange**.

—— Select Edge

- Drag the cursor downwards and click to see the preview of an Edge Flange.

- Select **Material Outside** 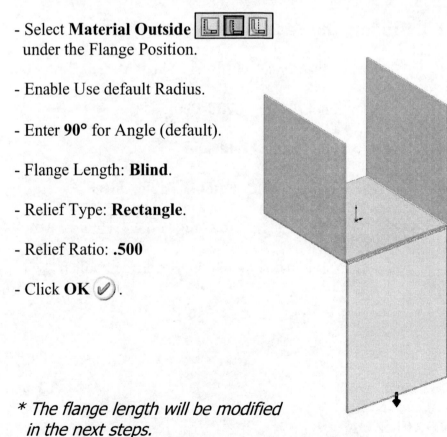 under the Flange Position.

- Enable Use default Radius.

- Enter **90°** for Angle (default).

- Flange Length: **Blind**.

- Relief Type: **Rectangle**.

- Relief Ratio: **.500**

- Click **OK** ✅.

* The flange length will be modified in the next steps.

4. Editing the Edge Flange sketch:

- Right click on the surface of the edge flange and select **Edit Sketch** .

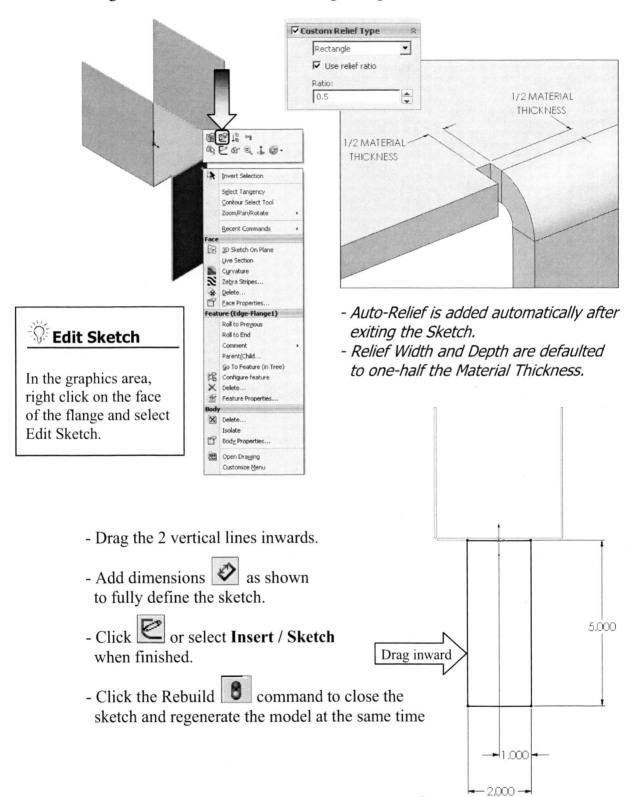

Edit Sketch

In the graphics area, right click on the face of the flange and select Edit Sketch.

- Auto-Relief is added automatically after exiting the Sketch.
- Relief Width and Depth are defaulted to one-half the Material Thickness.

- Drag the 2 vertical lines inwards.

- Add dimensions as shown to fully define the sketch.

- Click or select **Insert / Sketch** when finished.

- Click the Rebuild command to close the sketch and regenerate the model at the same time

5. Mirroring the Edge Flange:

- Click 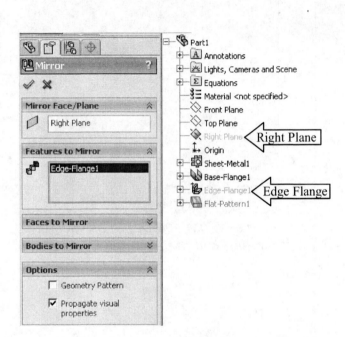 on the Features toolbar or select **Insert / Pattern-Mirror / Mirror**.

- Select the **Right** plane for Mirror Face/Plane.

- Select the **Edge Flange** either from the Feature tree or in the graphics area.

- Click **OK** ✓.

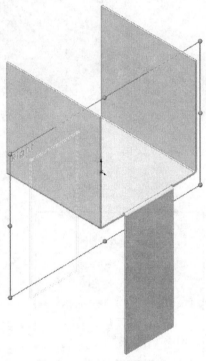

- The Edge Flange is mirrored and automatically receives the same sheet metal parameters as the original.

Note:
The second edge flange can be created at the Same time with the first edge flange; the mirror Option was demonstrated here instead.

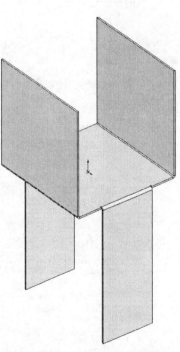

6. Creating a Sketch Bend:

- Select the side surface as indicated.

- Click 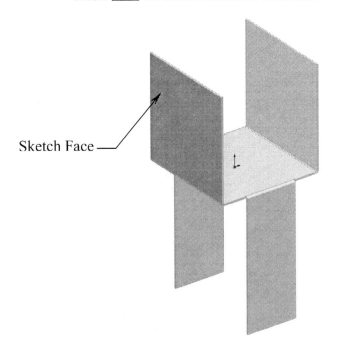 or select **Insert / Sketch**.

Sketch Face —

> ### ☼ Sketch Bends
>
> Add Bends or Tabs to
> the Sheet metal part
> with the sketch lines.
>
> Only sketch lines are
> allowed, but more than
> one line can be used in
> a same sketch, to create
> multiple bends.

- Sketch a line ╲ starting at one edge and Coincident with the other.

- Add dimensions ◇ to fully define the sketch.

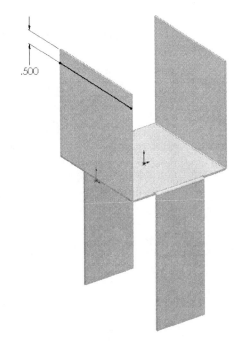

.500

- Click 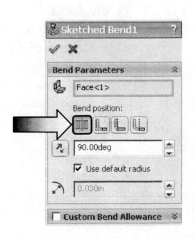 or select **Insert / Sheet Metal / Sketch Bends**.

- Select the **lower portion** of the surface as Fixed Face .

- Select **Bend Centerline** (default) under Bend Position .

- Enter **90.00** deg for Bend Angle (default) 90.00deg .

- Enable Use Default Radius.

- Click **OK** .

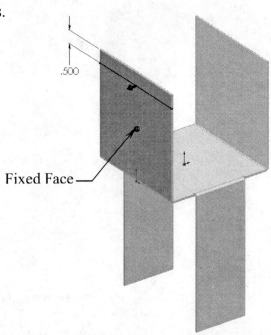

Fixed Face

- The resulting bend.

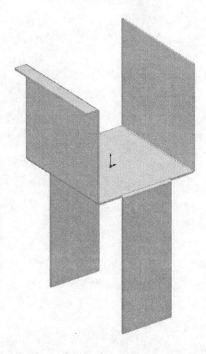

- The upper portion of the surface
  is bent outwards 90°, leaving the
  the lower portion fixed.

7. Creating another Sketch Bend:

- Select the surface on the right and open a sketch 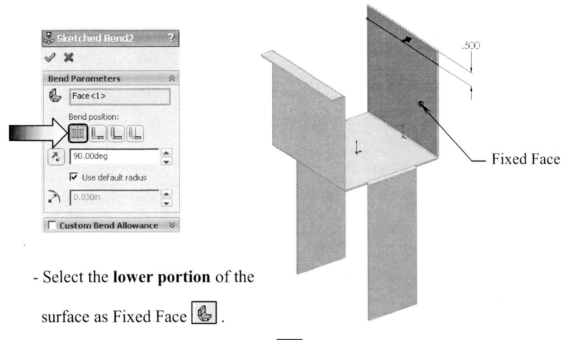 or select **Insert / Sketch**.

- Sketch a line as shown and add dimensions to fully define it.

- Click or select **Insert / Sheet Metal / Sketch Bend**.

Fixed Face

- Select the **lower portion** of the surface as Fixed Face.

- Select **Bend Centerline** (default) under Bend Position.

- Enter **90.00** deg for Bend Angle (default) | 90.00deg |.

- Enable Use Default Radius.

- Click **OK**.

- The resulting bend.

- The upper portion of the surface is bent outwards 90°, leaving the the lower portion fixed.

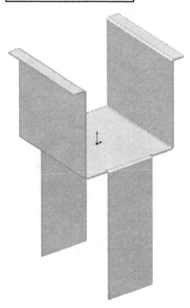

8. Adding holes on the Edge Flange:

- Select the surface as shown and open a new sketch 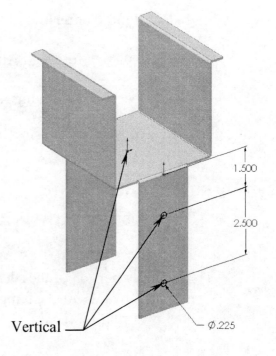,
  or select **Insert / Sketch**.

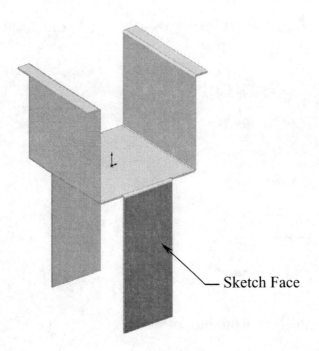

— Sketch Face

- Sketch two circles ⊕ on the face.

- Add dimensions ◇ as shown to
  position the circles.

- Add **Vertical** relations ⌐
  between the centers of the circles
  and the Origin to fully constrain
  them.

1.500

2.500

Vertical —

Ø.225

- Click 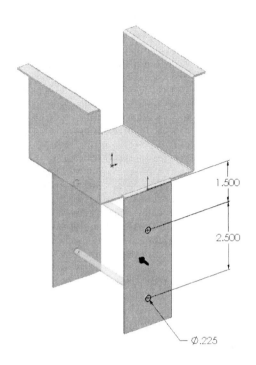 or select **Insert / Cut / Extrude**.

- End Condition: **Through All**.

- Enable **Normal Cut** (default).

- Click **OK**.

9. Adding holes on the Sketch Bend Flanges:

- Select the face as noted and open a new sketch or select **Insert / Sketch**.

- Sketch 4 circles and add dimensions as shown.

- Add the relations as needed to fully define the sketch.

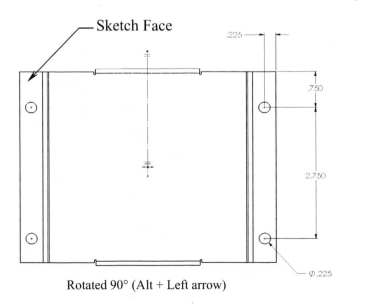

Rotated 90° (Alt + Left arrow)

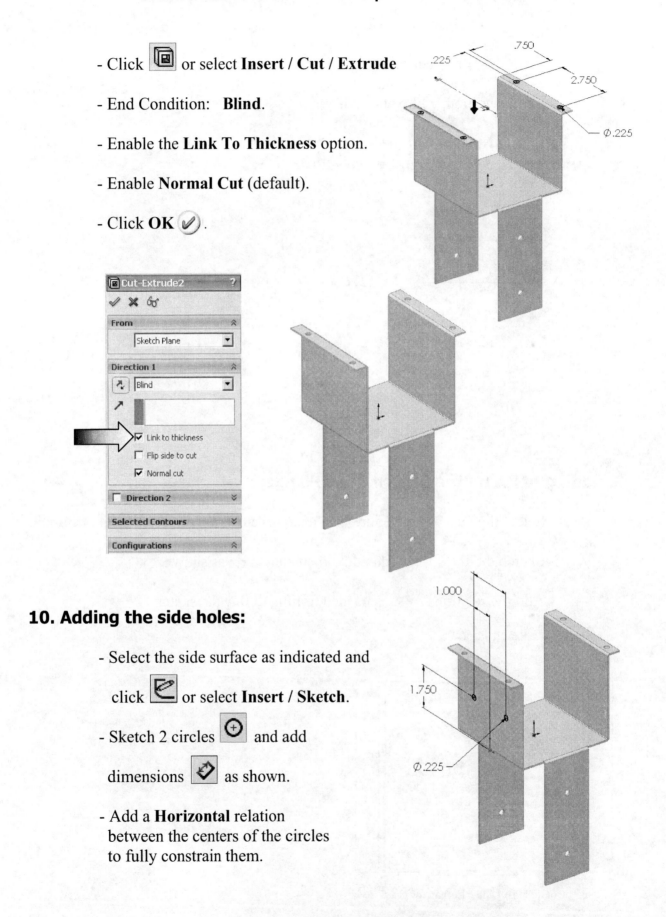

- Click or select **Insert / Cut / Extrude**

- End Condition: **Blind**.

- Enable the **Link To Thickness** option.

- Enable **Normal Cut** (default).

- Click **OK**.

10. Adding the side holes:

- Select the side surface as indicated and

  click or select **Insert / Sketch**.

- Sketch 2 circles and add

  dimensions as shown.

- Add a **Horizontal** relation
  between the centers of the circles
  to fully constrain them.

- Click 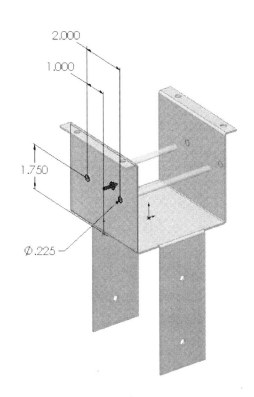 or select **Insert / Cut / Extrude**.

- End Condition: **Through All**.

- Enable **Normal Cut** (default).

- Click **OK** ✅.

11. Making the Flat Pattern:

- Click **Flat Pattern** on the Sheet Metal toolbar.

- The part is flattened with the bend lines shown (centerline).

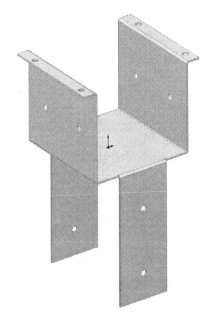

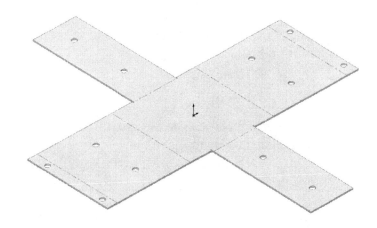

12. Saving your work:

- Select **File / Save As / Post Cap / Save**.

Questions for Review

Sheet Metal

1. A sheet metal part can have multiple thicknesses.
   a. True
   b. False

2. A solid model can be converted into a sheet metal part after it has been shelled and sheet metal parameters such as rips, bend radius, thickness, and bend allowance are added to it.
   a. True
   b. False

3. A sheet metal part can be created right from the beginning using the Base flange option.
   a. True
   b. False

4. Auto relief option is not available when extruding a Base Flange.
   a. True
   b. False

5. When the Sketched Bend option is used to create a bend, you'll have to specify at least two parameters:
   a. A fixed side and a sketched line.
   b. Fixed side and a bend angle value.
   c. A bend radius and a bend angle value.

6. The only time when the K-Factor option can be changed to Bend Table is when extruding the Base Flange.
   a. True
   b. False

7. A sheet metal part can be designed from a flat sheet and other bends can be added later using Sketched Bend, Edge Flange, etc.
   a. True
   b. False

8. Link-to-Thickness option allows all sheet metal features in a part to have the same wall thickness, and they can all be changed at the same time.
   a. True
   b. False

7. TRUE   8. TRUE
5. A   6. FALSE
3. TRUE   4. FALSE
1. FALSE   2. TRUE

CHAPTER 12 (cont.)

Sheet Metal Parts

Sheet Metal Parts

Sheet metal parts can be created using one of the following methods:

- Create the part as a solid and insert the sheet metal parameters such as rips, bend radius, material thickness, bend allowance, and cut relief so that the part can be flattened.

- Create the part as a sheet metal part from the beginning using the Base-Flange command to extrude the first feature.

- Sheet metal parameters can be applied onto the sheet metal part during the extrusion or after the fact.

This chapter will guide you through the use of the sheet metal and forming tool commands to create a sheet metal part.

Some of the sheet metal features are:

- Create a sheet metal part with the Base Flange command.
- Using the Miter-flange command.
- Create a sheet metal part in the flat or folded stage.
- Create Revolved features.
- Create forming tool to form the louvers.
- Create Linear patterns of features.
- Create Circular patterns of features.
- Create patterns of patterned features.

Vents
Sheet Metal Parts

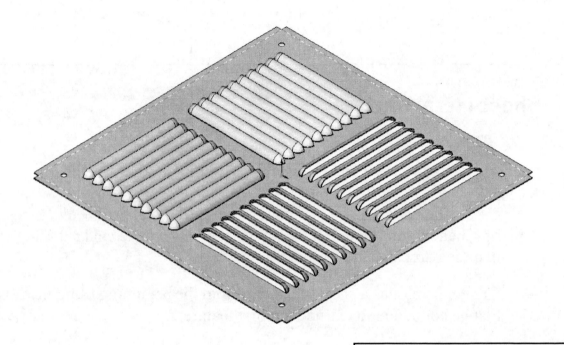

Dimensioning Standards: **ANSI**
Units: **INCHES** – 3 Decimals

Tools Needed:

Insert Sketch	Line	Dimension
Rectangle	Add Geometric Relations	Linear Pattern
Base Flange	Miter Flange	Circular Pattern
Flat Pattern	Extruded Cut	Design Library

1. Sketching the first profile:

- Select FRONT plane from FeatureManager tree.

- Click 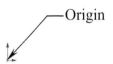 from Sketch toolbar OR select **Insert / Sketch**.

- Click ⟍ and sketch a horizontal line **below the Origin**.

- Click ⬦ and dimension the length of the line to **18.00 in**.

—Origin

2. Adding a Midpoint relation:

- Click ⌐ from the Sketch toolbar OR select **Tools / Relations /Add**.

- Click on the Origin point and select the line as shown.

- Select **Midpoint** option from the Add Geometric Relation dialog box.

- Click **OK** ✓.

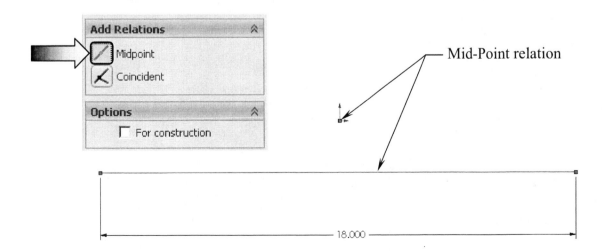

Mid-Point relation

3. Extruding with the Base-Flange command:

- Click 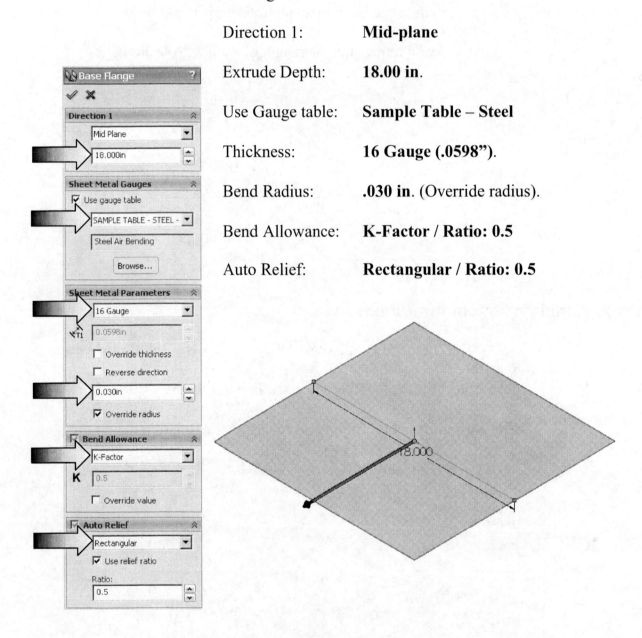 (Base Flange) from the Sheet Metal toolbar OR select:
Insert /Sheet Metal / Base Flange.

- Enter / select the following:

Direction 1:	**Mid-plane**
Extrude Depth:	**18.00 in**.
Use Gauge table:	**Sample Table – Steel**
Thickness:	**16 Gauge (.0598")**.
Bend Radius:	**.030 in**. (Override radius).
Bend Allowance:	**K-Factor / Ratio: 0.5**
Auto Relief:	**Rectangular / Ratio: 0.5**

- Click **OK** ✅.

4. Creating the Miter-Flanges:

- Select the <u>Edge</u> as indicated below and click 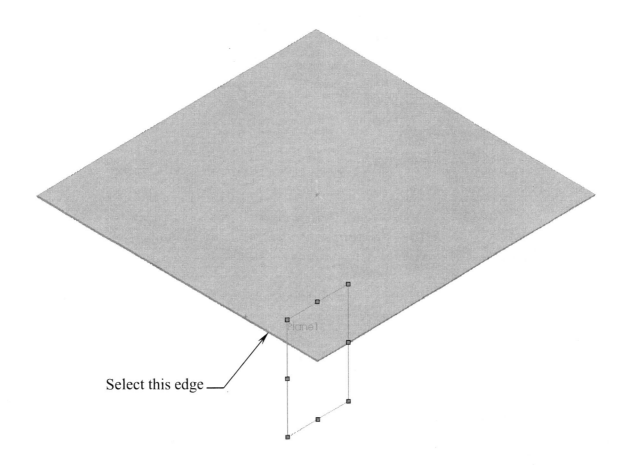 OR **Insert / Sketch**.

- The system automatically creates a new plane <u>normal</u> to the selected edge.

Select this edge ——

- Click **Zoom-to-Area** from the View toolbar and zoom in on the corner as shown below.

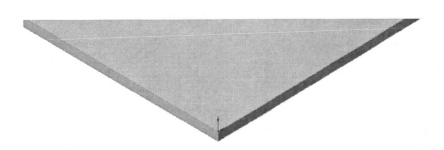

- Sketch a vertical line 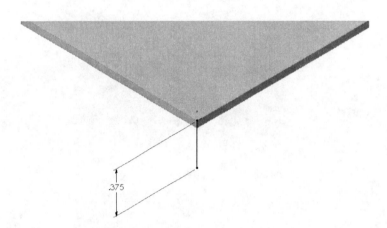 staring at the upper corner.

- Click (Dimension), and make the length of the line **.375 in**.

- Click **(Miter-Flange)** from the Sheet Metal toolbar OR select:
Insert / Sheet Metal / Miter Flange.

- Select the **4** upper edges as indicated.

- Choose **Material Outside** under Flange Position

- Set Gap Distance to **.010 in**

- Click **OK**.

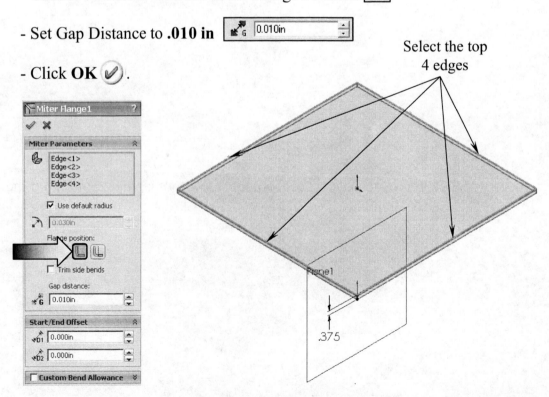

Select the top
4 edges

5. Flattening the part:

- The Flat Pattern can be toggled at anytime during or after the part is created.

- Click ⬛ (Flat-Pattern) from the Sheet Metal toolbar, to flatten the part.

6. Switching back to the folded-model:

- Click ⬛ (Flat-Pattern) again to take it back to the folded stage.

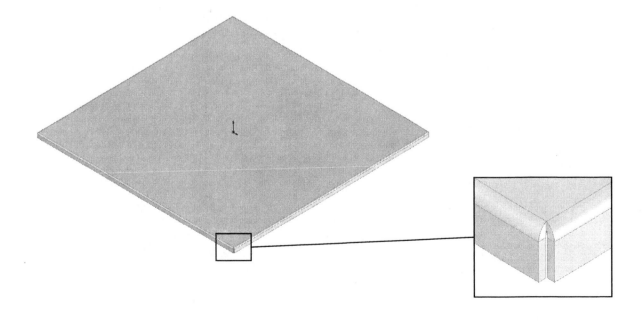

7. Saving your work: Select **File / Save As / Sheet Metal Vent / Save**.

---

8. Making a new Forming Tool – The Louver:

- Start a new Part file, click **File / New / Part / OK**.

- Set Units to Inches – 3 Decimal (Tools/Options/Document Properties/ Units).

9. Sketching on the TOP reference plane:

- Select the TOP plane and click [icon] **Insert / Sketch** from the Sketch toolbar.

- Select the [icon] (Center Rectangle) from the Sketch-Tools toolbar.

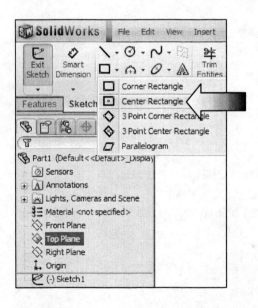

- Sketch a rectangle that starts from the Origin, as shown below.

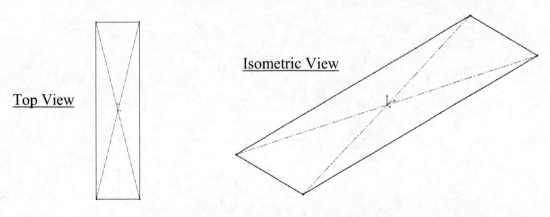

Top View   Isometric View

10. Other Rectangle options:

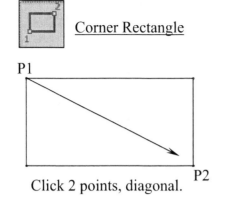

Corner Rectangle

Click 2 points, diagonal.

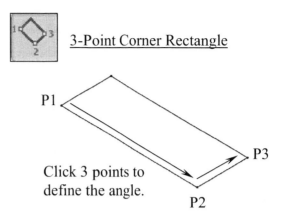

3-Point Corner Rectangle

Click 3 points to define the angle.

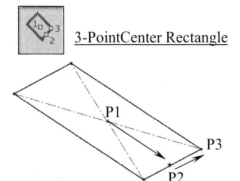

3-PointCenter Rectangle

Start at Center point and click 2 other points to define the angle.

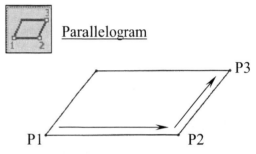

Parallelogram

Click 3 points to define the parallelogram.

11. Adding dimensions:

- Click 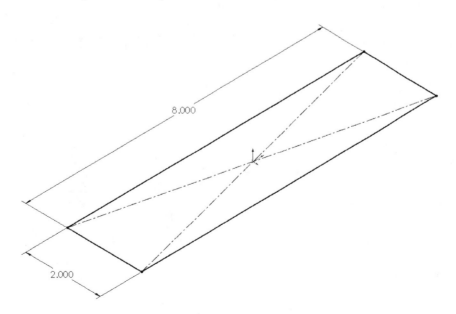 (Dimension) and add the dimensions as shown below.

12. Extruding the Base:

- Click 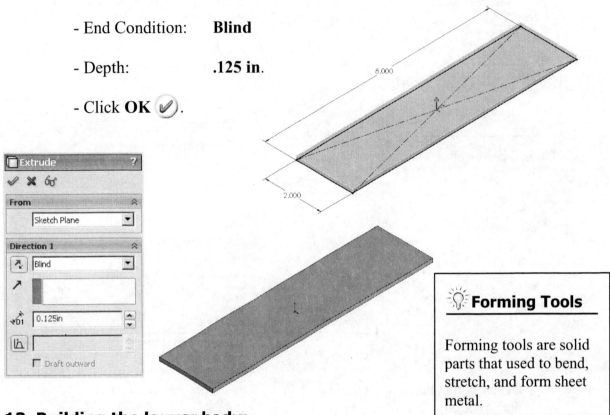 (**Extruded Boss/Base**) and fill in the following parameters:

- End Condition: **Blind**

- Depth: **.125 in**.

- Click **OK** ✓.

> **Forming Tools**
>
> Forming tools are solid parts that used to bend, stretch, and form sheet metal.

13. Building the louver body:

- Select the upper face of the part and open a new sketch.

- Change to the TOP View Orientation.

- Sketch the profile of the Louver-Forming tool and add Dimensions as illustrated below:

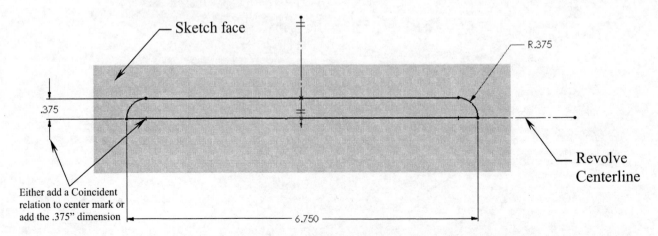

Sketch face

R.375

.375

Revolve Centerline

Either add a Coincident relation to center mark or add the .375" dimension

6.750

- Select the Horizontal Centerline and click 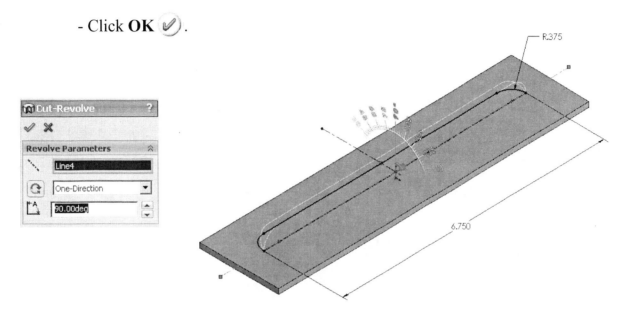 (**Revolve Boss/Base**).

- Use **One-Direction** for Revolve Type.

- For revolve Angle, enter **90°**.

- Toggle (Reverse) and make sure the preview looks like the one below.

- Click **OK** .

- The resulting of a 90° revolved.

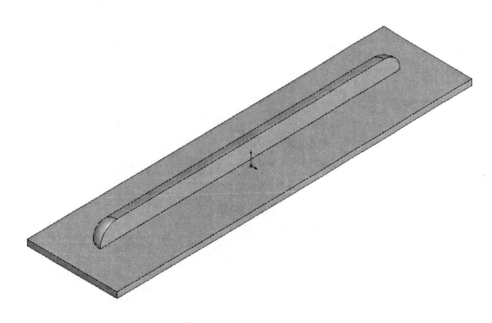

14. Adding a fillet at the base:

- Click (Fillet) and enter **.125** in. under Radius .

- Select the edge as indicated .

- Select Tangent Propagation check box (default), the system applies the same fillet to all connected tangent edges .

- Click **OK** .

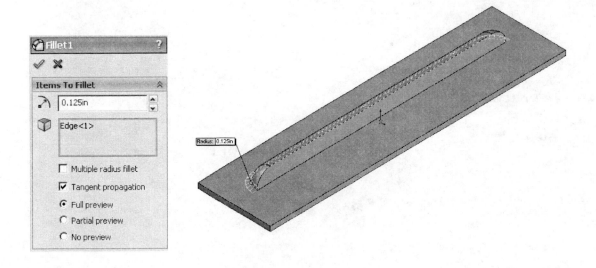

- The revolved feature viewed from the backside.

- The resulting fillet viewed from the backside.

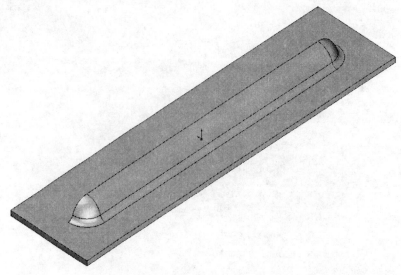

15. Creating the Positioning Sketch:

- The Positioning Sketch displays the preview of the Form tool while it is being dragged from the Design Library. Its sketched entities can be dimensioned to position the Form tool.

- Select the upper surface of the part and click to insert a new sketch.

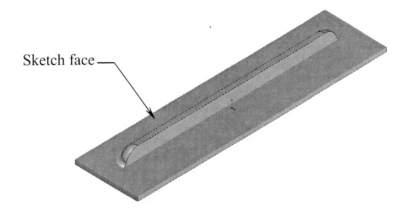

Sketch face

- Select the outer edges of the louver and click **Convert Entities**

- Add a Centerline as shown, to help in positioning the sketch in the future.

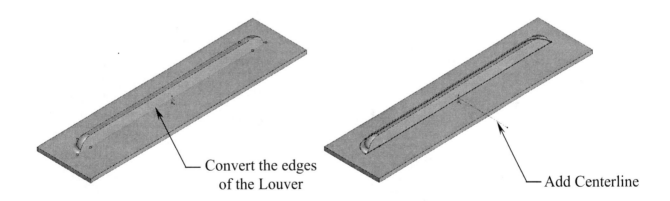

Convert the edges
of the Louver

Add Centerline

- **Exit the sketch** or click .

- Re-name the sketch to **Position Sketch** from the FeatureManager tree.

16. Establishing the Stop and Remove faces:

- In order for the forming tools to work properly, the Stopping Face and the Removing Faces will have to be established prior to saving it as a forming tool.

- Click **Insert / Sheet Metal / Forming Tool**, from the pull down menu.

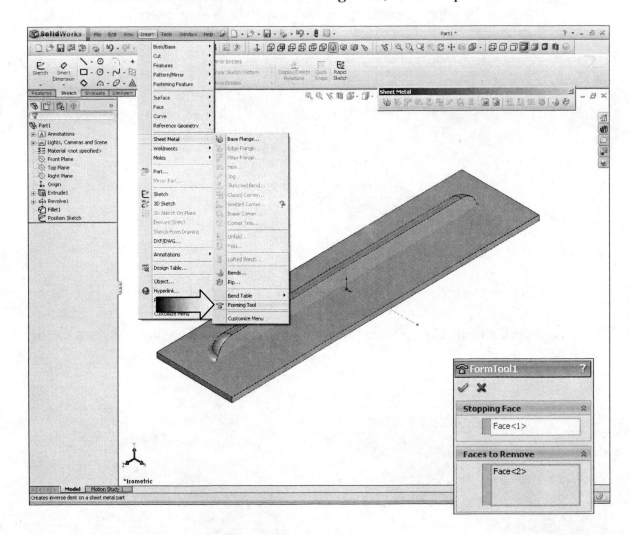

- For **Stopping Face**, select the Upper surface of the plate.

- For **Faces to Remove**, select the Flat surface of the louver.

- Click **OK**.

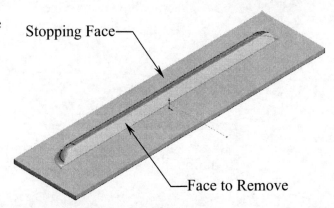

Stopping Face

Face to Remove

17. Saving the Forming Tool:

- Go to: **File / Save As.**

- Enter **Long Louver** for the file name.

- Select **Form Tool** (*.sldlfp) in the Save As Type.

- Change to the following directories: **Program Files\ SolidWorks\ Data\ Design-Library\ Forming Tools\Louvers.**

- Click **Save**.

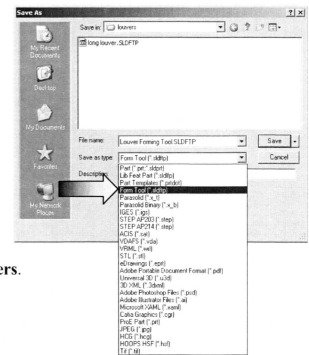

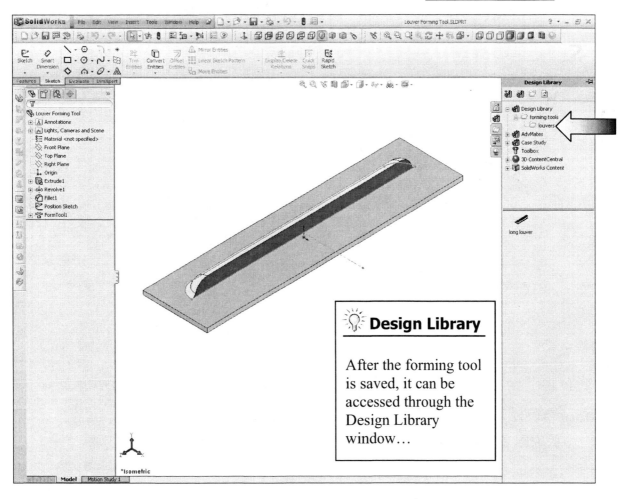

Design Library

After the forming tool is saved, it can be accessed through the Design Library window...

18. Opening the previous part:

- Open the Sheet Metal Vent that was saved earlier. (**File/Open/Sheet Metal Vent**).

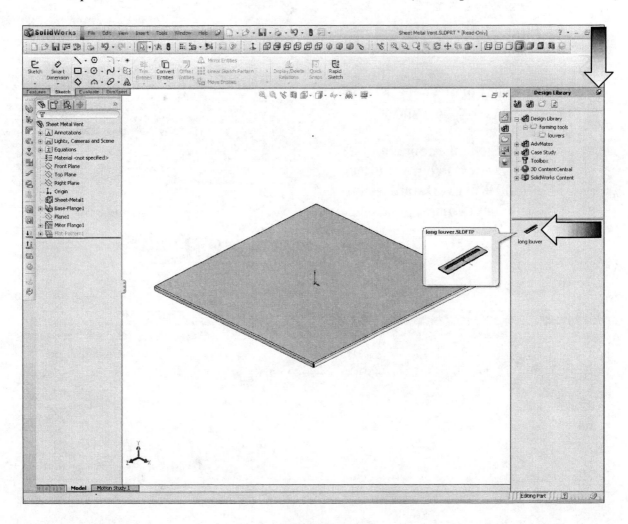

- Click the **Design Library** icon

- Click the push pin to lock the task pane (arrow).

- Expand the Forming Tool folder and double click on the Louvers folder to see its content.

- Move the mouse cursor over the name Long Louver to see the preview of the part (Arrow).

💡 Forming Tools

Forming tools should be inserted from the Design Library window and applied onto parts with sheet metal parameters such as material thickness, bend allowance, fixed face, cut relief, etc…

- Drag and drop the Long Louver from the Design Library onto the sheet metal part as pictured below.

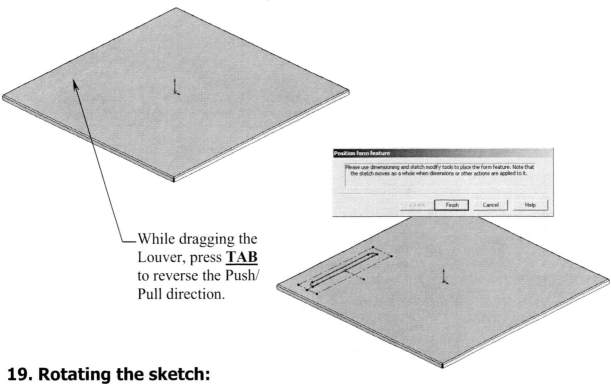

While dragging the Louver, press **TAB** to reverse the Push/ Pull direction.

19. Rotating the sketch:

- Select **Tools / Sketch Tools / Modify**

- In the Rotate section, enter **180 deg**. and press **Enter**.

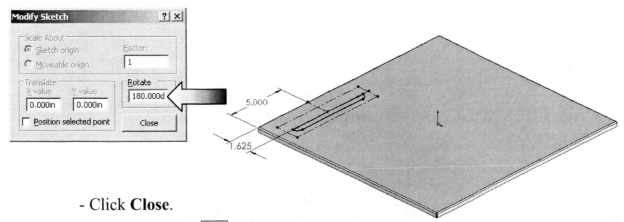

- Click **Close**.

- Add Dimension to position the Louver (use the outer edges of the part).

- Click **OK**.

- Click 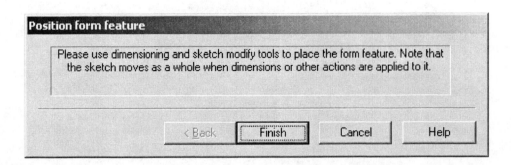 to complete the process.

- The formed Louver is created.

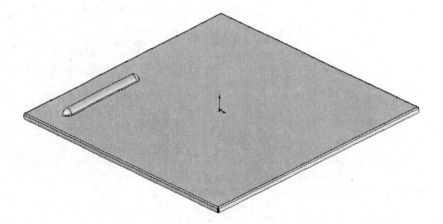

20. Adding a mounting hole:

- Select the upper face of the part as indicated.

- Click 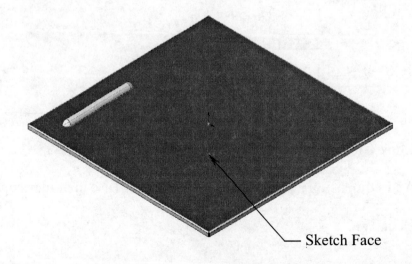 or select **Insert / Sketch**.

Sketch Face

- Sketch a circle 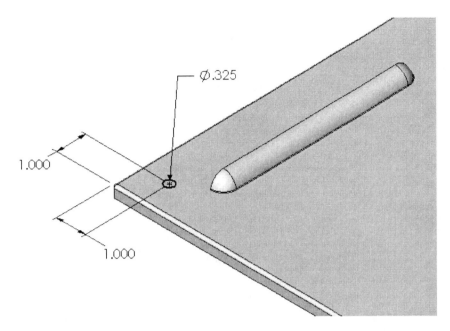 on the left side of the louver.

- Add dimensions to define the circle.

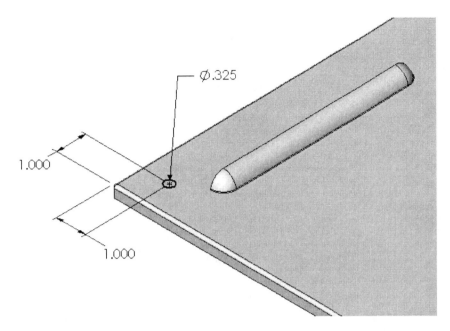

21. Extruding a cut:

- Click or select **Insert / Cut / Extrude**.

- End Condition: **Blind**

- Link to Thickness: **Enabled**

- Normal Cut: **Enabled**

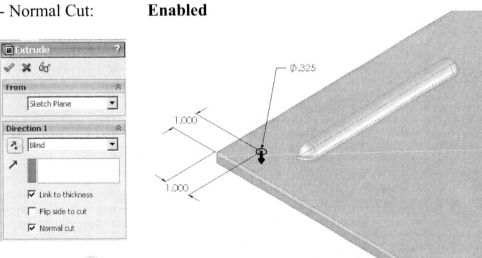

- Click **OK** .

22. Creating a Linear Pattern:

- Click 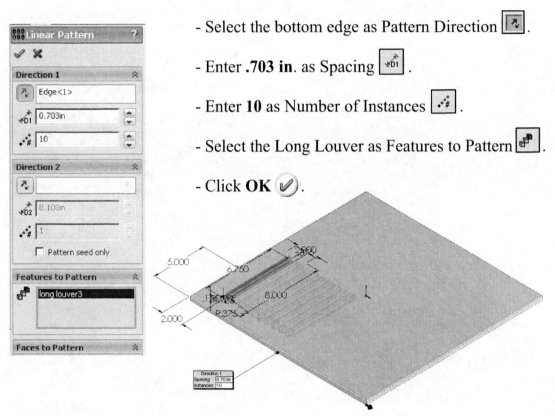 or select **Insert / Pattern Mirror / Linear Pattern**.

- Select the bottom edge as Pattern Direction.

- Enter **.703 in**. as Spacing.

- Enter **10** as Number of Instances.

- Select the Long Louver as Features to Pattern.

- Click **OK**.

- The completed Linear Pattern.

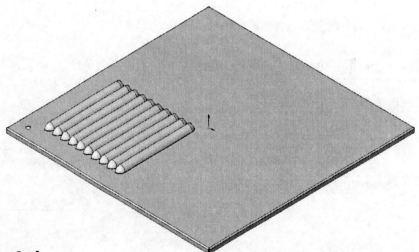

23. Creating an Axis:

- An axis can be created at anytime so features can be arrayed around it. In this case, an axis in the center of the part will be made and used as the center of the Circular Pattern.

- Click 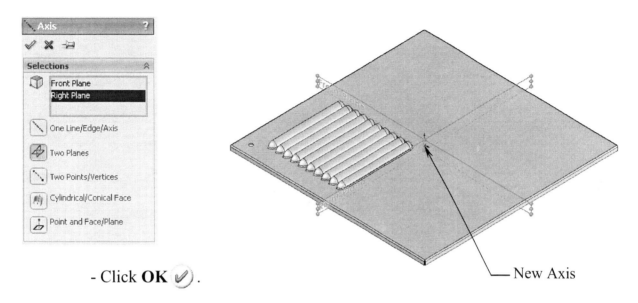 or select **Insert / Reference Geometry / Axis**.

- Choose **Two Planes** option.

- Select FRONT and RIGHT planes from Feature Manager tree.

New Axis

- Click **OK**.

24. Creating a Circular Pattern:

- Click or select **Insert / Pattern Mirror / Circular Pattern**.

- Select the new Axis for Pattern Axis

- Enter **360 deg.** for Pattern Angle

- Enter **4** for Number of Instances

- For Feature to Pattern choose Cut-Extrude1, LPattern1 and Long Louver from the Feature Manager tree.

- Click **OK**.

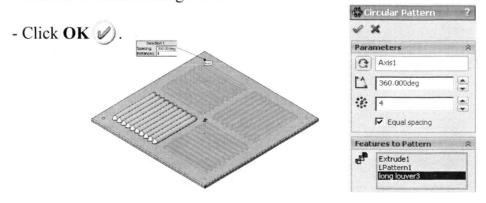

25. Saving your work:

- Either click on the Save icon 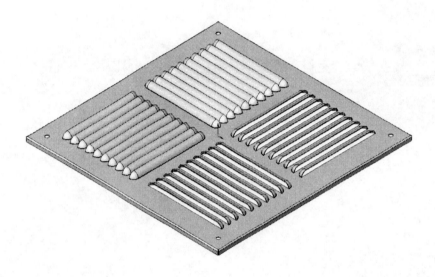 to save and override the previous file – or –

- Select **File / Save As / Sheet Metal Vent / Save**.

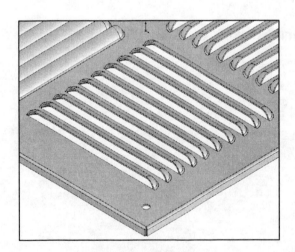

Finished Part (Folded)

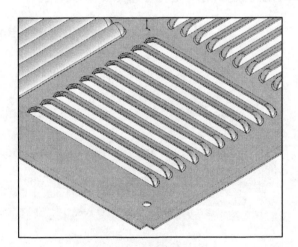

Flat Pattern

Questions for Review

Sheet Metal Parts

1. The mid-point relation can be used to center a line onto the Origin.
    a. True
    b. False

2. The base flange command can also be selected from Insert / Sheet Metal / Base Flange.
    a. True
    b. False

3. When a linear model edge is selected and the sketch pencil is clicked, the system creates a NORMAL TO CURVE plane automatically.
    a. True
    b. False

4. The Miter Flange feature can create more than one flange in the same operation.
    a. True
    b. False

5. The Flat and the Folded patterns cannot be toggled until the part is completed and saved.
    a. True
    b. False

6. An existing forming tool cannot be edited or changed; forming tools are fixed by default.
    a. True
    b. False

7. When applying a form tool onto a sheet metal part, the push or pull direction can be toggled when pressing:
    a. Up arrow
    b. Tab
    c. Control

8. The Modify Sketch command can be used to rotate or translate the entire sketch.
    a. True
    b. False

9. A formed feature(s) cannot be copied or patterned.
    a. True
    b. False

	9. FALSE
8. TRUE	7. B
6. FALSE	5. FALSE
4. TRUE	3. TRUE
2. TRUE	1. TRUE

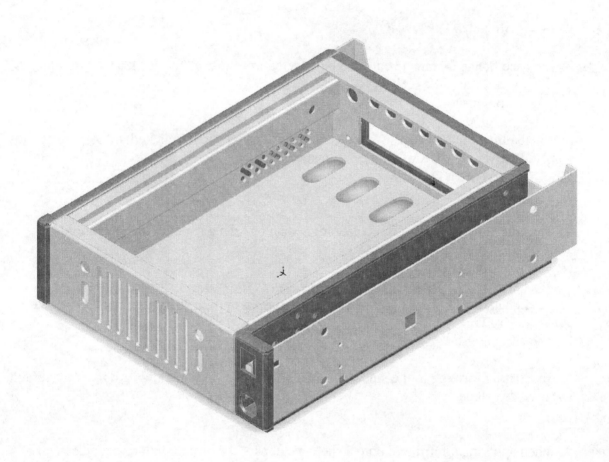

CHAPTER 13

Sheet Metal Forming Tools

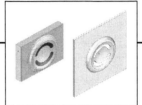

Sheet Metal Forming Tools

- Forming tools act as dies that bend, stretch, or otherwise form sheet metal.

- SolidWorks includes some sample forming tools to get you started. They are stored in: ***Installation_Directory\Data\Design Library\Forming Tools\folder_name.***

- Some types of form features, such as louvers and lances, create openings on sheet metal parts. To indicate which forming tool faces create openings, the system changes the color of these faces to **red (255,0,0)**.

- The user can only insert (drag & drop) forming tools from the **Design Library** window and apply them only to sheet metal parts.

- The Design Library window gives you quick access to the parts, assemblies, and library features you use most often.

- Users can create their own forming tools and apply them to sheet metal parts to create form features such as louvers, lances, flanges, and ribs.

- The Design Library window has several default folders. Each folder contains a group of palette items, displayed as Thumbnail Graphics.

- Design Library can include:
  - Parts (.sldprt)
  - Assemblies (.sldasm)
  - Sheet Metal Forming Tools (.sldlfp)
  - Library Features (.sldlfp)

- This lesson is the 1ˢᵗ half of chapter 13.

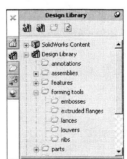

Button with Slots
Forming Tools

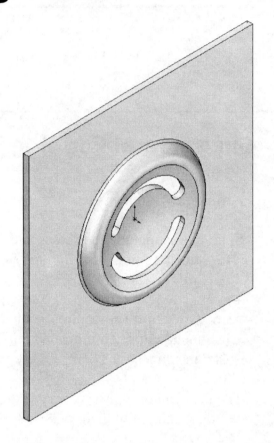

| Dimensioning Standards: **ANSI** |
| Units: **INCHES** – 3 Decimals |

Tools Needed:

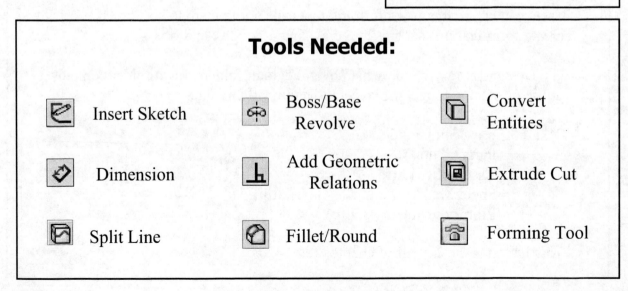

Insert Sketch	Boss/Base Revolve	Convert Entities
Dimension	Add Geometric Relations	Extrude Cut
Split Line	Fillet/Round	Forming Tool

1. Creating the base block:

- Select the RIGHT plane and Insert a new Sketch 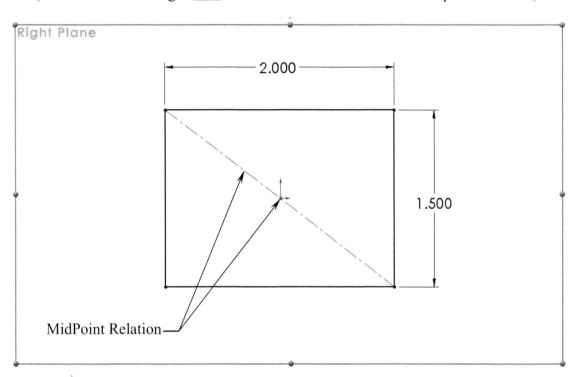 .

- Sketch the profile below and add Dimensions as shown.

- Add a Midpoint relation to position the sketch.

(The Center-Rectangle can be used to eliminate the midpoint relation).

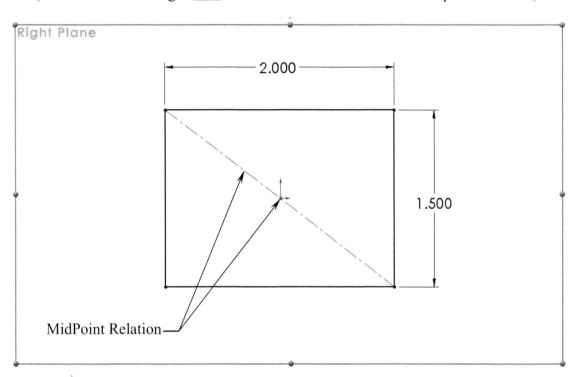

MidPoint Relation

3. Extruding the base:

- Click **Extruded Boss/Base** .

- Enter the followings:

- Direction 1: **Blind**.

- **Reverse** Direction.

- Depth: **.250in**.

- Click **OK** .

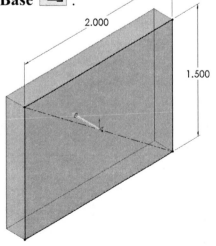

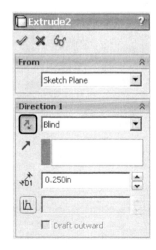

4. Creating the forming tool body:

- Select the FRONT plane and open a new sketch ✏️ .

- Sketch the profile as shown.

- Add dimensions 📐 and relations ⊥ to fully define the sketch.

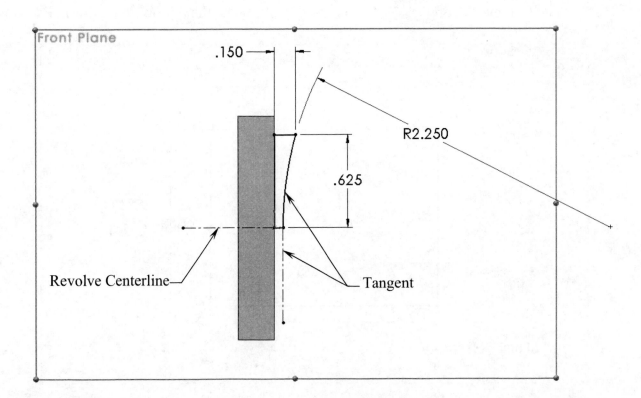

Revolve Centerline

Tangent

5. Revolving the body:

- Click **Revolved Boss/Base** ⊛ .

- Revolve a full **360 deg**.

- Click **OK** ✓ .

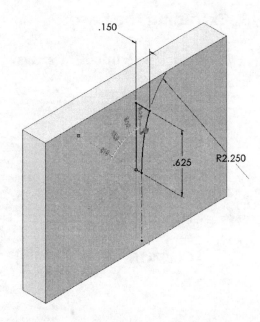

6. Adding fillet:

- Click **Fillet** and enter **.080 in**. for Radius.

- Select the edge as indicated.

- Click **OK**.

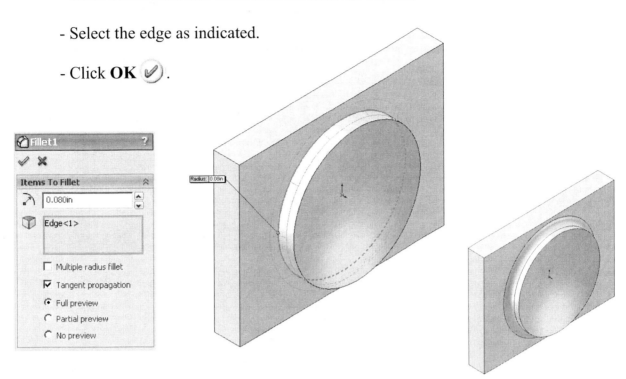

7. Sketching the 1ˢᵗ slot profile:

- Select the front face of the rectangular block and open a new sketch

- Sketch a Center point Arc as shown.

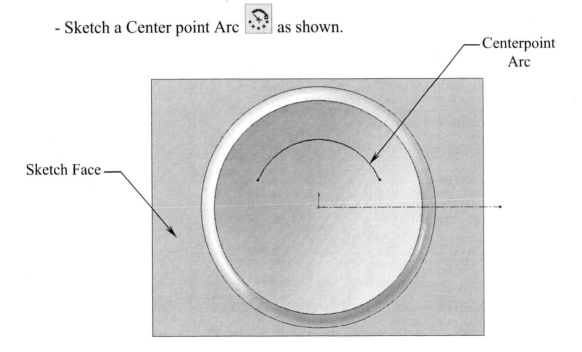

Centerpoint
Arc

Sketch Face

- From the Sketch Toolbar, click **Offset Entities**.

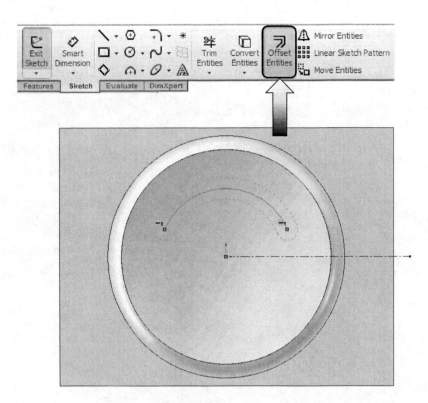

- Enter **.0625 in**. under Offset Distance.

- Enable the followings:

    * **Select Chain**   * **Bi-Directional**

    * **Make Base Construction**   * **Cap End / Arcs**.

- Click **OK** ✅.

Note:

- *The new Arc-Slot command* 🖊️ *can be used to create this shape.*

- Add dimensions 🖊️ and relations ⊥ as shown to fully define the sketch.

Horizontal

135.00°

.063

.063

R.388

8. Creating the 1st Split Line:

- Click Split Line  from the **CURVES** toolbar, or select:
Insert / Curve / Split Line.

- Select the face as indicated to split ⬦ .

- Click **OK** ✅ .

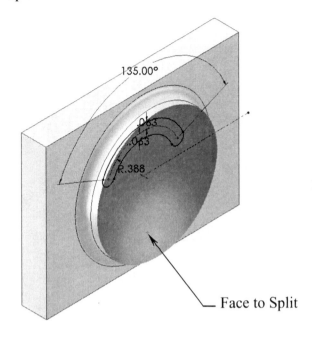

Face to Split

- The selected face is split into a new boundary.

- This new surface can now be used as Faces-to-Remove, when the form tool is inserted into a sheet metal part.

- The Faces to Remove option specifies what features/area will get a through cut.

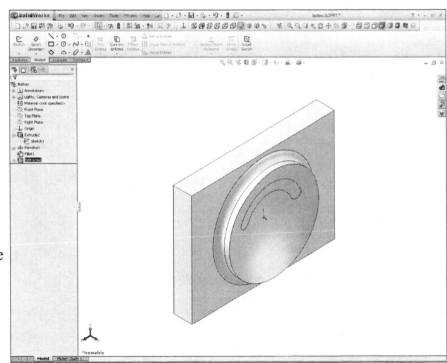

9. Creating the 2nd slot profile:

- Repeat step number 6 an 7 to create the 2nd split line.

- Either Copy and Paste to create the same sketch profile again – OR – the Derived Sketch option can also be used to fully maintain the relationships between the Original sketch and the Derived sketch.

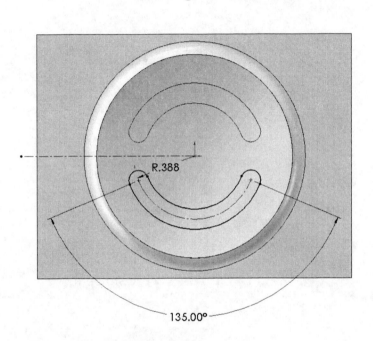

R.388

135.00°

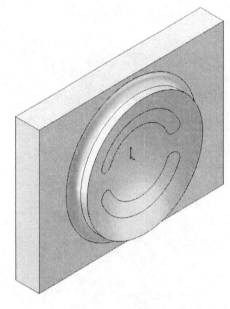

10. Adding more fillets:

- Click **Fillet**  and enter **.0625 in**. for Radius.

- Select the edge as indicated.

- Click **OK** .

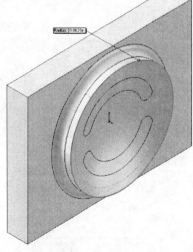

11. Inserting the Forming Tool feature:

- Select **Insert / Sheet Metal / Forming tool** 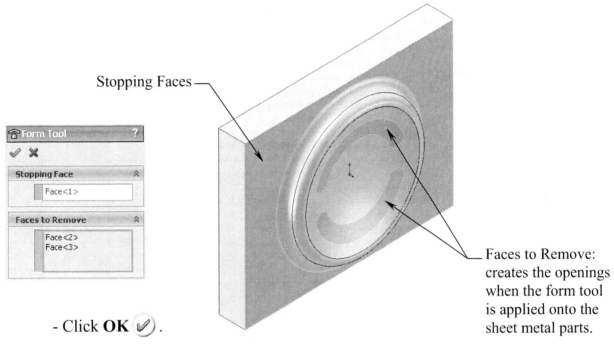 from the pull down menu

- Select the Stopping Face and the Faces to Remove as indicated.

Stopping Faces

Faces to Remove:
creates the openings
when the form tool
is applied onto the
sheet metal parts.

- Click **OK** .

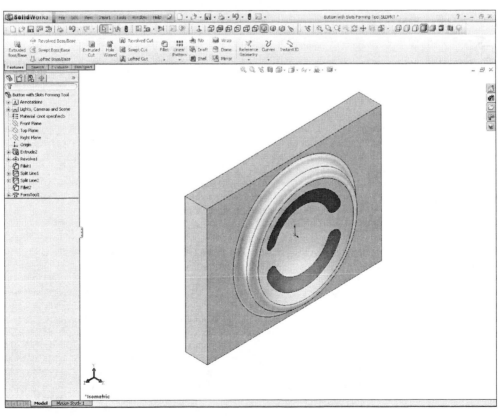

12. Saving the Forming tool:

- Click **File / Save As / Button w-Slots**, change the Save as Type to **Form Tool** and save the part in the following directories:

C:\Program Files\SolidWorks\Data\Design Library\Forming Tools\File Name.

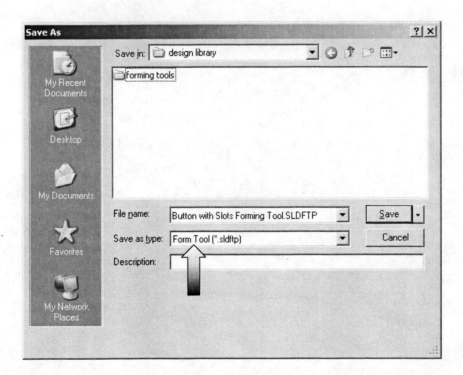

Note:

- *The Sheet metal forming tools can also be saved by dragging and dropping from the Feature Manager tree to a folder (i.e. Forming Tools) inside the Task pane.*

- *The file name, file type, and path can be selected to save the forming tool at this time.*

12. Applying the new forming tool: (Optional)

- Create a sheet metal part using the drawing below and test out your new forming tool.

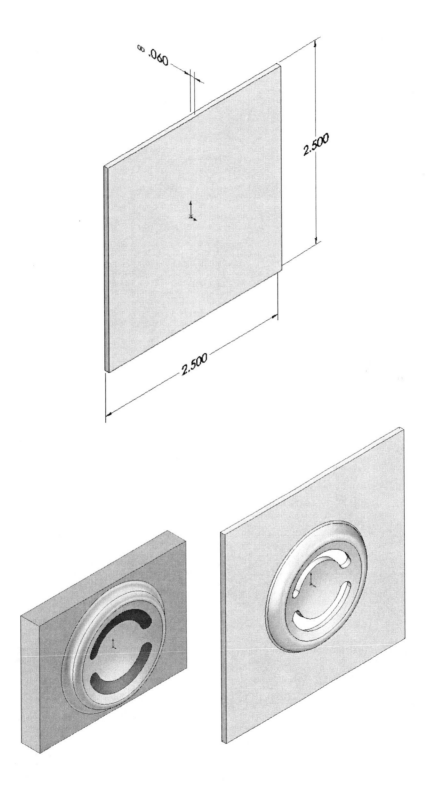

Questions for Review

Forming Tools

1. Forming tools can bend or stretch sheet metal parts.
    a. True
    b. False

2. Forming tools can be stored in the Design Library window using the file extension:
    a. slddrw
    b. sldprt
    c. dwg

3. Forming tools can be dragged and dropped from the Design Library window.
    a. True
    b. False

4. Forming tools can be used to form surfaces and solid parts as well.
    a. True
    b. False

5. The Red color on the face(s) of the forming tool creates openings on the sheet metal parts.
    a. True
    b. False

6. The Split Line command divides a selected face into multiple separate faces.
    a. True
    b. False

7. Only one single, closed sketch can be used with the Split Line command.
    a. True
    b. False

8. The _____ key is used to reverse the direction of the forming tool (push/pull):
    a. Shift
    b. Tab
    c. Alt

7. TRUE	8. b
5. TRUE	6. TRUE
3. TRUE	4. FALSE
1. TRUE	2. B

CHAPTER 13 (cont.)

Sheet Metal Parts

Sheet Metal Parts

- Sheet metal components are normally used as housing or enclosures for parts or to strengthen and support other parts.

- A Sheet Metal part can be created as a single part or it can also be designed in context of an assembly that has the components it will enclosed.

- Forming tools are dies that can bend, stretch, or form sheet metal.

- In SolidWorks, forming tools are applied using the "Positive Half" (the raised side) to form features.

- When inserting the forming tool, its direction can be reversed using the TAB key (Push or Pull).

- The Sheet Metal part can be flattened either by using the Unfold 🔽 or Flattened 🕮 button, and drawings can be made to show views of the bent or flattened part. Bend lines are also visible in the drawing views.

- By default, only the Bend-Lines are visible at all time but not the Bend-Regions. To show the Bend Regions, right click on the Flat-Pattern1 icon, at the bottom of the FeatureManager tree, select Edit Feature and <u>clear</u> the <u>Merge Faces</u> check box.

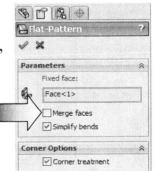

- This lesson is the 2nd half of chapter 13.

Mounting Tray
Sheet Metal Parts

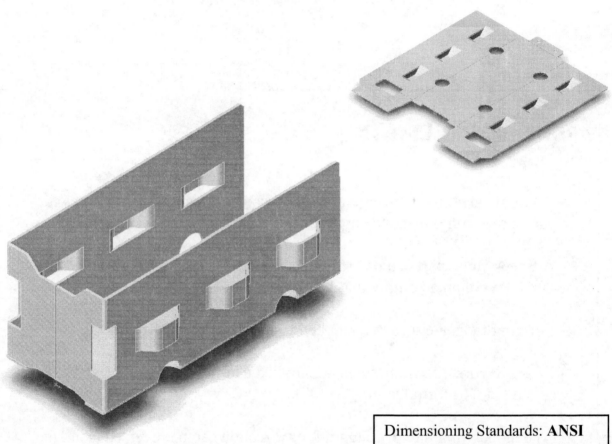

Dimensioning Standards: **ANSI**

Units: **INCHES** – 3 Decimals

Tools Needed:

Insert Sketch	Base Flange	Edge Flange
Unfold	Fold	Extruded Cut
Linear Pattern	Flattened	Break Corner

1. Starting with the base sketch:

- Select the FRONT plane from Feature Manager Tree.

- Click 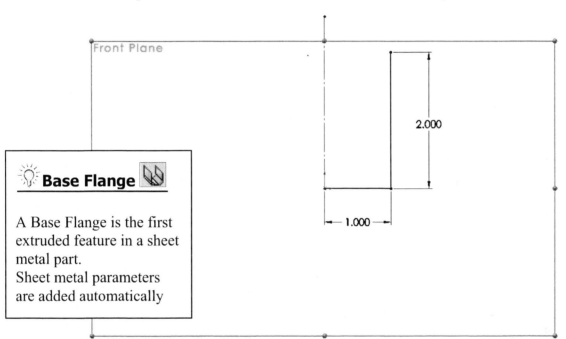 or select **Insert / Sketch**.

- Sketch the profile below and add dimensions to fully define the sketch.

> ### Base Flange
>
> A Base Flange is the first extruded feature in a sheet metal part.
> Sheet metal parameters are added automatically

2. Extruding the Base Flange:

- Click on the Sheet Metal toolbar, or select:

Insert / Sheet Metal / Base Flange.

- End Condition: **Blind**

- Extrude Depth: **5.000**

- Thickness: **18 Gauge**

- Bend Radius: **.010**

- Material: **Outside**

- Click **OK** .

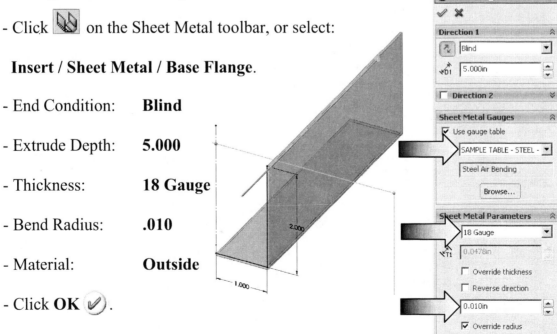

3. Creating an Edge Flange:

- Select the outer edge as shown and click  on the Sheet Metal toolbar, or select: **Insert / Sheet Metal / Edge Flange**.

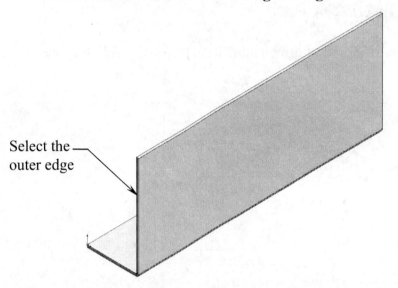

Select the outer edge

> 💡 **Edge Flange** 📐
>
> The Edge Flange command adds a flange to the selected linear edge and shares the same material thickness of the sheet metal part.

- Position the flange towards the left side and set the following:

- Use Default Radius: **Enabled**

- Flange Direction: **Blind**

- Bend Angle: **90deg**

- Flange Depth: **.985**

- Use **Inner Virtual Sharp**.

- Flange Position: **Material Outside**.

- Click **OK**.

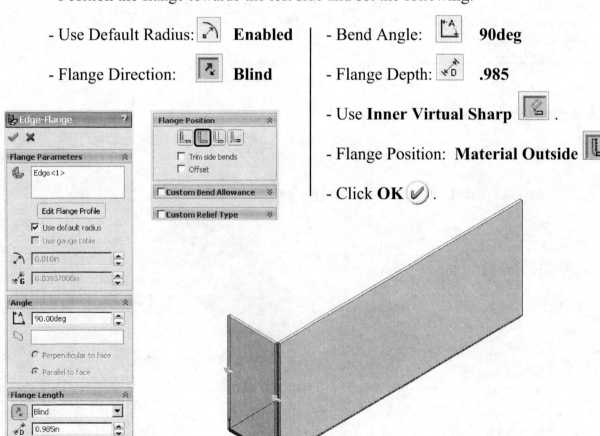

4. Adding cut features:

- Select the face as shown and insert a new sketch 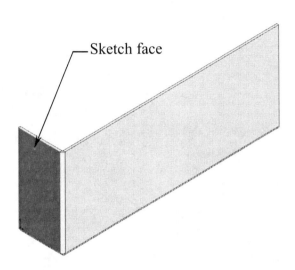.

- Sketch the profile and add dimensions .

- The horizontal dimensions are measured from the Centerline.

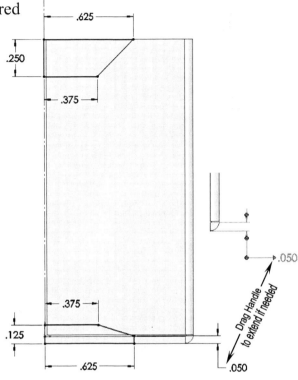

—Sketch face

.625

.250

.375

.375

.125

.625

.050

.050

Drag Handle
to extend if needed

5. Extruding a cut:

- Click  or select **Insert / Cut / Extrude**.

- End Condition: **Blind**.

- Extrude Depth: **.165 in.**

- Click **OK** .

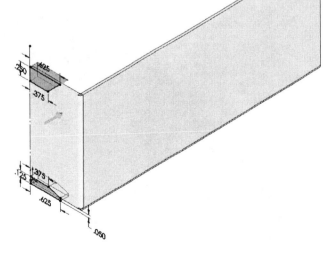

Extrude ?

From
Sketch Plane

Direction 1
Blind

D1 0.165in

☐ Link to thickness
☐ Flip side to cut
☑ Normal cut

6. Using the Unfold command:

- Click 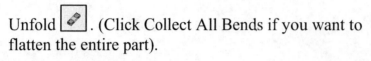 on the Sheet metal toolbar or select:
  Insert / Sheet Metal / Unfold.

- Select the right face as Fixed face .

- Select the bend radius as indicated for Bends to

  Unfold . (Click Collect All Bends if you want to
  flatten the entire part).

- Click **OK** .

> **Unfold**
>
> When adding cuts across a bend, the Unfold command flattens one or more bend(s) in a sheet metal part.

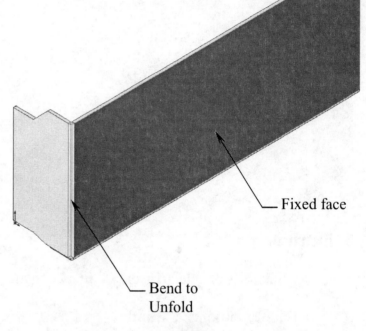

Fixed face

Bend to Unfold

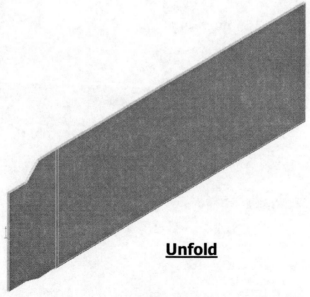

Unfold

7. Creating a Rectangular Window:

- Select the face as indicated and insert a new sketch 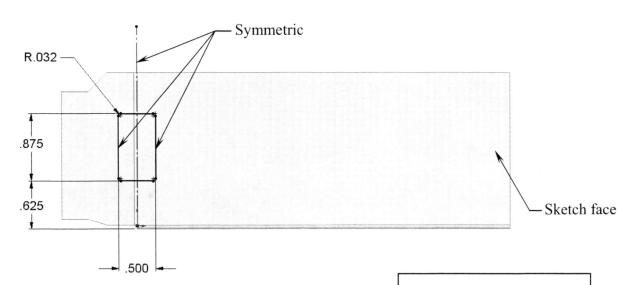 .

- Sketch a rectangle ☐ as shown below.

- Add dimensions ◇ and Sketch Fillets ⌐ .

Symmetric

R.032

.875

.625

.500

Sketch face

8. Extruding a Cut:

- Click  or select **Insert / Cut / Extrude**.

- End Condition: **Blind**

- Link to Thickness: **Enabled** (default)

- Normal Cut: **Enabled**

- Click **OK** ✔ .

💡 **Link To Thickness**

- The Link-to-Thickness option is only available in sheet metal parts.

- When this option is enabled, the extruded depth is automatically linked to the part' thickness.

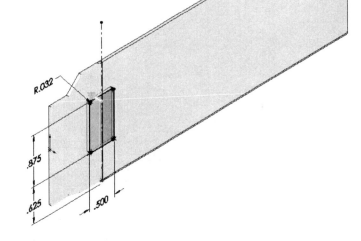

9. Using the Fold command:

- Click  on the Sheet metal toolbar or select:

Insert / Sheet Metal / Fold.

- Select the right face as Fixed face 🔧 .

- Select the bend radius as indicated for Bends to Fold 🖊 . (If Collect All Bends

was selected last time, click it again this time).

- Click **OK** ✓ .

> ◊ **Fold**
>
> _____
>
> The Fold command returns the bends to their folded states.

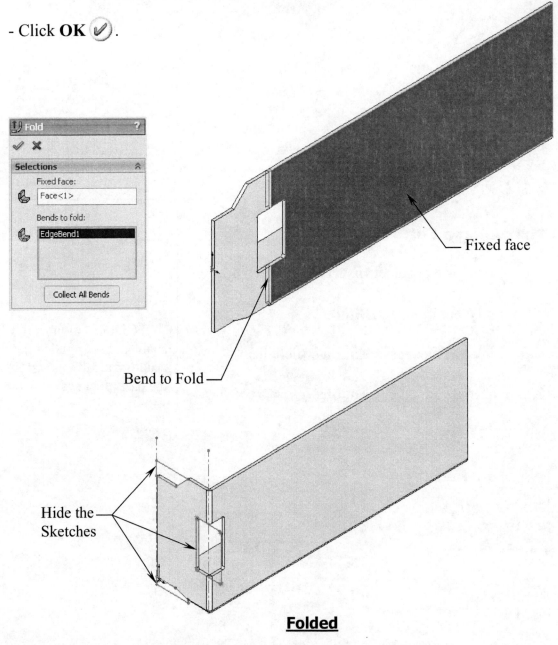

Fixed face

Bend to Fold

Hide the Sketches

Folded

10. Unfolding multiple bends:

- Click  or select **Insert / Sheet Metal / Unfold**.

- Select the bottom face as Fixed face .

- Select the 2 bend radii as shown for Bends To Unfold .

- Click **OK** .

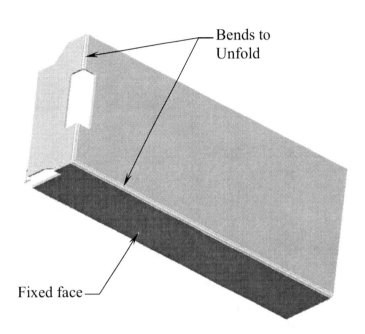

Bends to Unfold

Fixed face

11. Adding more Cuts:

- Select the upper face as noted and insert a new sketch .

- Sketch 2 Circles and add Dimensions for size and position.

- Add an Equal and a Vertical relation between the circles.

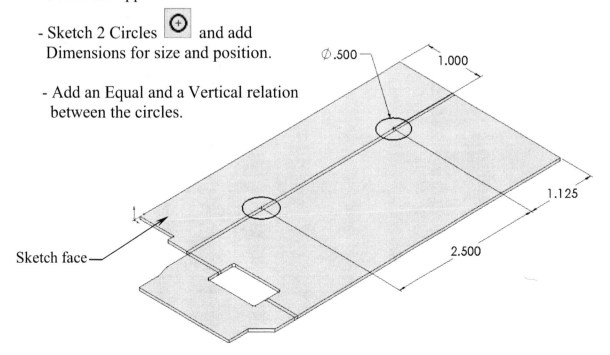

Sketch face

Ø.500

1.000

1.125

2.500

- Click  or select **Insert / Cut / Extrude**.

- End Condition: **Blind**.

- Link To Thickness: **Enabled**

- Click **OK** ✓.

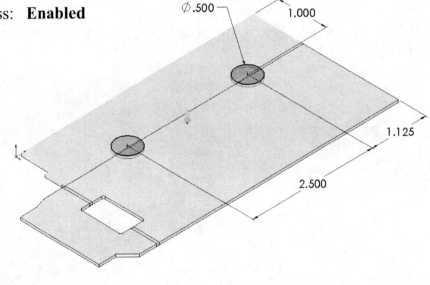

12. Folding multiple bends:

- Click 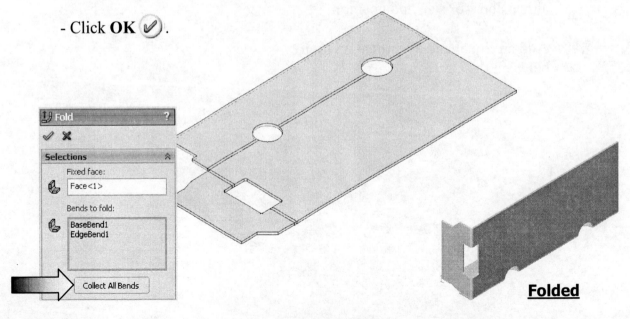 on the Sheet Metal toolbar or select: **Insert / Sheet Metal / Fold**.

- The Fixed face 🔩 is still selected by default.

- Under Bends to Fold 📐, click **Collect All Bends** `Collect All Bends` .

- Click **OK** ✓.

Folded

13. Inserting a Sheet Metal Forming Tool:

- Click the **Design Library** icon and click the push pin to lock it.

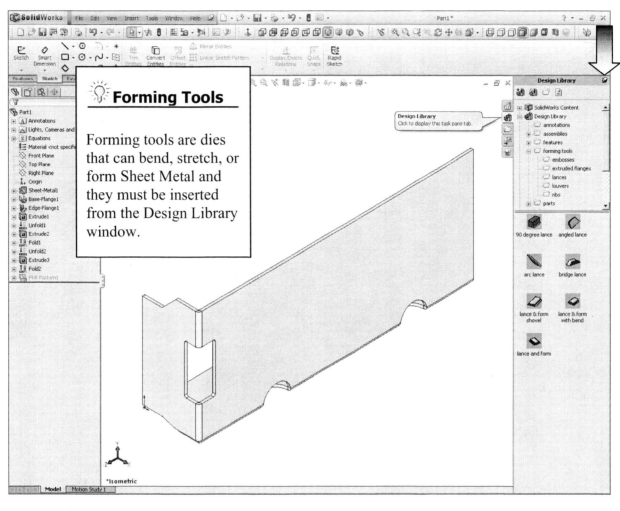

Forming Tools

Forming tools are dies that can bend, stretch, or form Sheet Metal and they must be inserted from the Design Library window.

- Double click on the Design Library folder to open it.

- Double click on the **Forming Tools** folder forming tools

- Double click on the **Lances** folder lances

- Locate the **Bridge Lance** form tool.

- Position the mouse cursor over the Bridge Lance icon to see its preview graphics.

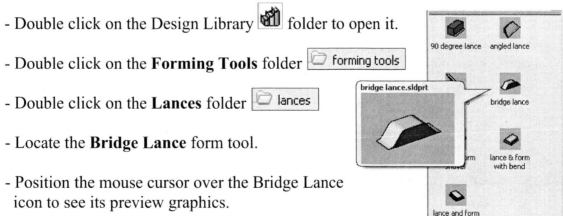

- SolidWorks includes some sample forming tools to get you started.

- Drag the Bridge Lance form tool out and position it approximately as shown.

- Do not release the mouse button just yet; let's look at the options of reversing the form tool.

- By default, the form-tool is inserted inwards (Pushed in).

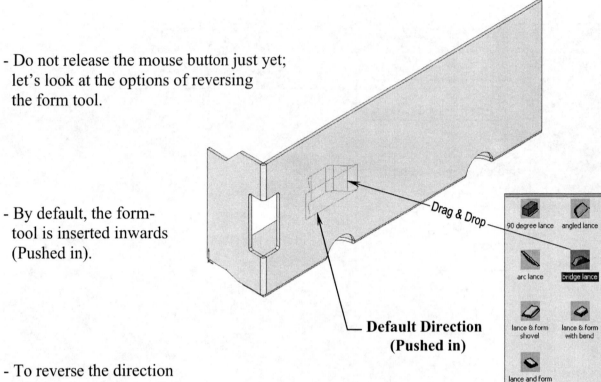

- To reverse the direction of the form tool, simply push the **TAB** key while holding the mouse button.

- Release the mouse button to place the Bridge Lance feature.

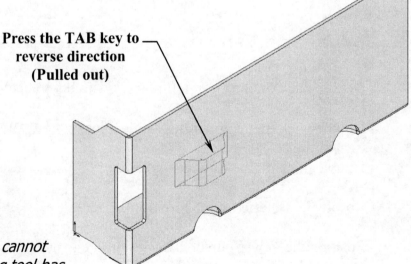

Note: The form direction cannot be reversed if the forming tool has already been dropped; click Undo to try it again.

14. Re-positioning the Bridge Lance feature:

- At the next pop-up screen, add dimensions 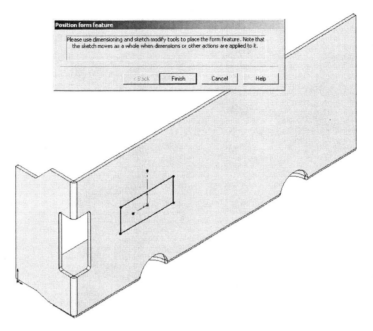 as shown below to correctly position the formed feature.

- Add dimensions <u>from the centerlines</u> to the outer-most edges of the part.

- Click Finish

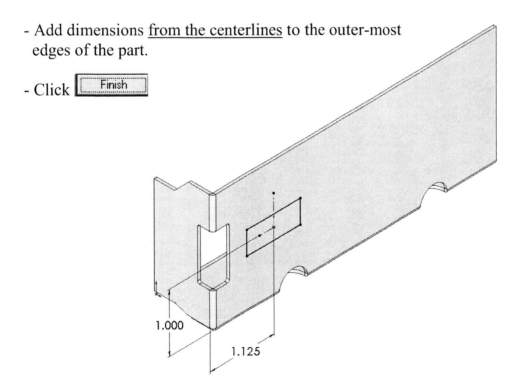

- Un-pin the Design Library Tree ⊞ to put it away temporarily.

15. Creating the Linear Pattern of the Bridge Lance:

- Click 🔲 or select **Insert / Pattern Mirror / Linear Pattern**.

- Select the Top Horizontal Edge of the part as Pattern Direction 🔲 .

- Enter **1.500** in for Instance Spacing 🔲 .

- Enter **3** for Number of Instances 🔲 .

- Select the Bridge-Lance as Features To pattern 🔲 .

- Click **OK** ✅ .

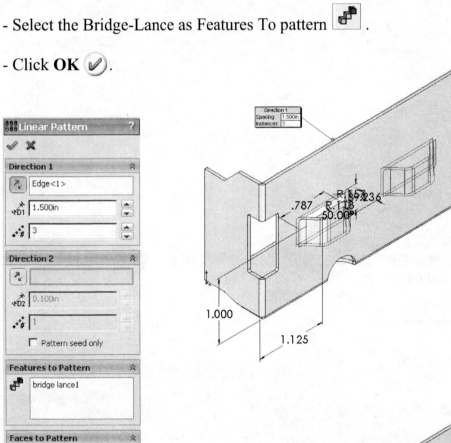

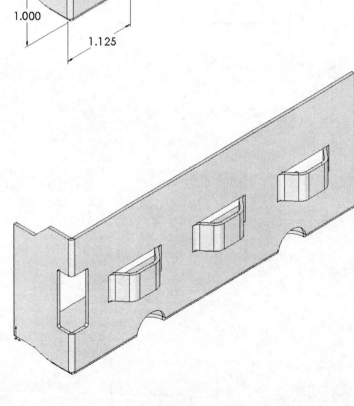

16. Mirroring the part:

- Rotate the part and select the face as indicated (for mirror face).

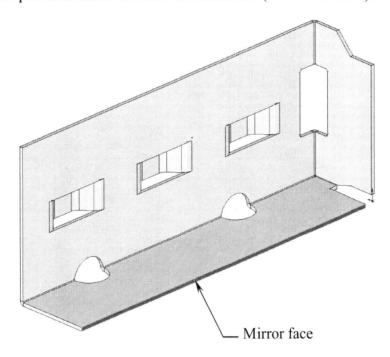

Mirror face

- Select **Insert / Pattern Mirror / Mirror**.

- Click inside the Bodies to Mirror section and select the body as shown.

- Click **OK** ✅.

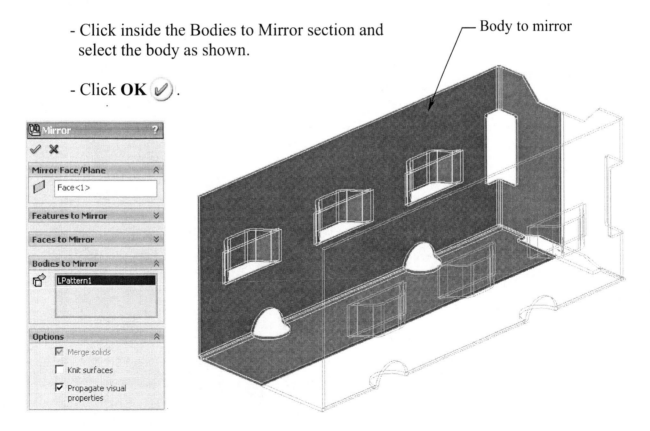

Body to mirror

17. Adding a lower Edge Flange:

- Select the edge as indicated.

- Click 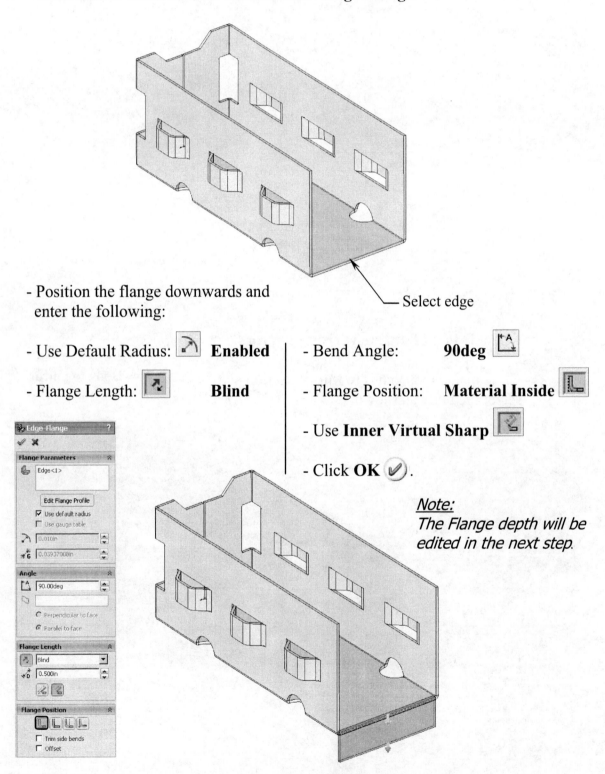 or select **Insert / Sheet Metal / Edge Flange**.

- Select edge

- Position the flange downwards and enter the following:

- Use Default Radius: **Enabled**

- Flange Length: **Blind**

- Bend Angle: **90deg**

- Flange Position: **Material Inside**

- Use **Inner Virtual Sharp**

- Click **OK**.

Note:
The Flange depth will be edited in the next step.

18. Resizing the Edge Flange:

- Expand the Edge Flange feature (click the + symbol) from FeatureManager tree.

- Right click on the sketch below the Edge Flange and select **Edit Sketch**.

- Drag the 2 outer-most vertical lines inwards (pictured).

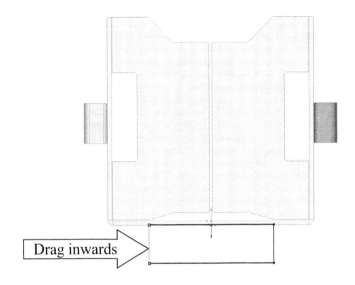

Drag inwards

- Sketch 2 Circles 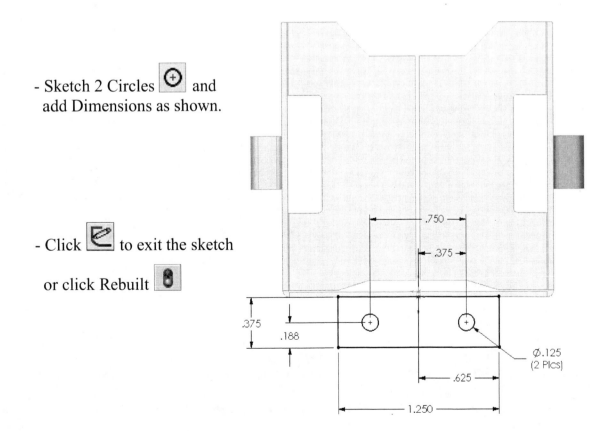 and add Dimensions as shown.

- Click to exit the sketch or click Rebuilt

19. Adding Chamfers:

- Click 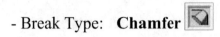 or select **Insert / Sheet Metal / Break-Corner**.

- Break Type: **Chamfer**

- Enter **.060** for chamfer depth

- Select the **4 Edges** as shown.

- Click **OK**.

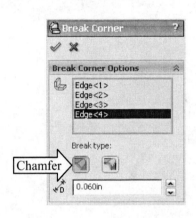

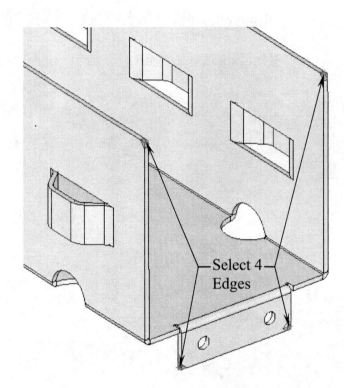

Select 4 Edges

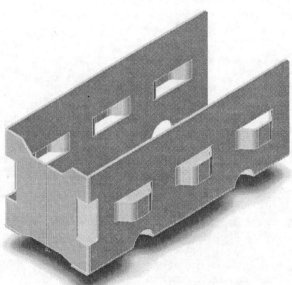

Front

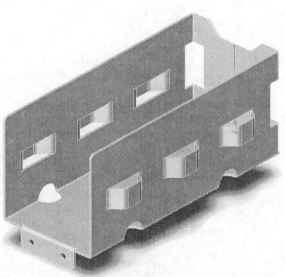

Back
Isometric

Rotation Options:
*(Set the View rotation to 15 degrees – Press the **Right** arrow 12 times and **Down** arrow 4 times).*
*(OR - View rotation set to 30 degrees – Press the **Right** arrow 6 times and **Down** arrow 2 times).*
*(OR - View rotation set to 60 degrees – Press the **Righ**t arrow 3 times and **Down** arrow 1 time).*

20. Switching to the Flat Pattern:

- Click 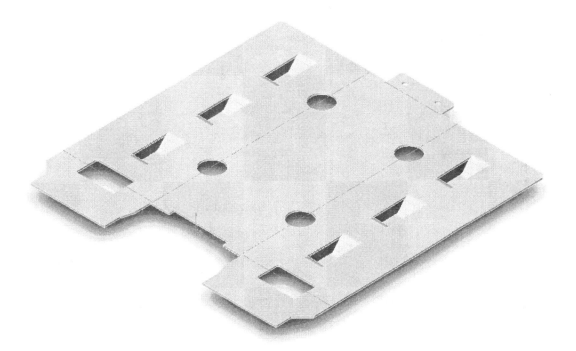 or select **Insert / Sheet Metal / Flattened**.

- Verify that the part is flattened properly and there are no rebuild errors.

21. Saving your work:

- Select **File / Save As / Mounting Tray / Save**.

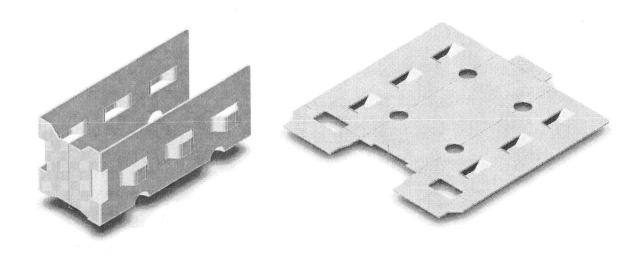

Questions for Review

Sheet Metal

1. A Sheet Metal part can be created as a single part or in context of an assembly that has the components it will enclose.
   - a. True
   - b. False

2. A Base Flange is the first extruded feature in a sheet metal part. Sheet metal parameters are added automatically.
   - a. True
   - b. False

3. A sheet metal part designed in SolidWorks can have multiple wall thickness.
   - a. True
   - b. False

4. The Edge Flange command adds a flange to the selected linear edge and shares the same material thickness of the sheet metal part.
   - a. True
   - b. False

5. Only one bend can be flattened at a time using the Unfold command.
   - a. True
   - b. False

6. Forming tools have to be inserted from the Feature Palette window.
   - a. True
   - b. False

7. To reverse the direction of the forming tool while dragging it from the Feature Palette window, press:
   - a. Tab
   - b. Control
   - c. Shift

8. After the features are formed by the forming tools, their sketches can only be moved or re-positioned and their dimension values cannot be changed.
   - a. True
   - b. False

1. TRUE	2. TRUE
3. FALSE	4. TRUE
5. FALSE	6. TRUE
7. A	8. TRUE

CHAPTER 14

Sheet Metal Conversions

Sheet Metal Conversions
From IGES to SolidWorks

- Parts created from other CAD systems (IGES or Initial Graphics Exchange Specification) can be imported and converted into SolidWorks Sheet Metal.

- When importing other CAD formats into SolidWorks, read them as follows:

  • If there are blank surfaces, they are imported and added to the Feature Manager design Tree as surface features.
  • If the attempt to knit the surfaces into a solid succeeds, the solid appears as the base feature (named **Imported1**) in a new part file.
  • If the surfaces represent multiple closed volumes, then one part is made for each closed volume.
  • If the attempt to knit the surfaces fail, the surfaces are grouped into one or more surface features (named **Surface-Imported1...**) in a new part file.
  • If you import a **.dxf** or **.dwg** file, the **DXF/DWG import wizard** appears to guide you through the import processes.

- The imported parts must be of uniform thickness to fold and unfold properly.
- After the part is opened in SolidWorks, sheet metal parameters such as Rip 🔲 , Fixed face or edge 🔲 , Bend radius 🔲 , etc., and should be added to it before the Flat Pattern can be created.

- The converted part appears on the Feature Manager Design tree, it contains the features Sheet Metal1 🔲 , Flatten Bend1 🔲 , and Process Bend1 🔲 .

- The part can now be Flattened and Folded as a sheet metal part by toggling the Suppression state 🔲 of the Process Bends.

Sheet Metal Conversions
From IGES to SolidWorks Flat Pattern

Dimensioning Standards: **ANSI**

Units: **INCHES** – 3 Decimals

Tools Needed:

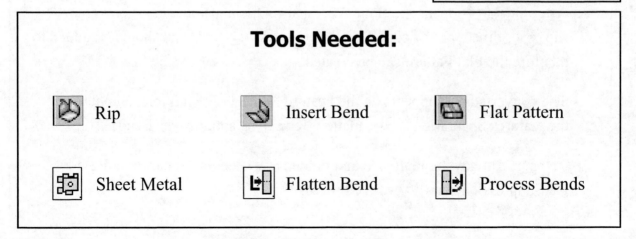

Rip   Insert Bend   Flat Pattern

Sheet Metal   Flatten Bend   Process Bends

1. Opening the existing IGES document:

- Select **File / Open** and change Files of Type to **IGES**.

- Select: **Sheet Metal Conversion** and click **Open**.

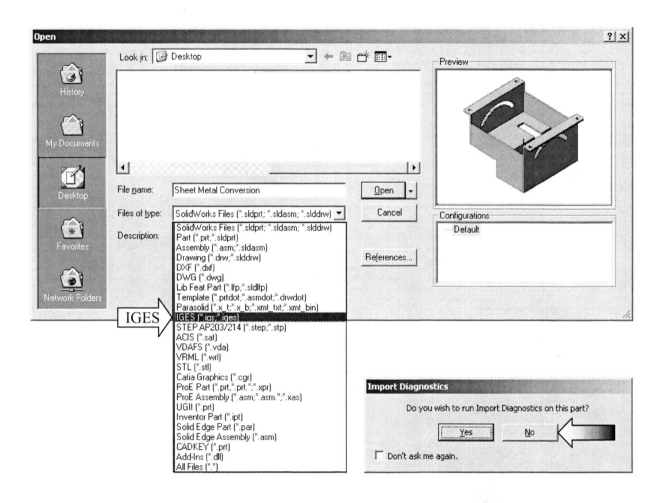

- Click NO to skip the Import Diagnosis option.

- The part is imported into **Solid**Works as the base feature with no history.

2. Creating the Rips:

- Click **Rip** on the sheet metal toolbar or select **Insert / Sheet Metal / Rip**.

- Select the **inner edge** as shown.

- The 2 arrows indicate that the Rip command is going to effect both walls.

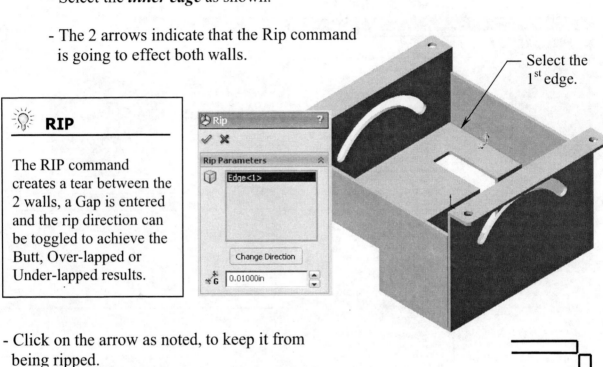

Select the 1ˢᵗ edge.

RIP

The RIP command creates a tear between the 2 walls, a Gap is entered and the rip direction can be toggled to achieve the Butt, Over-lapped or Under-lapped results.

- Click on the arrow as noted, to keep it from being ripped.

- Stay with the **Default Gap** (.010)

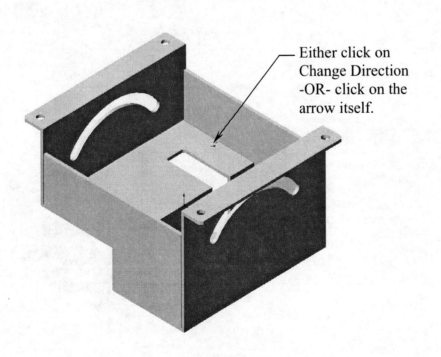

Either click on Change Direction -OR- click on the arrow itself.

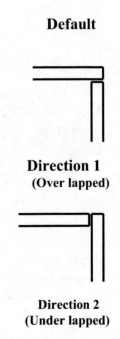

Default

Direction 1
(Over lapped)

Direction 2
(Under lapped)

- Select a total of 4 edges (2 on each side) as indicated.

- Click **OK** ✅.

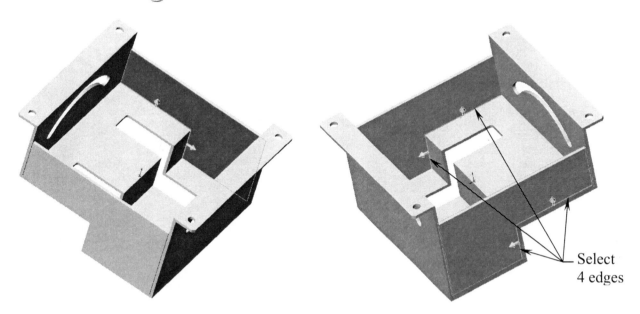

Select
4 edges

3. Inserting the Sheet Metal Parameters:

- Click **Insert Bends** command or select **Insert / Sheet Metal / Bends**.

- Select the inside
  face for use as the

  Fixed Face.

- Enter **.015 in.** for
  inside Bend-

  Radius.

- Click **OK** ✅

- The system reports
  some Auto Relief
  Cuts were made for
  some bends.

- Click OK.

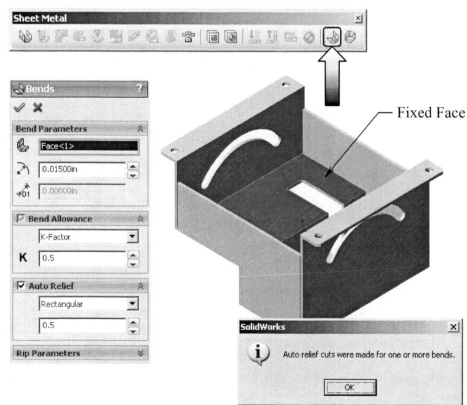

Fixed Face

4. Adding Fillets:

- Click **Fillet** command  or select **Insert / Features / Fillet/Round**.

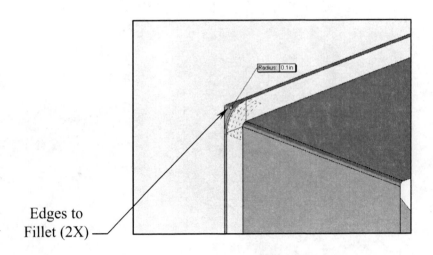

Edges to
Fillet (2X) —

- Enter **.100 in**. for Radius

- Select the **2 edges** as noted.

- Click **OK**.

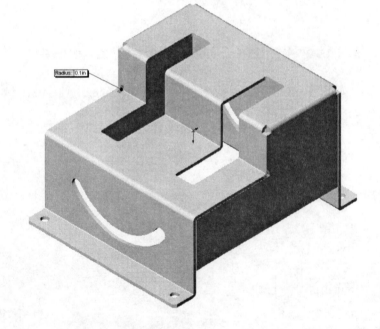

- Verify the resulted fillets.

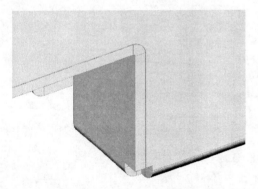

5. Switching to the Flat pattern:

- To examine the part in the

flattened view; click **Flatten** 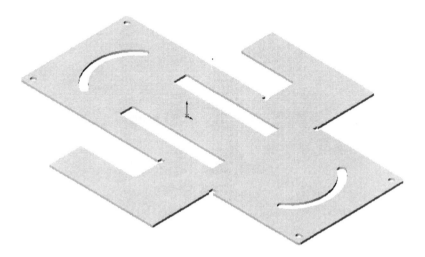 on the Sheet Metal toolbar.

6. Saving your work:

- Click **File / Save As**.

- Enter **Sheet Metal Conversion** for file name.

- Click **Save**.

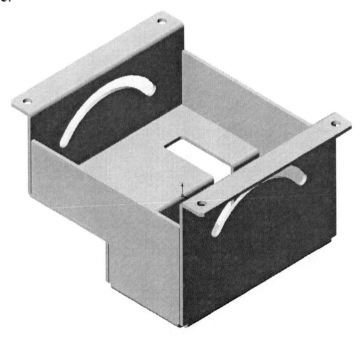

Questions for Review

Sheet Metal Conversions

1. An IGES file can be imported into SolidWorks and converted into a sheet metal part.
   - a. True
   - b. False

2. DXF and DWG are imported into SolidWorks as 2D Sketches, using the DXF/DWG import wizard.
   - a. True
   - b. False

3. After imported into SolidWorks, the IGES file can be flattened instantly.
   - a. True
   - b. False

4. The imported parts must be of uniform thickness to fold and unfold properly.
   - a. True
   - b. False

5. The Rip feature removes 1 material thickness, based on the side of the direction arrow that you select.
   - a. True
   - b. False

6. When applying the sheet metal parameters, you do not have to specify a fixed face.
   - a. True
   - b. False

7. The width and depth of the relief cuts are fixed and cannot be changed.
   - a. True
   - b. False

8. The Folded and the Flat pattern can be toggled by moving the Rollback Line up or down.
   - a. True
   - b. False

7. FALSE
8. TRUE
5. TRUE
6. FALSE
3. FALSE
4. TRUE
1. TRUE
2. TRUE

Sheet Metal Assembly **STEP Files** and **Smart Fasteners**

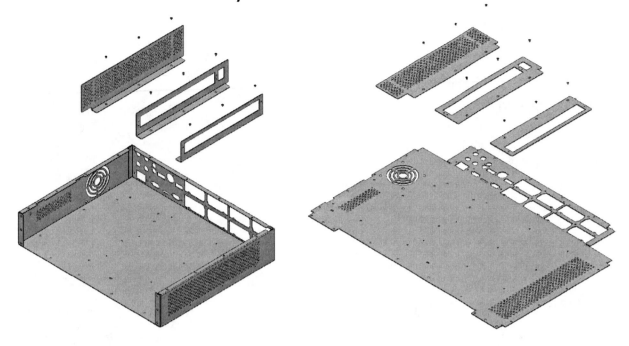

STEP files translator: (**ST**andard for the **E**xchange of **P**roduct data).

- The STEP translator supports <u>import and export</u> of body, face and curve colors of STEP AP214 files.

- The STEP AP203 standard does not have any color implementation.

- The STEP translator <u>imports</u> STEP files as SolidWorks part or assembly documents.

- The STEP translator <u>exports</u> SolidWorks part or assembly documents to STEP files. You can select to export individual parts or subassemblies from an assembly tree, limiting export to only those parts or subassemblies. If you select a subassembly, all of its components are automatically selected. If you select a component, its ascendants are partially selected, preserving the assembly structure.

1. Opening an Assembly Step file:

- Change the Files of Type to STEP and open the STEP document named **SM-Assembly.step**, from the Training CD or from the Web link.

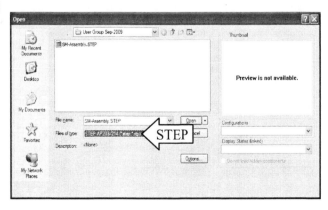

- The part files from the STEP document will appear as SolidWorks documents on the FeatureManager tree.

- There are 4 components in this assembly and they have not yet been constrained.

- The Housing will be used as the Fixed Component and the 3 Card Guides will be left un-constrained for the purpose of this exercise.

- Change the Shading option to: **Shaded with Edges** (arrow).

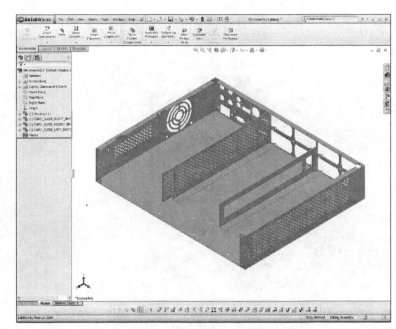

2. Mating the components:

- In order to mate the Fixed-Component to the assembly's Origin, we'll need to align the 3 Front, Top & Right planes.

- Click the Mate command from the Assembly toolbar.

- Select the **Front** plane of the Housing and the **Front** plane of the Assembly.

- Select **Coincident** from the list.

- Click **OK**.

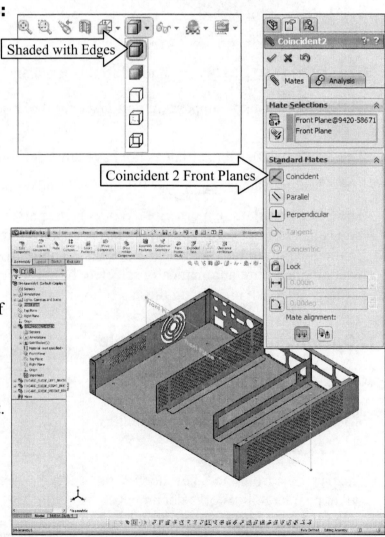

- Add the same Coincident mate to the **Top** plane of the Housing and the **Top** plane of the Assembly.

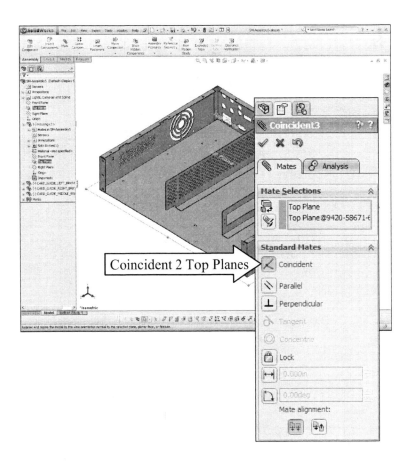

Coincident 2 Top Planes

- Repeat the Coincident mate for the **Right** plane of the Housing and the **Right** plane of the Assembly.

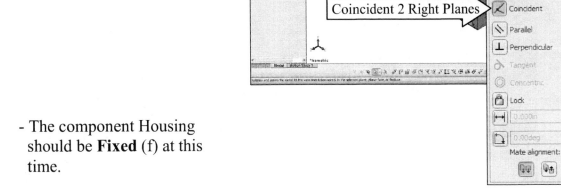

Coincident 2 Right Planes

- The component Housing should be **Fixed** (f) at this time.

3. Other Mates:

- Other mates can be added to constrain the other components but later on, they'll need to be suppressed so that the final sheet metal components can be flattened properly.

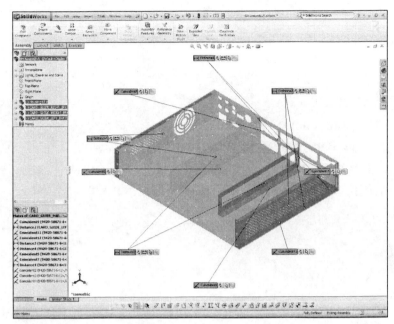

- In this exercise, we will leave the components un-constrained to help focus in other areas).

4. Examine the components:

- The imported components have **Sharp corners** all around them, which is not suitable for the Sheet Metal processes.

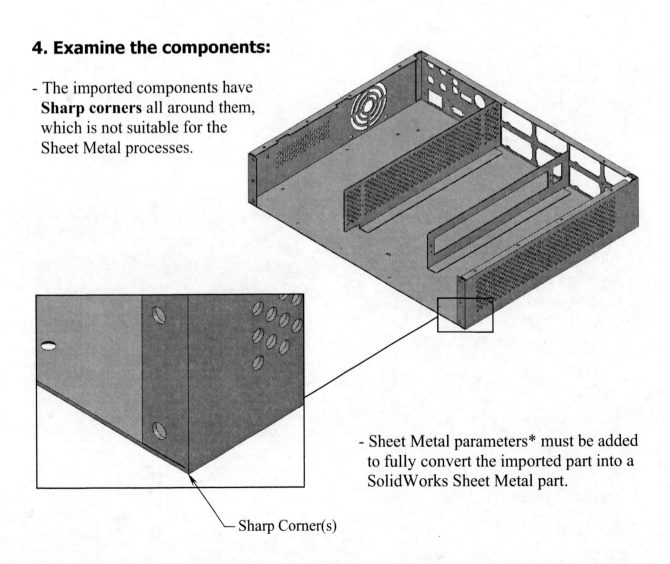

- Sheet Metal parameters* must be added to fully convert the imported part into a SolidWorks Sheet Metal part.

Sharp Corner(s)

5. Adding the Sheet Metal tool tab:

- If the Sheet Metal tool tab is not visible on the CommandManager, do the following to add it:

- Right click on the Assembly tool tab and select the **Customized CommandManager** option (arrow).

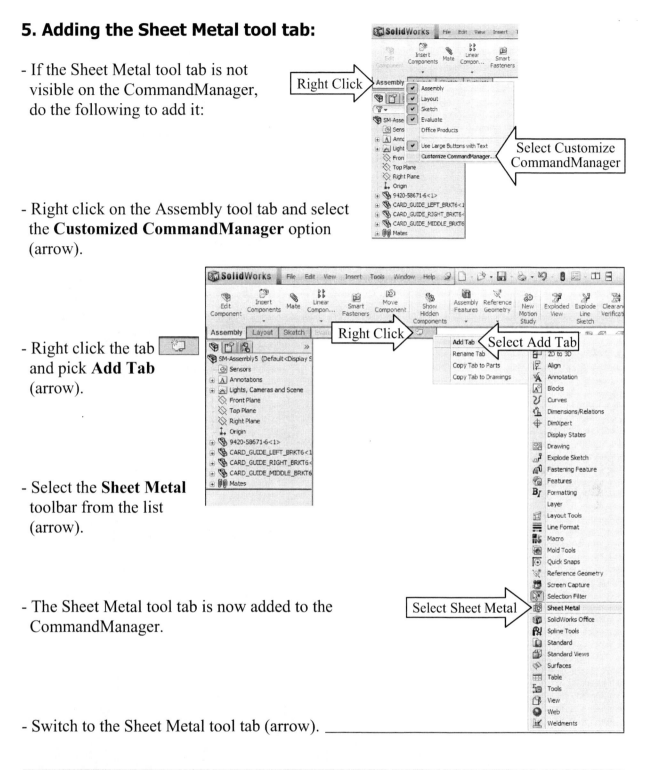

- Right click the tab and pick **Add Tab** (arrow).

- Select the **Sheet Metal** toolbar from the list (arrow).

- The Sheet Metal tool tab is now added to the CommandManager.

- Switch to the Sheet Metal tool tab (arrow).

6. Inserting Sheet Metal parameters*:

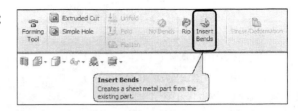

- Select the component **Housing** and click the

  Edit Component command.

- From the Sheet Metal tool tab

  click the **Insert Bends**
  command.

- Select the **Fixed face** as noted.

- Enter **.010"** for Bend Radius.

- Use the **default settings** for
  Bend Allowance and **Auto-
  Relief**.

- Click **OK**.

- A message pops up indicating
  that Auto Relief Cuts were
  added to some of the corners
  of the part.

- Click **OK** OK .

Select Fixed face

Auto relief cuts were made for one or more bends.

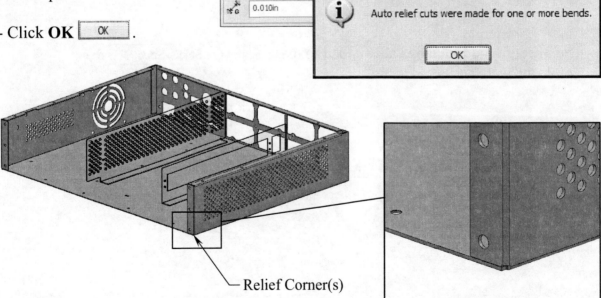

Relief Corner(s)

- Zoom in to see the relief corners.

7. Viewing the Flat Pattern:

- From the Sheet Metal tool tab, click the

Flatten command  .

- The Housing is flattened. The
Orientation of the flattened
view is based on the Fixed
face that was specified
in the step number 6.

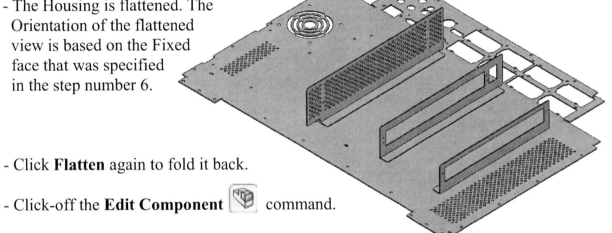

- Click **Flatten** again to fold it back.

- Click-off the **Edit Component** command.

8. Converting the 2nd component:

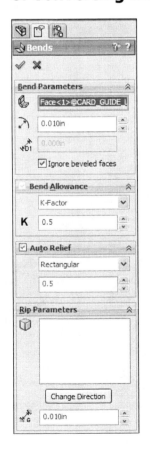

- Select the **Card Guide Left** as shown and

click the **Edit Component** command.

- From the Sheet Metal tool tab, select **Insert Bends** command.

- Select the **Fixed face** as noted.

- Enter **.010"** for Radius.

- Click **OK** .

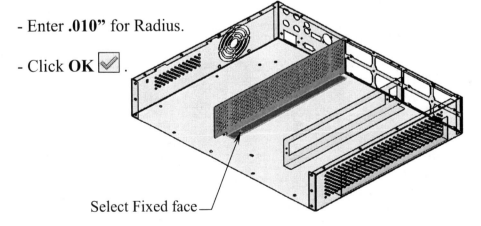

Select Fixed face

- Click-off the **Edit Component** command.

9. Converting the 3rd component:

- Select the **Card Guide Middle** as shown and click the **Edit-Component**  command.

- From the Sheet Metal tool tab select **Insert Bends** [Insert Bends icon]

- Select the **Fixed face** as noted.

- Enter **.010"** for Bend Radius and use the **default settings** for the Bend Allowance and K-Factor.

- Click **OK** ✓.

- Click-off the **Edit Component** command.

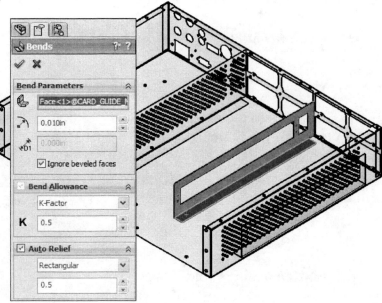

10. Converting the 4th component:

- Select the **Card Guide Right** as shown and click the **Edit Component** command.

- From the Sheet Metal tool tab, click: **Insert Bends** [Insert Bends icon].

- Select the **Fixed face** as noted.

- Enter **.010"** for Bend Radius.

- Click **OK** ✓.

- Click-off the **Edit Component** command.

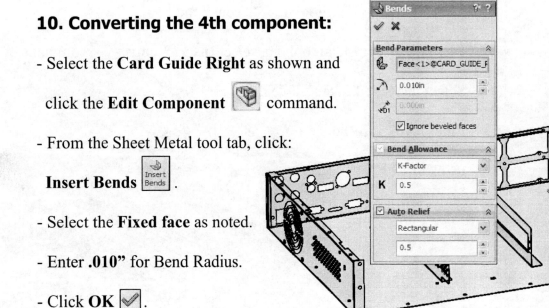

Select Fixed face

11. Using the Hole-Series:

- The hole series is an Assembly Feature, it is used to create a series of holes through the individual parts of an assembly.

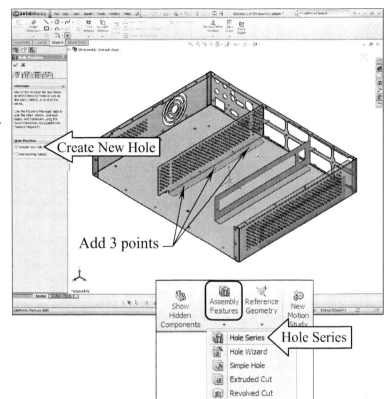

- Unlike other assembly features, the holes are contained in the individual parts as externally referenced features. If you edit a hole series within an assembly, the individual parts are modified.

- From the Assembly tool tab, select **Assembly Features** / **Hole Series**.

- From the FeatureManager, click **Create New Hole**.

- The mouse cursor changes into the **Sketch Point** command.

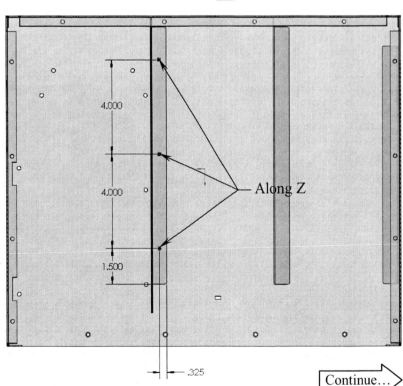

- Click approximately as shown to create **3 points**.

- Each point represents the center for that hole.

- Add an **ALONG Z** relation (Vertical) between the 3 points.

- Add the dimensions as indicated to fully define the positions of the points.

Continue...

- Click the **First Part** tab.

- Click the **Countersink** option.

- Select the followings:

  Standard: **Ansi Inch**

  Type: **Flat Head Screw**

  Size: **#4**

  Fit: **Normal**

- Use the default settings for Custom Sizing.

- Click the **Middle Part** tab.

- Enable the check box:

  Auto Size Based On Start Hole.

- Click on the **Last Part** tab.

- Click the **Tap** button.

- Enable **Auto Size Based On Start Hole**.

- Set Type to **Tapped Hole**.

- Set Size to **#4-40**.

- Set both End Conditions to **Through All**.

- Enable the **Cosmetic Thread** and **With Thread Callout**.

- Click **OK** ✓.

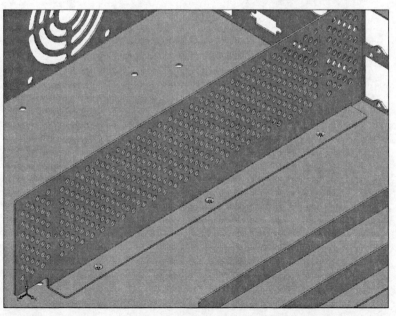

12. Using the Hole Wizard:

- Hole wizard is an Assembly Feature, it creates these types of holes:

  • Counterbore
  • Countersink
  • Hole
  • Straight Tap
  • Tapered Tap
  • Legacy

- From the Assembly tool tab, click **Assembly Features / Hole Wizard**.

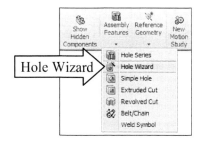

- Select the **Countersink** option under the **Type** tab.

- Set the options to match the last 3 holes in step number 11.

- Switch to the **Positions** tab.

- Click approximately as shown to create **3 points**.

- Each point represents the center for that hole.

- Add relation and dimensions as indicated.

- Click **OK** ☑.

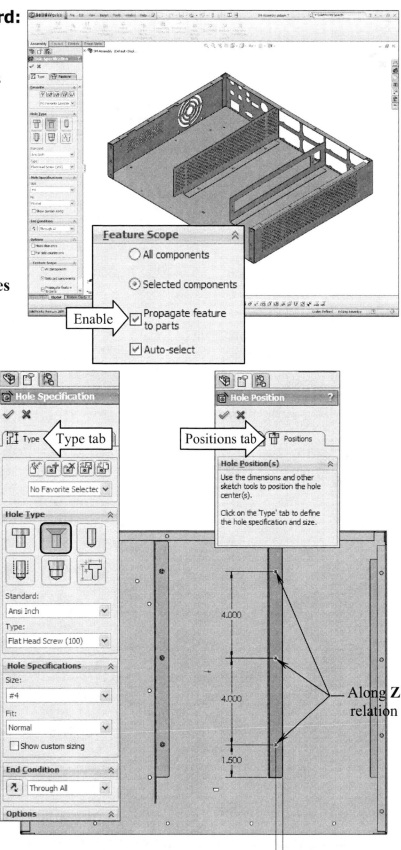

13. Verifying the two hole types:

- Even though the 6 holes were created with 2 different hole options, but they are exactly identical.

- Open the Card Guide Middle to verify that the holes are actually there on the part.

- The new feature in step 12 (propagate feature to parts) allows these Assembly Features to appear in the part mode as well.

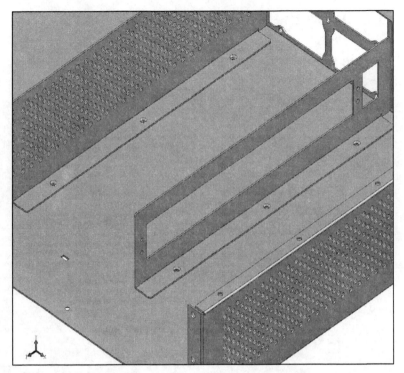

14. Adding holes on the Card Guide Right:

- Repeat either step number 11 (Hole Series) or step number 12 (Hole Wizard) and create 3 more holes for the last Card Guide.

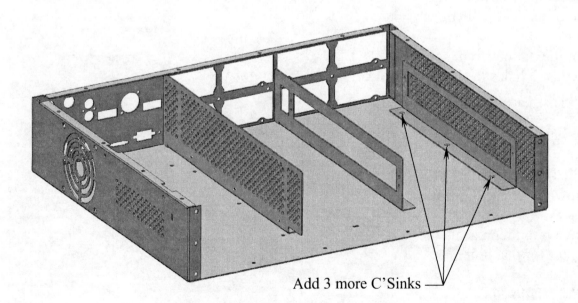

Add 3 more C'Sinks

- Use the same dimensions from the previous step to position the holes.

15. Adding the Smart Fasteners:

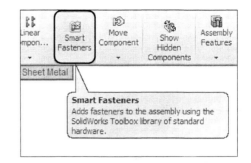

- Click **Smart Fasteners** 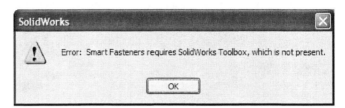 from the Assembly tool tab.

- An error message pops up asking for SolidWorks Toolbox to be present** (Required SolidWorks Office Pro. or SolidWorks Premium).

**To activate Toolbox, go to:

  - **Tools / Add Ins**.

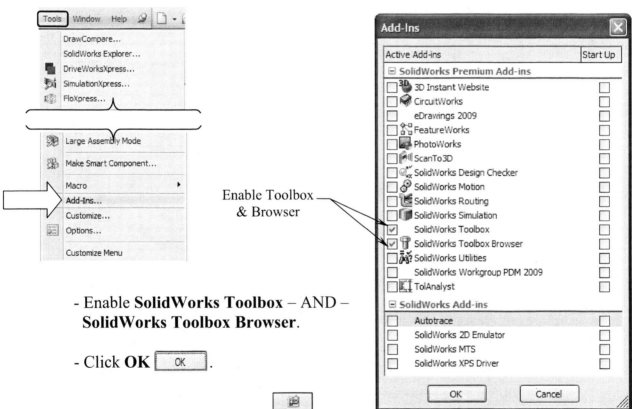

Enable Toolbox & Browser

  - Enable **SolidWorks Toolbox** – AND – **SolidWorks Toolbox Browser**.

  - Click **OK** ⌷ OK ⌷.

- Click the **Smart Fasteners** button ⌷ Smart Fasteners ⌷ once again.

- Another message pops up indicating that the Smart Fasteners calculation may take extra time, click **OK** ⌷ OK ⌷.

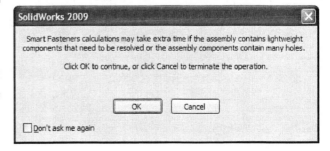

- Select one of the C'sink holes from the graphics area.

- Click **Populate All** (arrow).

- The system searches for the best matched screws from its Toolbox library and inserts them into each hole automatically.

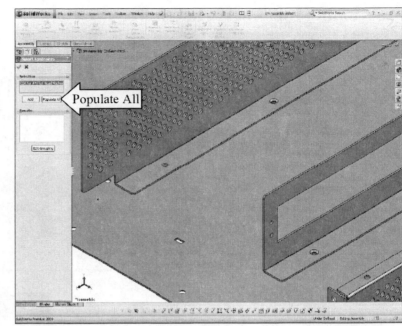

- Set the following properties:

    - Size: **#4-40**   Length: **.125"**   Drive Type: **Cross**

    - Thread Display: **Simplified**

    - Click **OK** ✓.

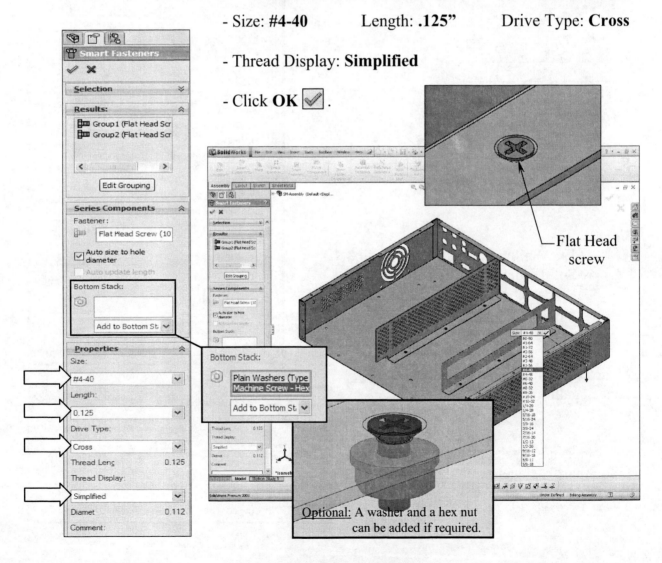

Flat Head screw

Optional: A washer and a hex nut can be added if required.

16. Creating an Exploded View:

Option 1

- Optionally, create an exploded view with all 4 parts show in folded stage as shown.

- Every time an exploded view is created, SolidWorks also creates an animated configuration, which can be played back and saved as an AVI file format.

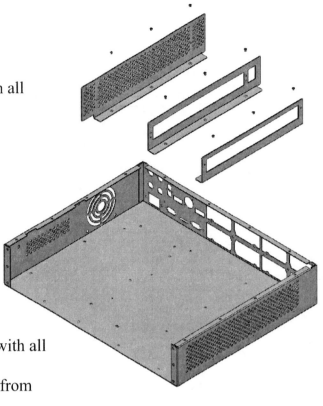

Option 2

- Optionally, create a 2nd exploded view with all 4 parts show in Flatten stage as shown.
(Edit each component in order to switch from Folded to flatten).

17. Saving your work:

- Click **File / Save As**.

- Enter **SM_Assembly_Smart Fasteners**.

- Click **Save**.

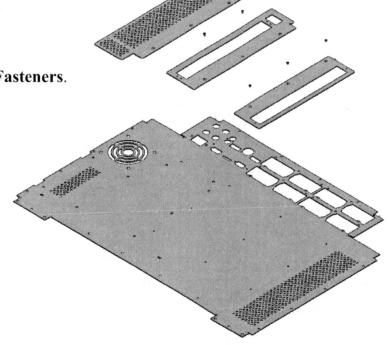

Weldments – Structural Members

The options in Weldments allows you to develop a weldment structure as a single multibody-part. The basic framework is defined using a 2D or a 3D sketch, then structural members like square or round Tubes are added by sweeping the tube profile along the framework. Gussets, end caps, and weld-beads can also be added using the tools on the **Weldments** toolbar.

1. Opening an existing document:

- Open the file named **Weldment_Frame** from the Training CD or from the web link.

2. Enabling the Weldment toolbar:

- Click **View / Toolbar** and select the **Weldment toolbar** from the list (arrow).

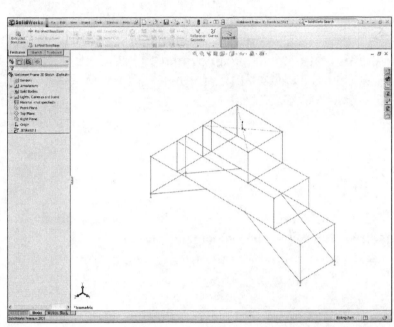

- Click the **Weldment button** from the weldment toolbar.

Weldment
Creates a weldment feature to enable the weldment environment.

- A Weldment Feature appears on the feature tree along with a Weldment Cut List (arrows), which indicates the items from the model to include in this cut list.

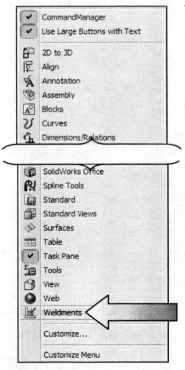

- A single 3D Sketch is created for the purpose of this exercise. In reality, multiple sketches (2D & 3D) can be used to work with weldments.

3. Adding Structural Members:

- Click the **Structural Member** button from the Weldment toolbar.

- Select the following:

  • **Ansi Inch.**
  • **Square Tube**
  • **4 X 4 X 0.25**

- Click the **4 lines** on topmost.

- Select the **MITER** under Apply Corner-Treatment.

- Click **OK** .

- By default, the profile of the tube is automatically centered on the end of each line.

- Try out all 3 options for corner treatments: End Miter, End Butt1 and End Butt2.

- Go back to the End Miter option when finished.

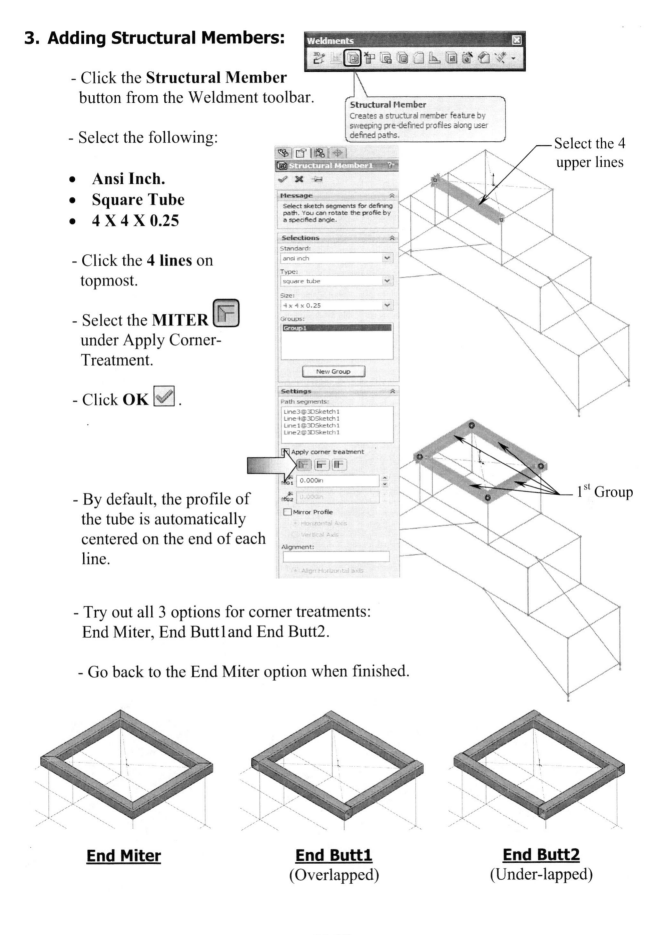

Select the 4 upper lines

1st Group

End Miter

End Butt1
(Overlapped)

End Butt2
(Under-lapped)

4. Adding Structural Members to Contiguous Groups*:

- Repeat the previous Step and add another 4 square tubes to the 2nd group as shown.

- Use these same settings:

- **Ansi Inch.**
- **Square Tube**
- **4 X 4 X 0.25**

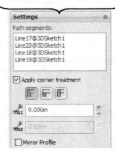

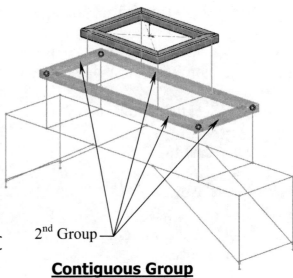

2nd Group

Contiguous Group

* *A group is a collection of related segments in a structural member. There are 2 types of groups, one is called Contiguous, where a continuous contour of segments joined end-to-end, and the other is called Parallel, where a discontinuous collection of parallel segments. Segments in the group cannot touch each other.*

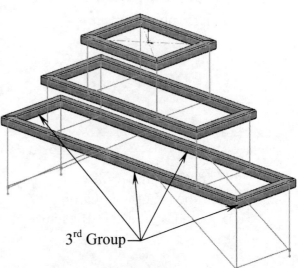

3rd Group

Contiguous Group

- Repeat the same step for the 3rd group.

- Follow the same procedure and add the same size tubing to the vertical members as note for the 4th group.

Note: *select the exact same members on both sides (total of 12).*

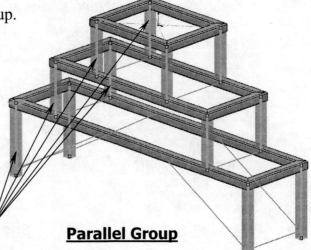

4th Group
(both sides)

Parallel Group

5. Adding Structural Members to the Parallel Groups:

- Repeat the previous step and add the same structural members to the 5th group as indicated.

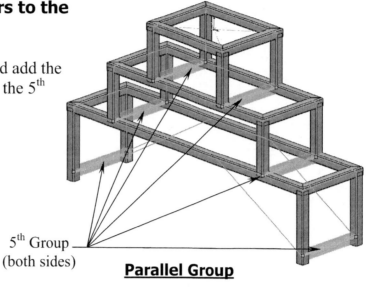

5th Group
(both sides)

Parallel Group

 Note

You can define a group in a single plane or in multiple planes. A 3D sketch is best suited for weldment designs since all entities can be drawn and controlled in the same sketch.

- Create the same type of structural Members for the 6th and 7th group, which has only 2 lines in each group...

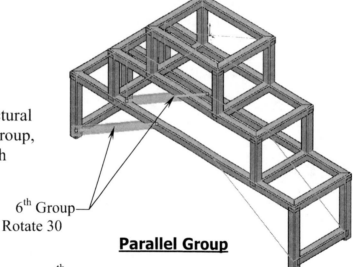

6th Group
Rotate 30

Parallel Group

- Rotate the profile to **30 deg.** for the 6th group, and **60 deg.** for the 7th group.

- There are several over-lapped areas that need trimming, we will look into that in the next steps.

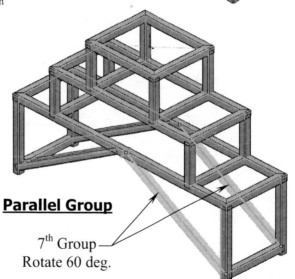

Parallel Group

7th Group
Rotate 60 deg.

6. Hiding the 3D sketch:

- Right click on one of the lines in

3D sketch and select **Hide** 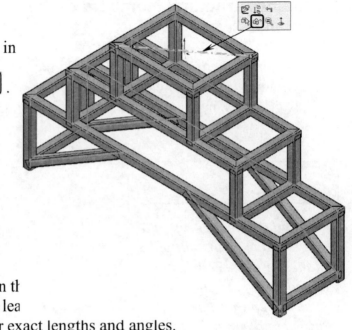 .

- Notice the overlapping areas in th
  For practice purposes, we will lea
  options to cut the tubes to their exact lengths and angles.

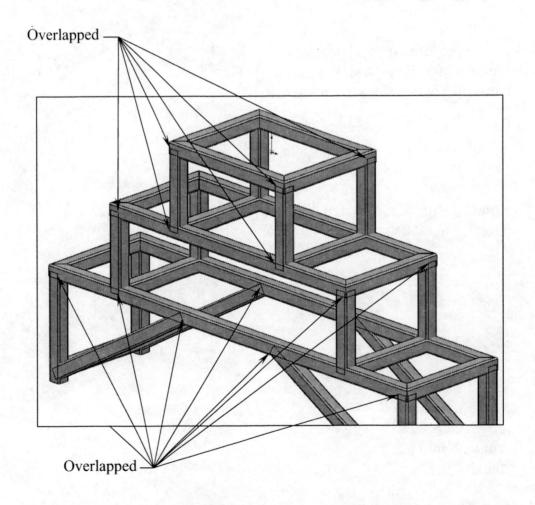

Overlapped

Overlapped

7. Trimming the Structural Members:

- Click **Trim/Extend** on the Weldment toolbar.

- Under **Corner Type**, use the default **End Trim**.

- Under **Bodies To Be Trimmed**, select the 4 vertical tubes as shown.

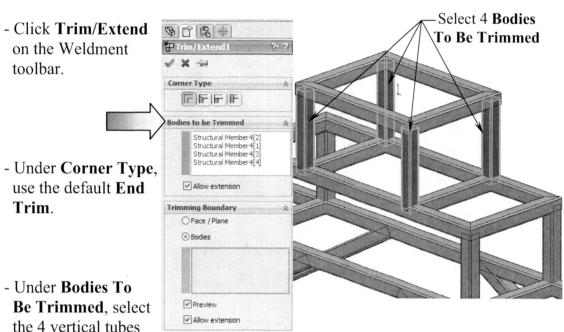

Select 4 **Bodies To Be Trimmed**

- Under **Trimming Boundary**, select the **Body** option (arrow).

- Select the 6 horizontal tubes as indicated, for use as trimming bodies.

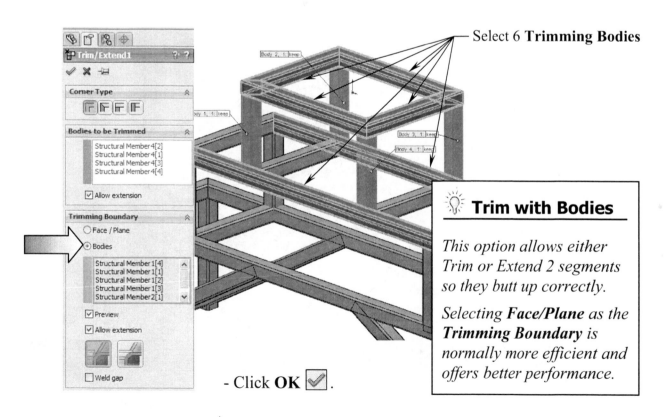

Select 6 **Trimming Bodies**

- Click **OK**.

> ### Trim with Bodies
>
> *This option allows either Trim or Extend 2 segments so they butt up correctly.*
>
> *Selecting **Face/Plane** as the **Trimming Boundary** is normally more efficient and offers better performance.*

8. Trimming the Parallel Groups:

- Select the **Trim/Extend** command once again, from the weldment toolbar.

- Click in the **Bodies To Be Trimmed** dialog to activate it and select the next 4 vertical tubes as noted.

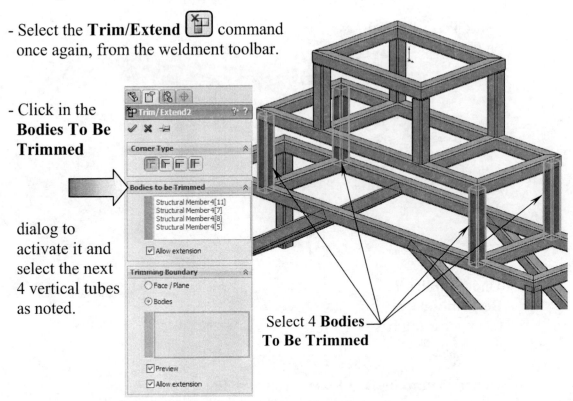

Select 4 **Bodies To Be Trimmed**

- For **Trimming Boundary**, select the **Body** option again (Arrow).

- Select the 6 horizontal tubes as shown for use as trimming bodies.

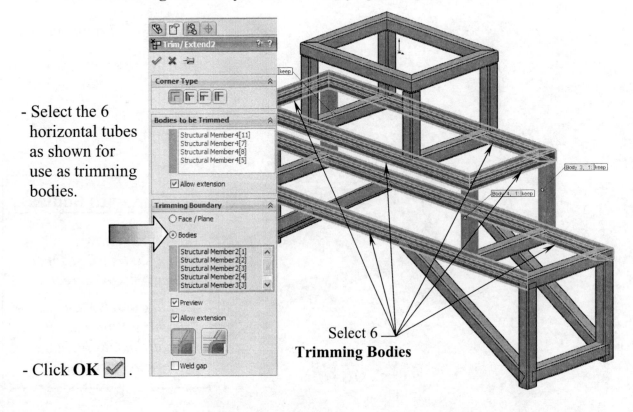

Select 6 **Trimming Bodies**

- Click **OK**.

9. Trimming the next sets of Parallel Groups:

- Select the **Trim/Extend** command from the weldment toolbar.

- Click in the **Bodies To Be Trimmed** dialog to activate it, and select the 4 structural members as noted.

Select 4 **Bodies To Be Trimmed**

- For **Trimming Boundary**, click the **Body** option (Arrow).

- Select the 4 horizontal tubes as shown, for use as **Trimming Bodies**.

Select 4 **Trimming Bodies**

- Click **OK**.

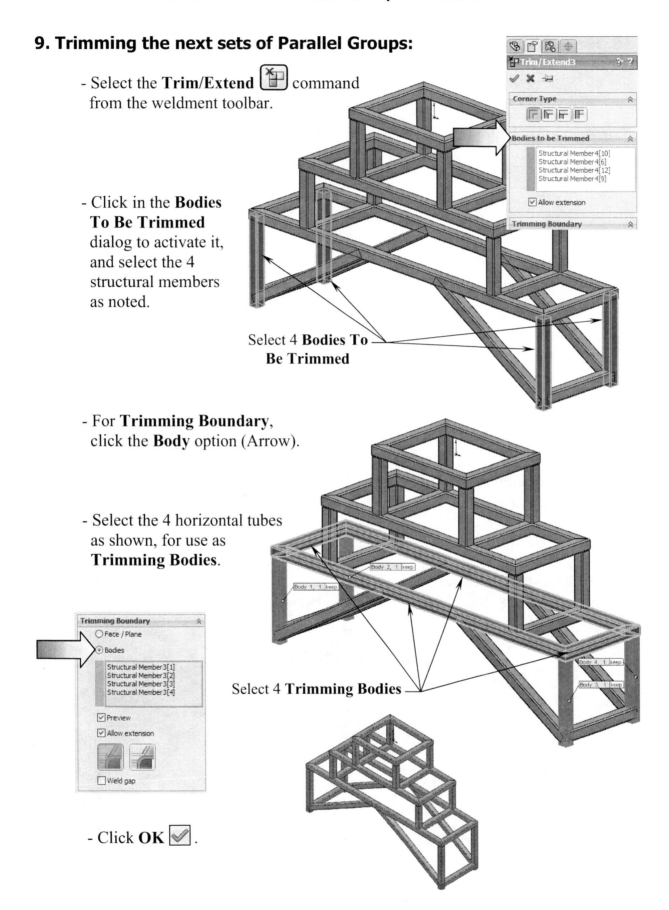

10. More Trimming using Bodies:

- Select the **Trim/Extend** command from the weldment toolbar.

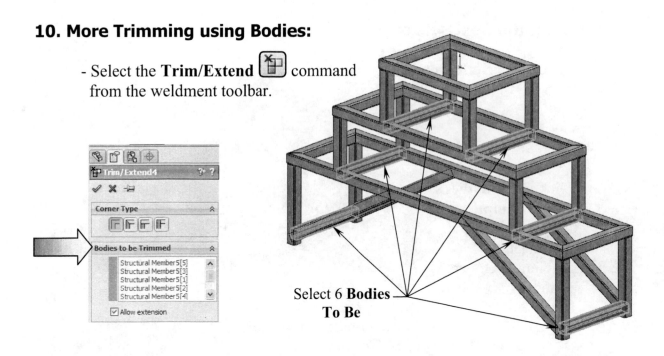

Select 6 **Bodies To Be**

- For **Bodies To Be Trimmed** select the 6 structural members as indicated.

- For **Trimming Boundary**, click the **Body** option (Arrow).

- Select the 8 horizontal structural members as shown, for **Trimming Bodies**.

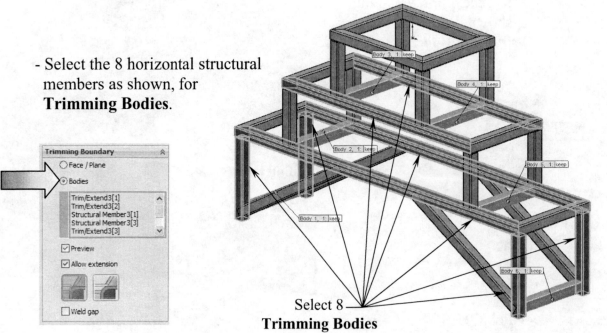

Select 8 **Trimming Bodies**

- Click **OK** .

11. Trimming with Face/Plane:

- Select the **Trim/Extend** 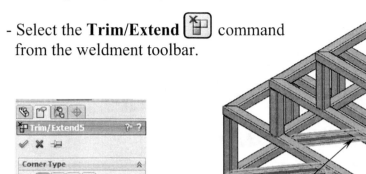 command from the weldment toolbar.

Select 2
**Bodies To
Be Trimmed**

- For **Bodies To Be Trimmed** select the 2structural members as indicated.

- For **Trimming Boundary**, click the **Face / Plane** option (Arrow).

- Select the planar surface as noted for **Trimming Bodies**.

Select **Face**
for **Trimming
Boundary**

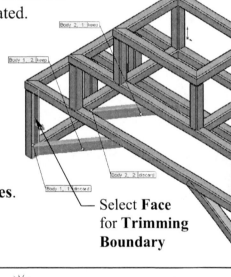

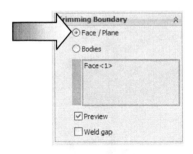

🔆 Trim with Face/Plane

This option allows a planar face(s) as a trimming boundary to trim one or more solid bodies.

*Selecting **Face/Plane** as the **Trimming Boundary** is normally more efficient and offers better performance.*

- Click **OK** ✓.

12. More Trimming using Face/Plane:

- Select the **Trim/Extend** 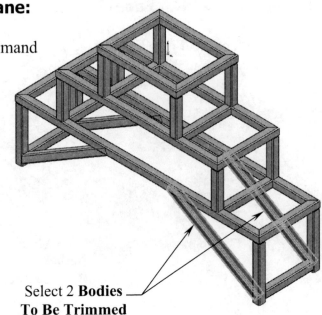 command from the weldment toolbar.

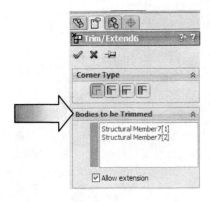

Select 2 **Bodies
To Be Trimmed**

- For **Bodies To Be Trimmed** select the 2 structural members as indicated.

- For **Trimming Boundary**, click the **Face / Plane** option (Arrow).

- Select the planar surface on the back of the vertical tube as noted for **Trimming Bodies**.

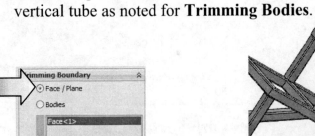

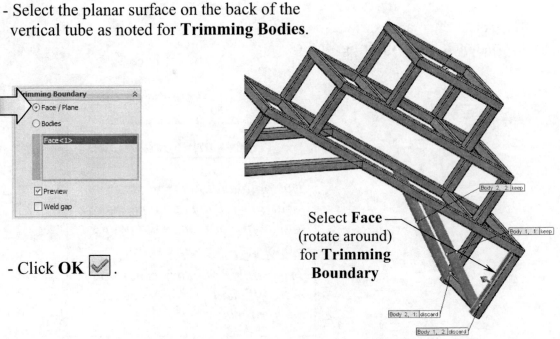

Select **Face**
(rotate around)
for **Trimming
Boundary**

- Click **OK** ☑ .

13. Trimming the last 4 structural members:

- Select the **Trim/Extend** command from the weldment toolbar.

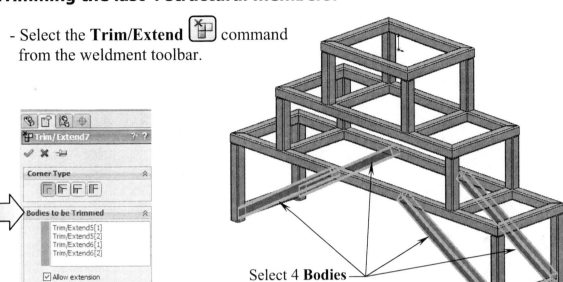

Select 4 **Bodies To Be Trimmed**

- For **Bodies To Be Trimmed** select the 4 structural members as shown.

- For **Trimming Boundary**, click the **Body** option (Arrow).

- Select the 2 horizontal tubes as noted, for **Trimming Bodies**.

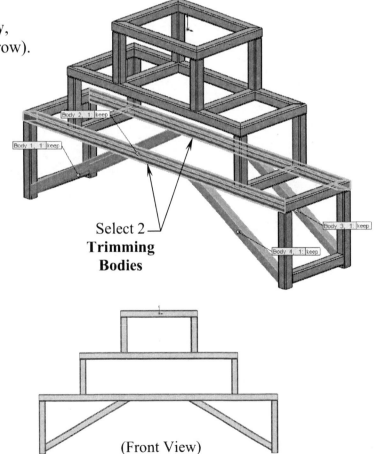

Select 2 **Trimming Bodies**

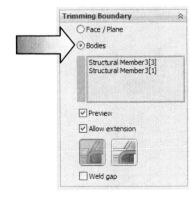

- Click **OK** .

(Front View)

14. Adding the foot pads:

- Insert a new sketch on the bottom surface of one of the 4 legs.

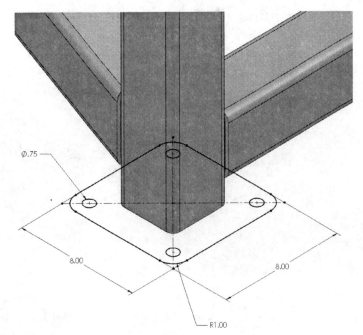

- Sketch the profile as shown.

- The 4 circles are concentric with the corner radius.

- Add the dimensions and relations needed to fully the sketch.

- Mirror the sketch to make a total of 4 foot pads.

Note:
Add a couple of centerlines as shown prior to making the mirror.

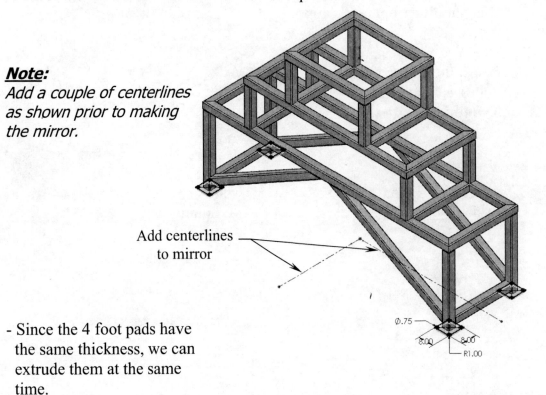

Add centerlines to mirror

- Since the 4 foot pads have the same thickness, we can extrude them at the same time.

- Click **Extruded Boss/ Base**.

- Enter the following:

   * Type: **Blind**

   * Depth: **1.000**

- Click **OK** ✓.

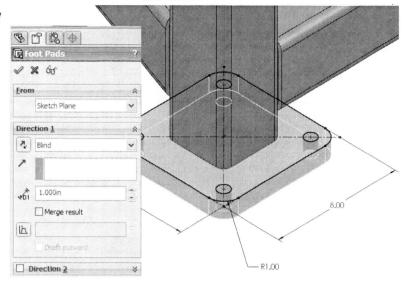

15. Adding the Gussets:

- Rotate and zoom to an orientation that looks similar to the view below.

- Click the **Gusset** Command.

- For **Supporting Faces**, Select the **2 faces** as indicated.

- Enter the following:

   * Distance1: **5.00 in.**

   * Distance2: **5.00 in.**

   * Distance3: **.500 in.**

   * Thickness: **.500"**
      (Both Sides)

   * Location: **Midpoint**

- Click **OK** ✓.

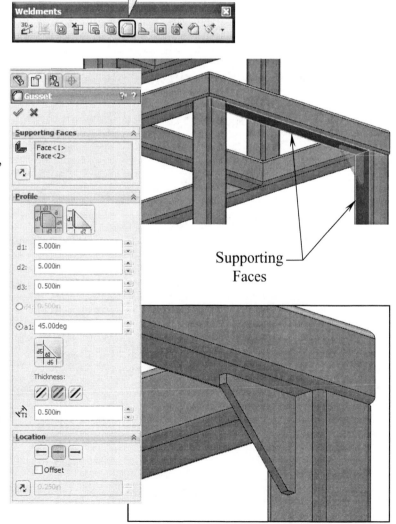

Supporting Faces

16. Adding more Gussets:

- Repeat the step 15 and add a gusset to each corner of the frame.

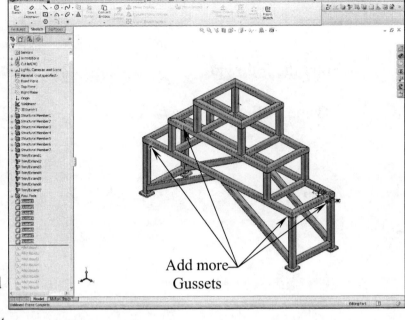

- Next we are going to add the weld beads around the gussets. Weld beads can be added full length, intermittent, or staggered. Fillet weld beads between any intersecting weldment entities, such as structural members, plate weldments, or gussets.

Add more Gussets

17. Adding the Weld Beads:

- Click Fillet Bead 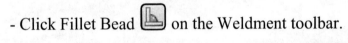 on the Weldment toolbar.

Fillet Bead
Adds a fillet weld bead feature between two disjoint bodies.

- From the Weld Bead properties tree, enter the following:

* Bead Type: **Full Length**

* Fillet Size: **.250 in.**

* Tangent Prop: **Enabled**

* Face Set1: **Select the 2 faces** as noted.

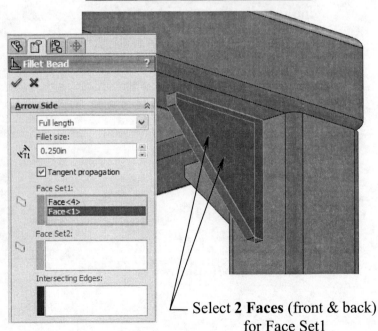

Select **2 Faces** (front & back) for Face Set1

(continue on next page...)

- For **Face Set2**, select the next 2 faces as indicated.

Intersecting Edges.
Highlights edges where
Face Set1 *and* ***Face Set2***
intersect. You can right-
click an edge and select
Delete *to remove it from*
the weld bead.

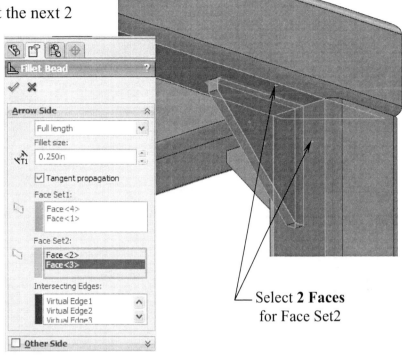

Select **2 Faces**
for Face Set2

- Enable the **Other Side** check box and apply the same settings to the back end of the gusset.

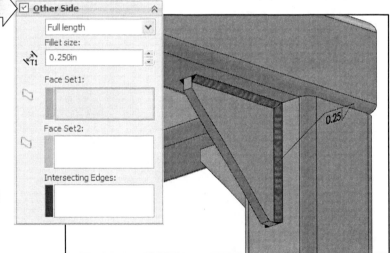

- Different bead type or fillet size can be added to the other side, but we are going to use the same settings as the first side.

- Click **OK** ☑.

- A bead call out is added automatically (see example below).

Example: 0.25 = Length of the leg of the fillet bead
0.375 = Length of each bead segment.
0.7 = Distance between the start of each bead.

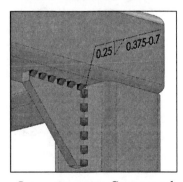

Intermittent or Staggered

18. Adding more Fillet Beads:

- Repeat step 17 and add a set of fillet beads to each one of the gusset created earlier.

- When adding the fillet beads, try out the different types of beads such as: Full Length, Intermittent and Staggered to see the different results and callouts.

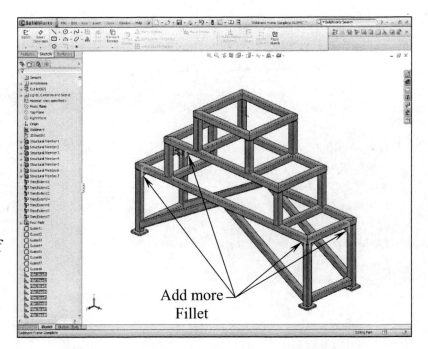

Add more Fillet

19. Viewing the Weldment Cut List:

- Locate the **Cut List** on the FeatureManager tree and click the Plus (+) sign to expand it.

- The Cut List needs to be Updated every time something is added to the model.

- The icon [⊞] in front of the cut list indicates that it needs updating.

- The icon [⊞] indicates that the list is up to date.

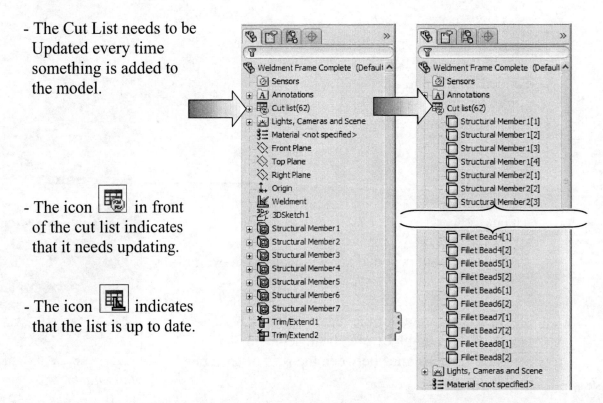

20. Updating the Cut List:

- Right click on the cut list and select **Update** (arrow).

- Notice the option **Automatic** is enabled by default? This option organizes all of the weldments entities in the cut list for the new weldment parts.

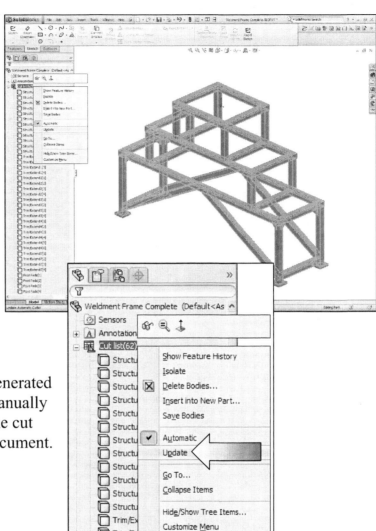

- Although the cut list is generated automatically, you can manually specify when to update the cut list in a weldment part document.

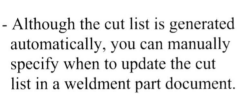

- This enables you to make many changes, then update the cut list once. However, the cut list updates automatically when you open a drawing that references the cut list.

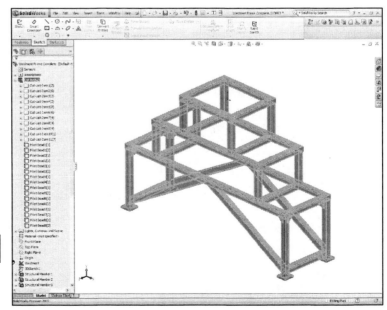

- At this time, the icon in front of the cut list gets changed to this which indicates the cut list is now up to date.

21. Making a drawing (OPTIONAL):

- A drawing that includes the cut list can be generated. (Refer to the Part 1 of this textbook for more information on how to create a detail drawing).

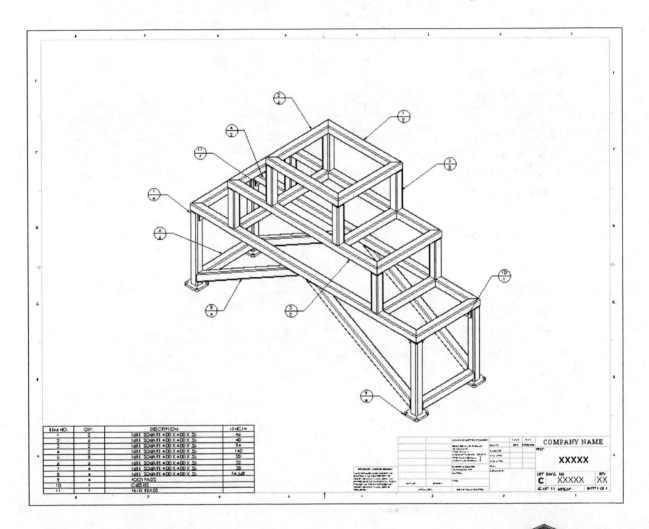

22. Saving your work:

- Click **File / Save As**.

- Enter **Weldment Frame** for the name of the file.

- Click **Save**.

- Replace the existing File when prompted.

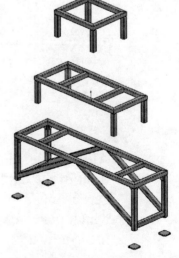

CHAPTER 15

Core & Cavity

Creating a Core & Cavity
Assembly Level

- Create new parts in the context of an assembly by using the existing geometry and positions of other parts, in order to build and reference the new parts. This allows the components involved to be fully associated with each other.

- In the Top down Assembly mode (also referred to as In-Context Assembly), when a face or a plane is selected as a sketch plane for the new part, the system creates an INPLACE mate to reference the new part, (only one Inplace mate for each component).

- The Inplace Mates can be suppressed so that components can be moved or re-positioned.

- When a part is being edited, the Edit Component icon 🗗 is selected and the part's color on the Feature tree is changed to Blue or Magenta, depending on the color settings selected by the user.

- In Top Down Assembly mode, the active component remains its default color while other components turned into transparent. (This option can be changed under: ***Tools/Options/Display Selection/Assembly Transparency For In Context Edit***, and drag the transparency slider back and forth.

- The Scale feature 🗗 is used when creating the core and cavity to increase the overall size of the part to accommodate the shrinkage; the scale feature changes the part's size but not its dimensions. Changes done to the engineered part will be passed onto the 2 halves automatically.

Creating a Core and Cavity
Assembly Level

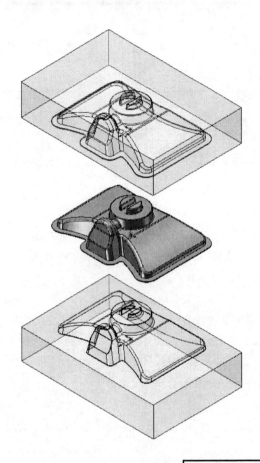

Dimensioning Standards: **ANSI**	
Units: **INCHES** – 3 Decimals	

Tools Needed:

Insert Sketch	Convert Entities	Scale
Radiate Surface	Knit Surface	Plane
Base/Boss Extrude	Edit Component	Exploded View

1. Opening the existing IGES document:

- Click **File / Open**. (Change the File Type to IGS)
  (Go to Training CD or the Weblink)).

- Select the file **Tooling.IGS** and click **Open**.

2. Scaling the part:

- Click  or select **Insert / Features / Scale**.

- Scale About: **Centroid**.

- Uniform Scaling: **Enabled**.

- Scale Factor: **1.05%**

- Click **OK** ✅.

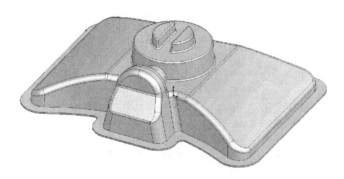

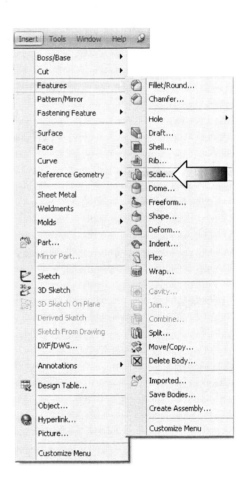

Notes:

- The scale feature changes the part's size but not its dimensions to accommodate for the Material shrinkage.
- When a drawing is made from the scaled part, the original dimensions will be shown in The drawing views.
- The scaled feature appears in the Feature Manager tree, where its value can be altered.

3. Creating the Radiate Surface:

- Click 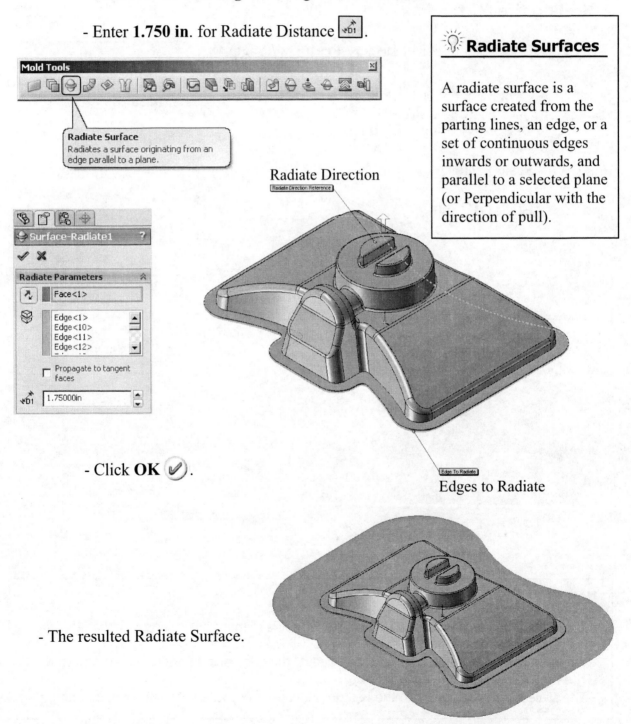 or select **Insert / Surface / Radiate**.

- Select the upper face for Radiate Direction.

- Select the **bottom edges** for Edges to Radiate.

- Enter **1.750 in**. for Radiate Distance.

Mold Tools

Radiate Surface
Radiates a surface originating from an edge parallel to a plane.

> 💡 **Radiate Surfaces**
>
> A radiate surface is a surface created from the parting lines, an edge, or a set of continuous edges inwards or outwards, and parallel to a selected plane (or Perpendicular with the direction of pull).

Radiate Direction

Radiate Direction Reference

Surface-Radiate1

Radiate Parameters

Face<1>

Edge<1>
Edge<10>
Edge<11>
Edge<12>

☐ Propagate to tangent faces

1.75000in

- Click **OK**.

Edge To Radiate

Edges to Radiate

- The resulted Radiate Surface.

4. Transferring the part to Assembly:

- Click **Make Assembly from Part / Assembly** button, or select the same command from the File menu.

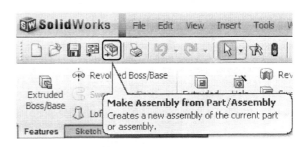

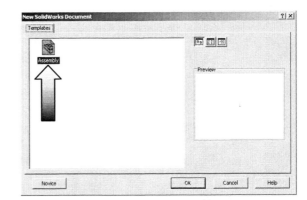

- Select an Assembly template and click OK.

- The Tooling Part is automatically attached to the mouse cursor.

- Place the part on the Origin as indicated.

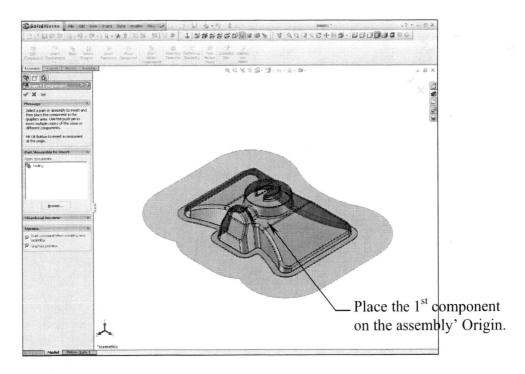

Place the 1st component on the assembly' Origin.

5. Saving the assembly:

- Save the assembly document as **Core and Cavity.**

- The 1st part (Tooling part) is fixed automatically onto the Origin.

- The symbol **(f)** next to the part's name indicates that it has been fixed and cannot be moved.

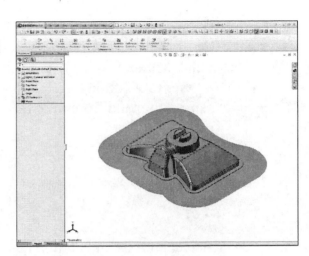

6. Creating the Core:

- Click **Insert / Components / New Part**.

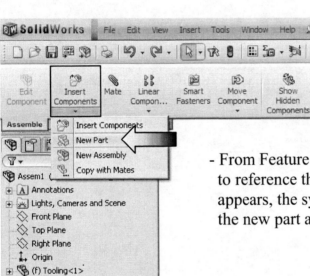

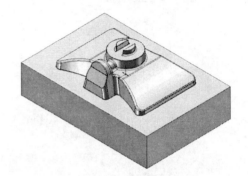

- From Feature Manager tree, select the TOP plane to reference the new part. (When this cursor symbol appears, the system creates an INPLACE mate between the new part and the reference plane).

- Right click on the default name: [Part1^Assem]<1> and select **Rename**.

- Enter: **Core** for the new name.

- **Exit the Sketch** the Knit surface has to be created first).

- The 1st component changes its appearance based on the settings in the options.

7. Knitting the surfaces to forming a new part:

- Click  or select **Insert** / **Surface** / **Knit**.

- First, select the Radiated surface as Surfaces and Faces to Knit .

- Second, select the face on the FAR SIDE as indicated, for Seed Faces .

- Click **OK** ✓.

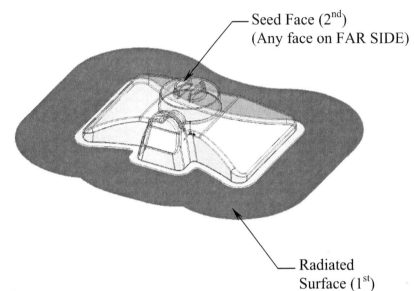

— Seed Face (2nd)
(Any face on FAR SIDE)

— Radiated
Surface (1st)

8. Hiding the engineered part:

- Right click over the part **Tooling** and select **Hide Components** .

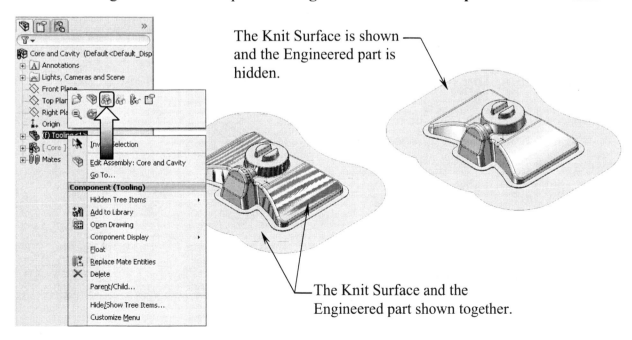

The Knit Surface is shown —
and the Engineered part is
hidden.

— The Knit Surface and the
Engineered part shown together.

9. Creating a new work plane:

- Click  or select **Insert / Reference Geometry / Plane**.

- Select **Offset Distance** option and enter **2.00 in**.

- Select the TOP plane of the assembly to offset from.

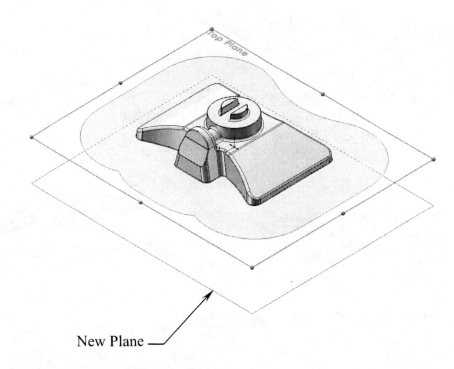

New Plane

- Click **OK** ✓.

10. Sketching the profile of the lower block:

- Select the new Plane1, either from the graphics area or from the Feature-Manager tree, and insert a new sketch.

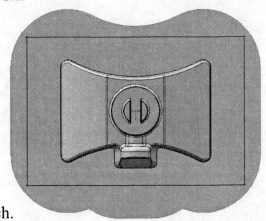

- Sketch a Rectangle ▢ as shown.

- Add a centerline, a midpoint relation and dimensions to fully define the sketch.

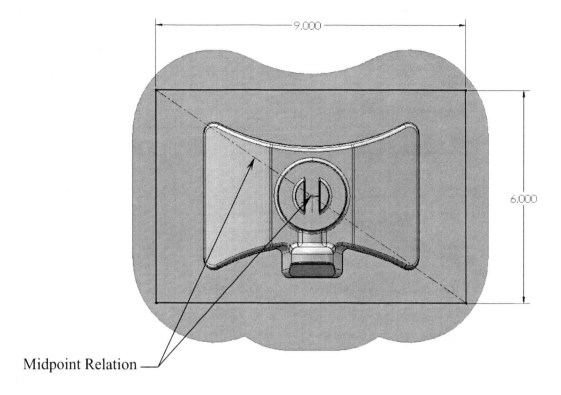

Midpoint Relation —

11. Extruding the lower block:

- Click 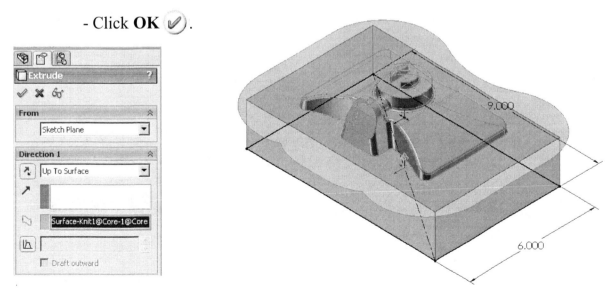 or select **Insert / Boss-Base / Extrude**.

- Direction 1: **Up to Surface**

- Click the Radiated surface as Face/Plane end condition.

- Click **OK** ✓.

- The Core is created; this is the 1st half of the mold.

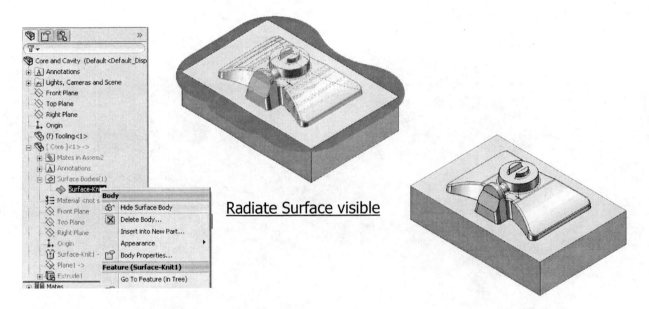

Radiate Surface visible

Radiate Surface hidden

12. Returning to the assembly mode:

- Click or right-click the part and select **Edit Assembly** to exit.

13. Showing the hidden part:

- Right click over the name **Tooling** and select **Show**.

- The engineered part reappears. It will be used again to help create the upper half of the mold (the cavity).

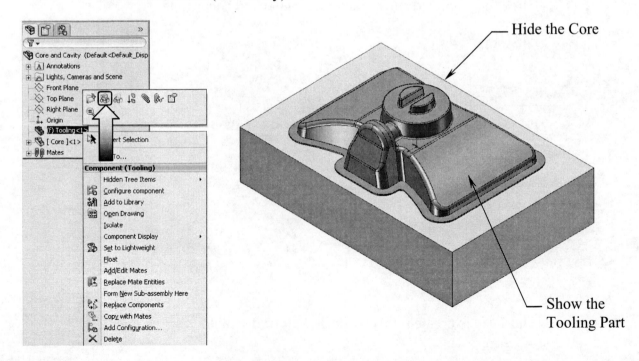

Hide the Core

Show the Tooling Part

14. Creating the Cavity: (Repeat from step 5)

- Select **Insert / Components / New Part**.

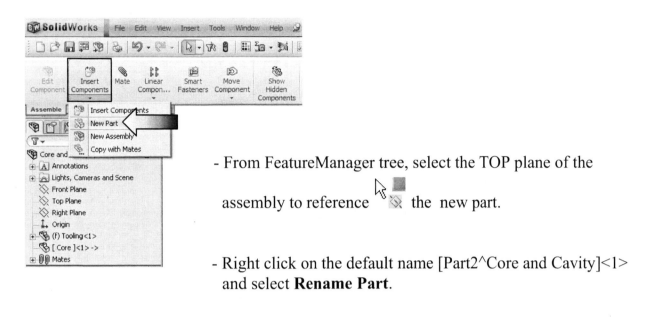

- From FeatureManager tree, select the TOP plane of the assembly to reference the new part.

- Right click on the default name [Part2^Core and Cavity]<1> and select **Rename Part**.

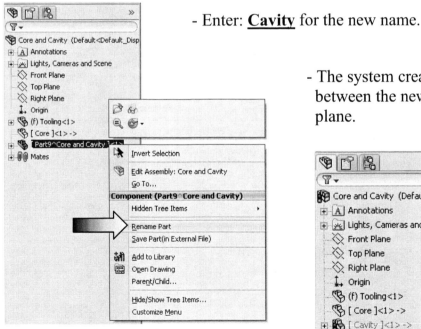

- Enter: **Cavity** for the new name.

- The system creates an INPLACE mate between the new part and the Top reference plane.

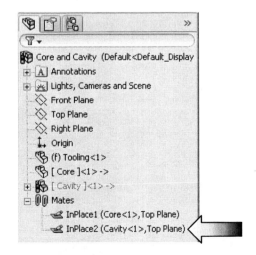

- **Exit the Sketch** or select **Insert / Sketch**; the Knit-Surface must be created first.

15. Knitting the surfaces to form a new part:

- Click ⬚ or select **Insert / Surface / Knit**.

- Select the Radiated surface as Surfaces and Faces to Knit ⬚ .

- Select the face indicated as Seed Faces ⬚ .

- Click **OK** ✓ .

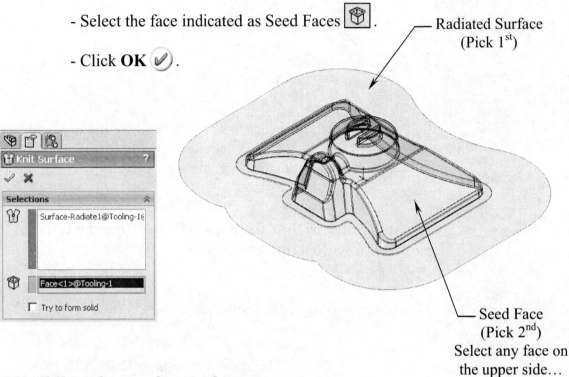

Radiated Surface
(Pick 1ˢᵗ)

Seed Face
(Pick 2ⁿᵈ)
Select any face on
the upper side…

16. Hiding the engineered part:

- Right click over the part named **Tooling** and select **Hide**.

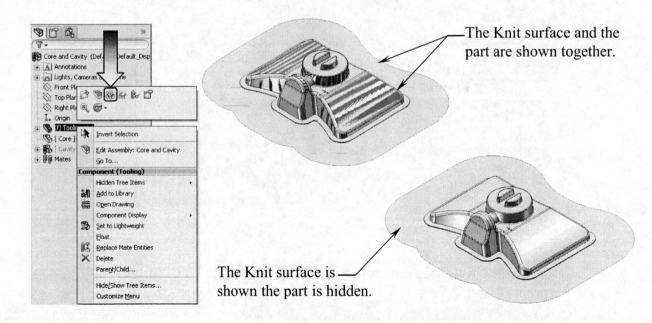

The Knit surface and the
part are shown together.

The Knit surface is
shown the part is hidden.

17. Creating a new work plane:

- Click 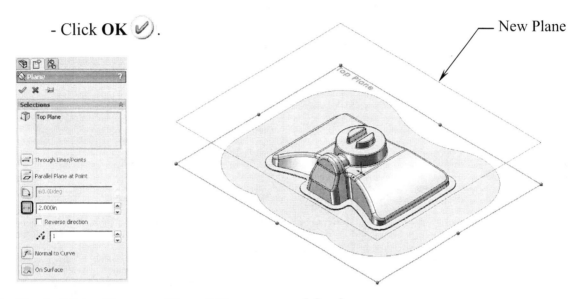 or select **Insert / Reference Geometry / Plane**.

- Select **Offset Distance** option and enter **2.00 in**.

- Select the TOP plane of the assembly from FeatureManager tree.

- Click **OK** .

New Plane

18. Sketching the profile of the upper block:

- Select the new plane either from the graphics area or from the Feature tree.

- Click or select **Insert / Sketch**.

- Convert the Rectangle from the previous sketch

Convert from the previous sketch

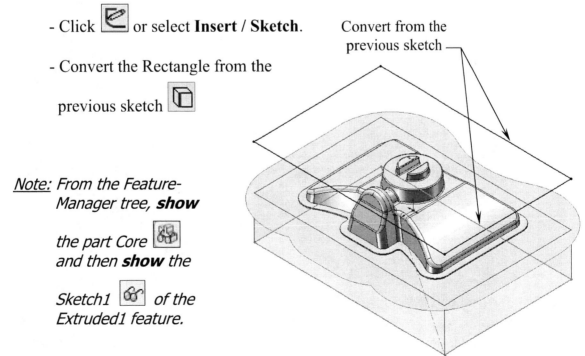

*Note: From the Feature-Manager tree, **show** the part Core and then **show** the Sketch1 of the Extruded1 feature.*

19. Extruding the upper block:

- Hide the Sketch1 and the part Core, from the previous step.

- Click  or select **Insert / Boss-Base / Extrude**.

- End Condition: **Up To Surface** .

- Select the Radiated surface as Face/Plane .

- Click **OK** .

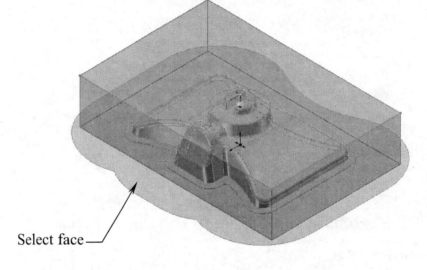

Select face

- Verify the resulted Cavity part.

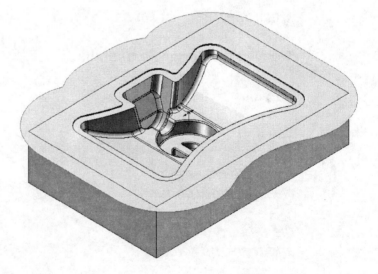

20. Returning to the assembly mode:

- Click or right-click on the component and select **Edit Assembly** to exit.

21. Showing all components:

- Right click on the part named **Tooling** and select **Show** .

- Right click on the part named **Core** and select **Show** .

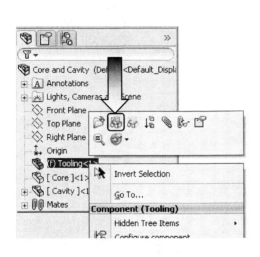

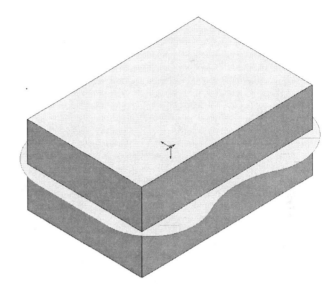

22. Hiding the Surface Bodies:

- Expand the part Tooling and click the plus symbol (+) next to the **Surface Bodies** folder to open it.

- Right click on Surface Radiate1 and select:
Hide-Surface Body.

Hide the
Surface Radiate

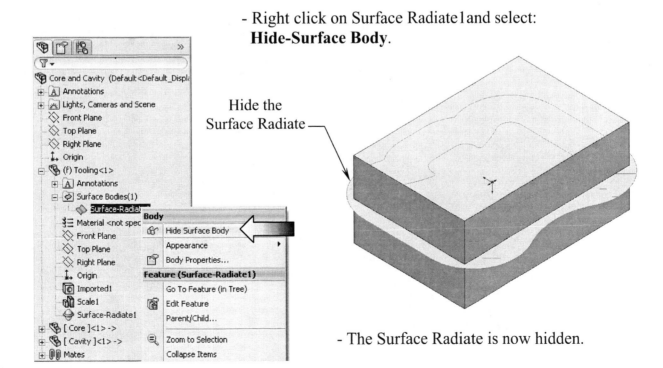

- The Surface Radiate is now hidden.

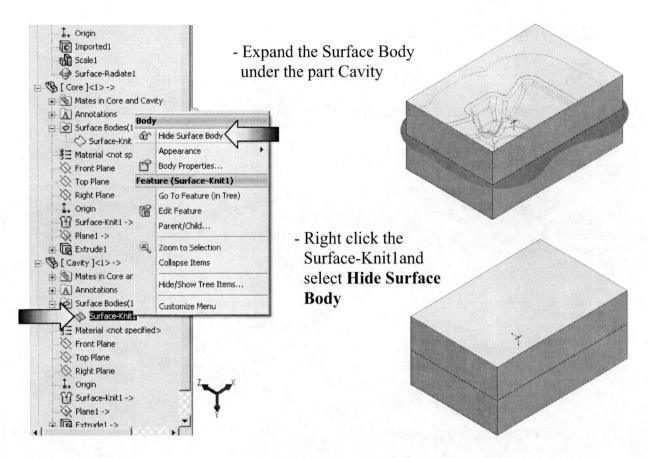

- Expand the Surface Body under the part Cavity

- Right click the Surface-Knit1and select **Hide Surface Body**

- The Surface-Knit1 is now hidden.

23. Making the parts transparent:

- Right click on the part named **Core** and select **Change Transparency** .

- Repeat the same step and make the part named Cavity also transparent.

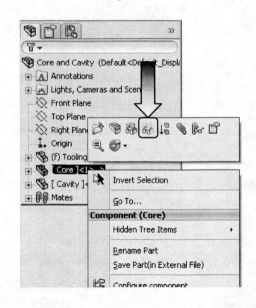

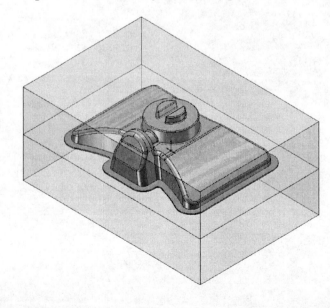

24. Creating an assembly Exploded view:

- Select **Exploded View** 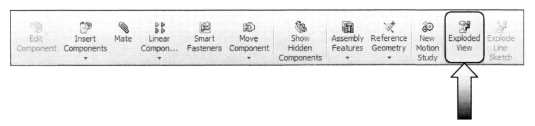 from the **Insert** menu OR click the Exploded
View Icon, from the Assembly toolbar.

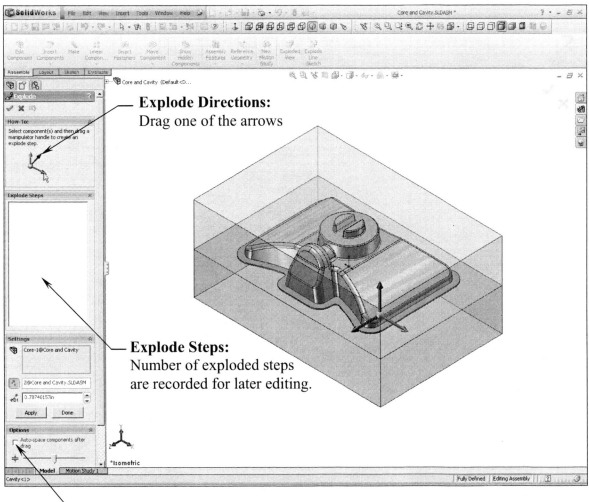

Explode Directions:
Drag one of the arrows

Explode Steps:
Number of exploded steps
are recorded for later editing.

Auto Spacing for Multi-Components:
Select several components, enable Auto-Space check box, drag one
of the arrows to move the components, and release the mouse cursor.
The components are automatically spaced evenly.

- Select the part **Cavity** either from the Feature tree or in the graphics area.

- For Direction, click the GREEN arrow (Y axis).

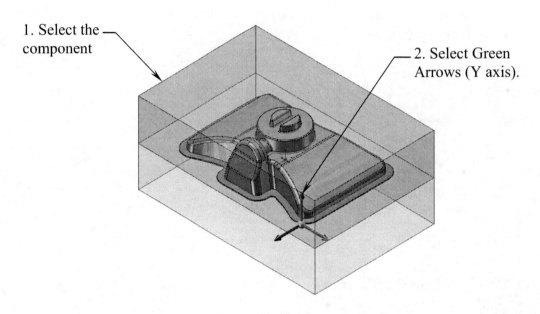

1. Select the component

2. Select Green Arrows (Y axis).

- Enter **6.00in.**, in the Explode Distance field and click Apply [Apply] .

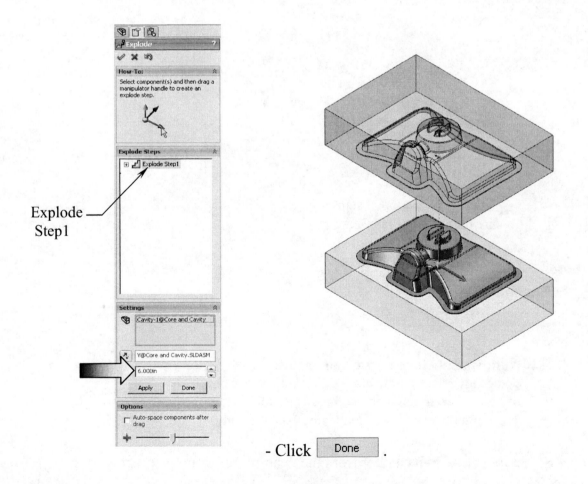

Explode Step1

- Click [Done] .

- Select the part **Core** either from the Feature tree or in the graphics area.

- Click the GREEN arrow (Y Axis)

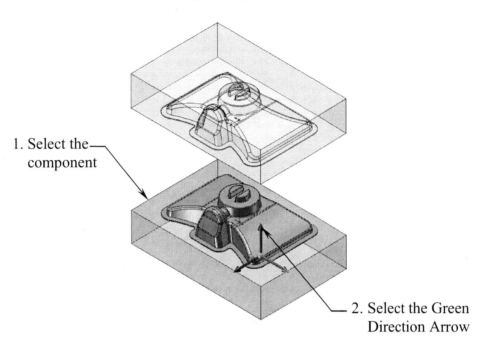

1. Select the component

2. Select the Green Direction Arrow

- Enter **-6.00in**., in the Explode Distance field (circled).

- Click **Apply** Apply and then click **Done** Done .

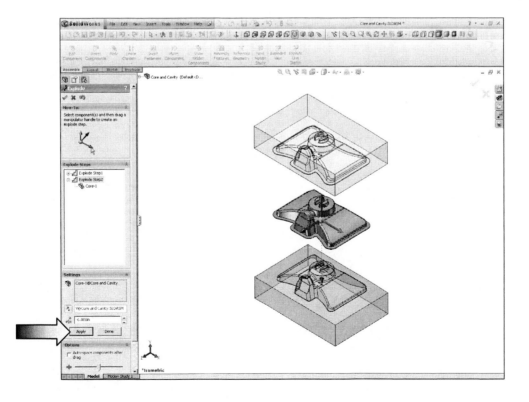

- The Explode Step2 is completed and recorded in the Explode Steps dialog.

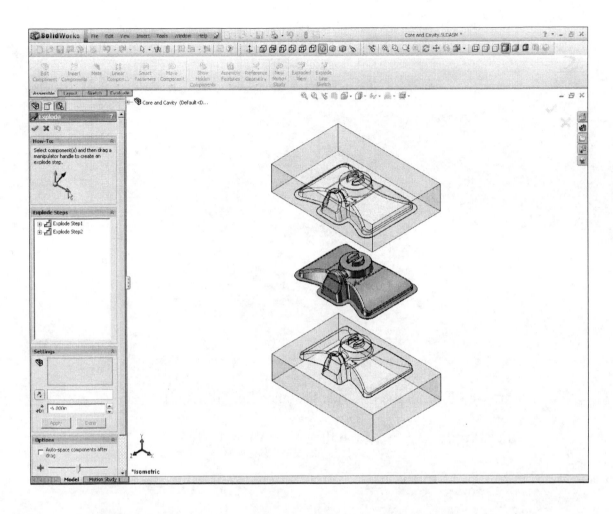

- Click **OK** to close out of the Explode mode.

25. Animating the Explode & Collapse:

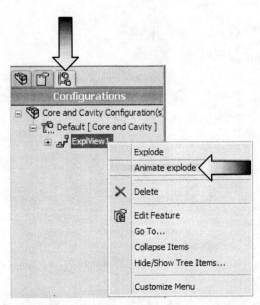

- Change to the Configuration Manager Tree (arrow).

- Expand the Default configuration.

- Right click on **ExplView1** and select: **Animate Collapse**.

- See the **Animation Controller** in the next step.

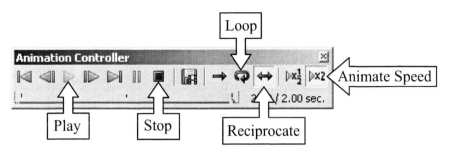

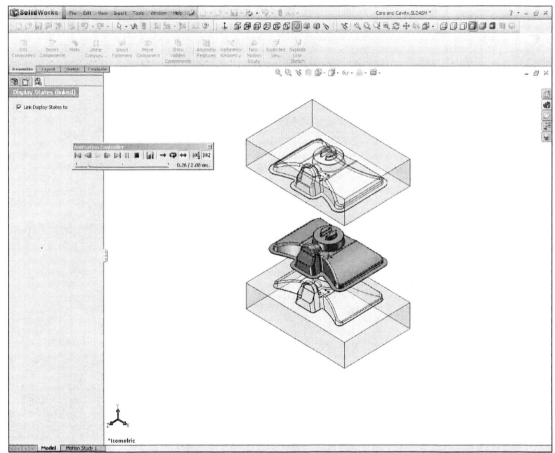

- Stop the animation when finished viewing.

26. Saving your work:

- The document was saved once before.

- Select **File / Save**.

- (Replace the previous
  document when prompted).

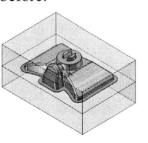

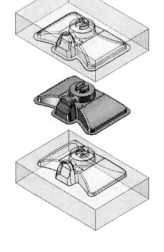

Questions for Review

Top Down Assembly

1. Existing geometry of other parts such as model edges, hole sizes, locations, sketches, surfaces, etc., can be converted and used to build new parts in the assembly level.
   a. True
   b. False

2. The first existing part inserted into an assembly document will be fixed (anchored) by the system automatically.
   a. True
   b. False

3. In Top-Down assembly, when selecting a plane or a model face to sketch the profile of a new part, the system creates the mate:
   a. Coincident
   b. Concentric
   c. Inplace

4. When the Edit Component button is selected, the part's color changes to Magenta, (or Blue, depends on the color settings), which means:
   a. The part is over defined
   b. The part is being edited
   c. The part is out of context

5. The Scale feature not only scales the part, but all of its dimensions as well.
   a. True
   b. False

6. When a radiate surface is created from a solid model, it can have thickness as well.
   a. True
   b. False

7. When a part is built in Top-Down assembly, it can only be moved when:
   a. Its mates are suppressed
   b. Its mates are deleted
   c. Create an exploded view
   d. All of the above

7. D

5. FALSE   6. FALSE

4. B   3. C

1. TRUE   2. TRUE

CHAPTER 15 (cont.)

Core & Cavity – Part Level

Creating a Core and Cavity Part Level

- A mold is normally designed in SolidWorks using a sequence of intergraded tools that control the mold creation process.
- Using the finished model, these mold tools can be used to analyze and correct deficiencies with the part.

- The process usually follows these steps: Draft analysis, Undercut Detection, Parting Lines, Shut-Off Surfaces, Parting Surfaces, Interlock Surfaces (Ruled Surfaces), and Tooling Split.

- The Parting Lines lie along the edge of the molded part, between the core and the cavity surfaces. They are used to create the Parting Surfaces and to separate the surfaces.

- The Shut-Off Surfaces are created after the Parting Lines. A shut-off surface closes up a through hole by creating a surface patch along the Edges that form a continuous loop -OR- a parting line you previously created to define a loop.

- After the Parting Lines and the Shut-Off Surfaces are determined, the Parting Surfaces are created. The Parting Surfaces extrude from the parting lines, and are used to separate the mold cavity from the core.

- After a parting surface is defined, the Tooling Split tool is used to create the core and cavity blocks for the model. To create a tooling split, at least three surface bodies are needed in the Surface Bodies folder Surface Bodies.

- With most mold parts, the interlock surfaces need to be created. The interlock surfaces help prevent the core and cavity blocks from shifting, and are located along the perimeter of the parting surfaces. Usually, they have a 5-degree taper.

Creating a Core and Cavity
In the Part Level

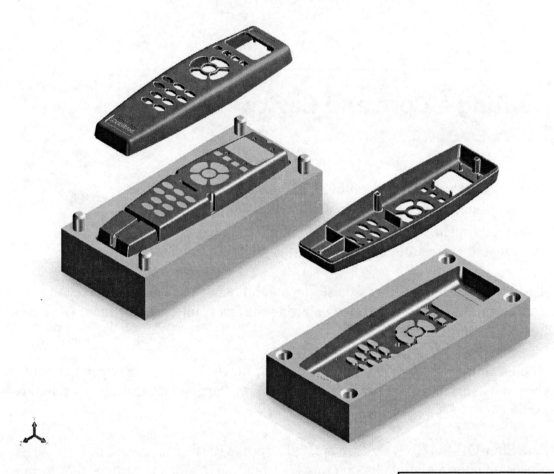

Dimensioning Standards: **ANSI**

Units: **INCHES** – 3 Decimals

Tools Needed:

 Parting Lines   Parting Surfaces   Shut-Off Surfaces

 Tooling Split   Planes   2D Sketch

1. Opening an existing IGES document:

- Select **File / Open**.

- Change the Files of Type to **Parasolid**.
  (From the Training CD or Class Files server).

- Select **Remote Control.x_b** and click **Open**.

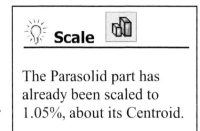

☀ **Scale**

The Parasolid part has already been scaled to 1.05%, about its Centroid.

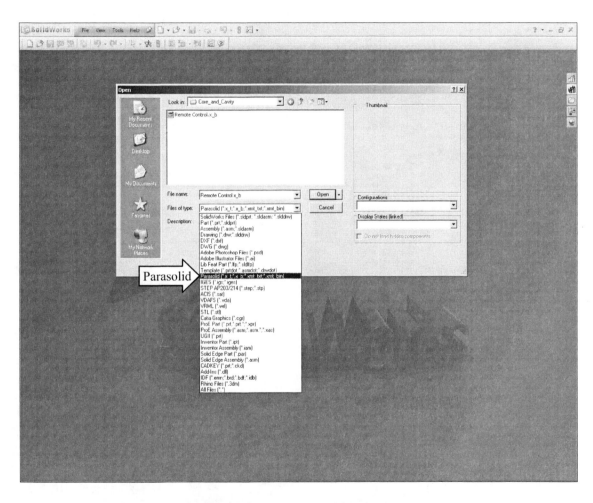

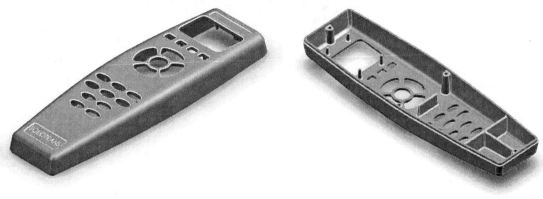

2. Creating the Parting Lines:

- Click  or select:

Insert / Molds / Parting Lines.

Parting Lines
Establishes parting lines to separate core and cavity surfaces.

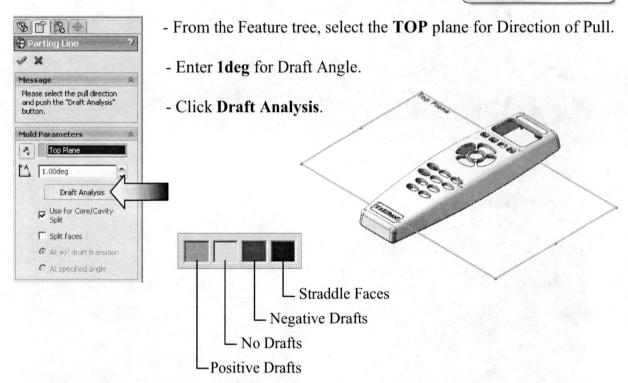

- From the Feature tree, select the **TOP** plane for Direction of Pull.

- Enter **1deg** for Draft Angle.

- Click **Draft Analysis**.

— Straddle Faces
— Negative Drafts
— No Drafts
—Positive Drafts

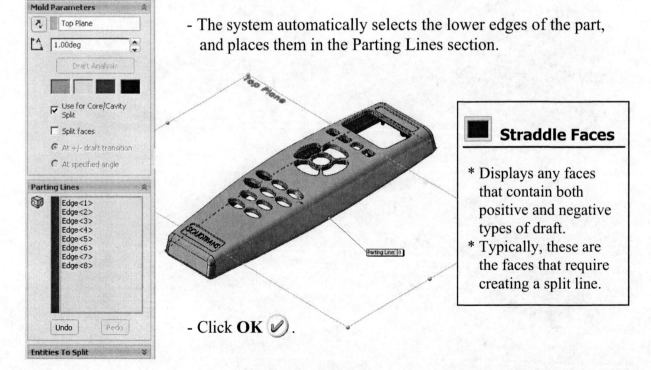

- The system automatically selects the lower edges of the part, and places them in the Parting Lines section.

Straddle Faces

* Displays any faces that contain both positive and negative types of draft.
* Typically, these are the faces that require creating a split line.

- Click **OK** ✓.

3. Creating the Shut-Off Surfaces:

- Click or select **Insert / Molds / Shut-Off Surfaces**.

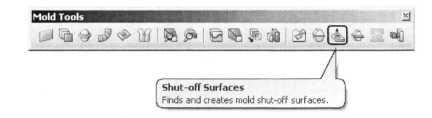

- The system automatically picks up all of the opened areas and labels them as Loop/Contacts.

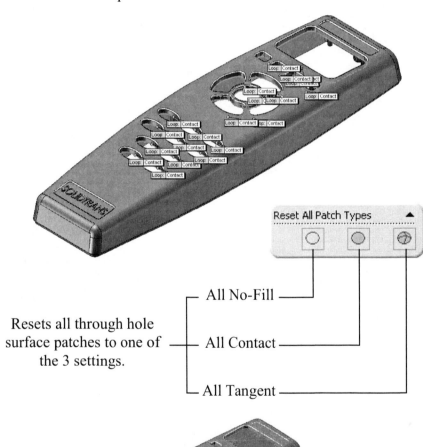

Resets all through hole surface patches to one of the 3 settings.

- All No-Fill
- All Contact
- All Tangent

💡 Patch Types

Only one Shut-Off Surface feature is allowed in a model. Therefore, within the one feature, you must assign a fill type of **Contact**, **Tangent**, or **No Fill** to every hole.

- Click **OK** ⊘ .

4. Creating the Parting Surfaces:

- Click 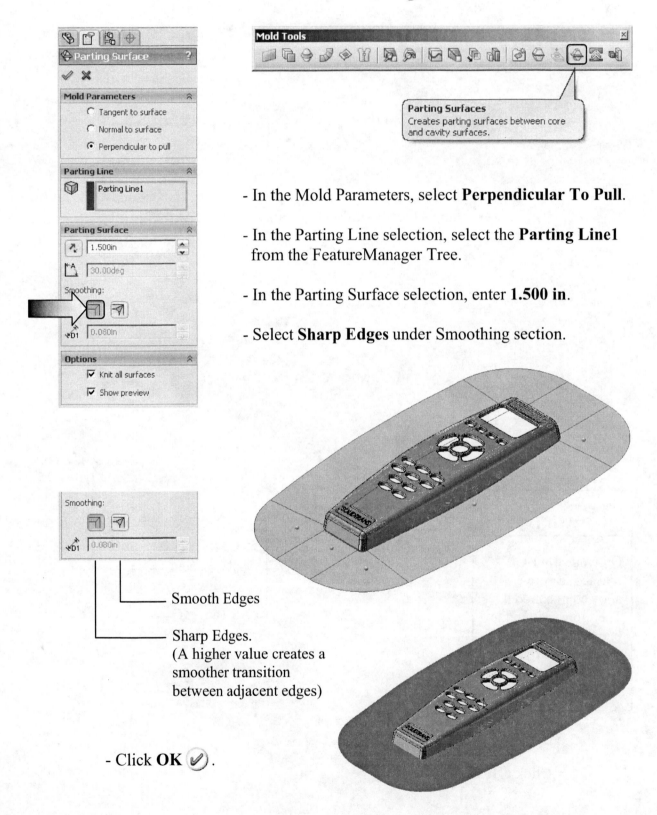 or select **Insert / Molds / Parting Surfaces**.

- In the Mold Parameters, select **Perpendicular To Pull**.

- In the Parting Line selection, select the **Parting Line1** from the FeatureManager Tree.

- In the Parting Surface selection, enter **1.500 in**.

- Select **Sharp Edges** under Smoothing section.

Smooth Edges

Sharp Edges.
(A higher value creates a smoother transition between adjacent edges)

- Click **OK** .

5. Sketching the profile of the mold-blocks:

- Select the TOP plane and open a new sketch.

- Sketch a Rectangle approximately as shown.

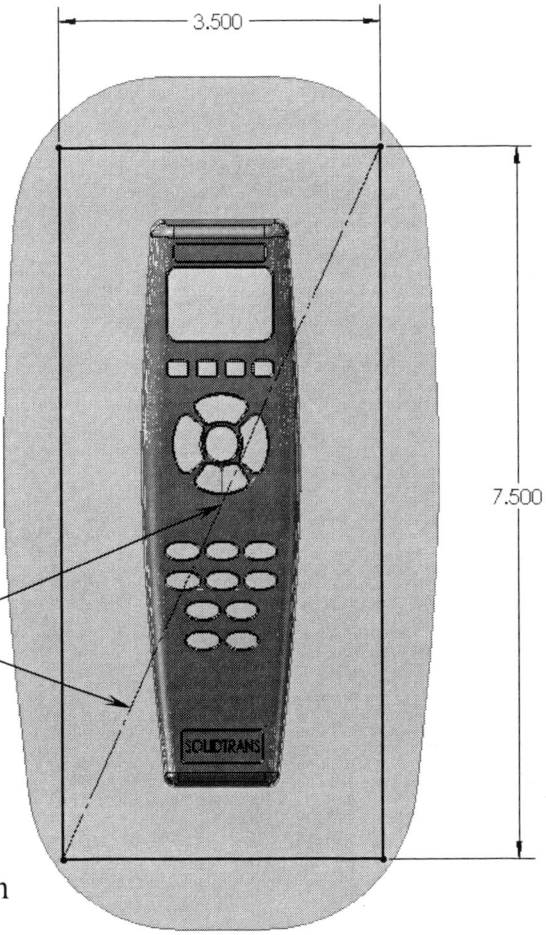

- Add the width and the height dimensions.

Midpoint Relation

- Add a Centerline as shown.

- Add a Midpoint relation between the centerline and the Origin to fully define the sketch.

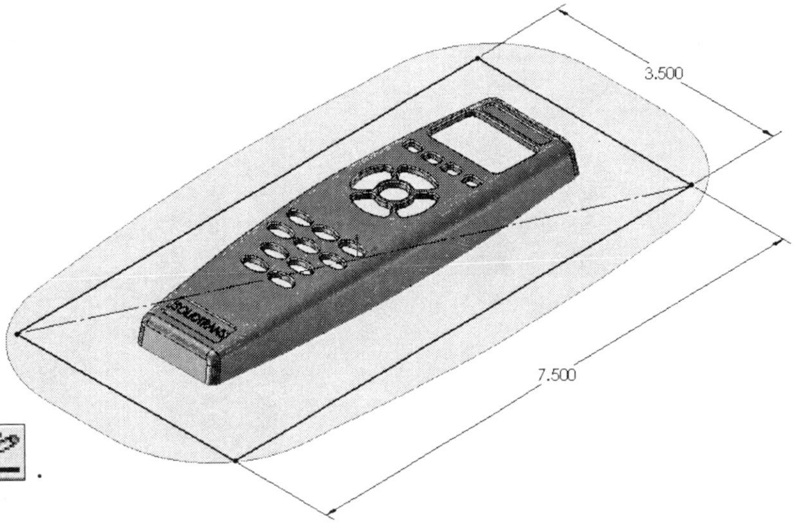

3.500

7.500

3.500

7.500

- **Exit the Sketch.**

6. Creating the Tooling Split:

- Click 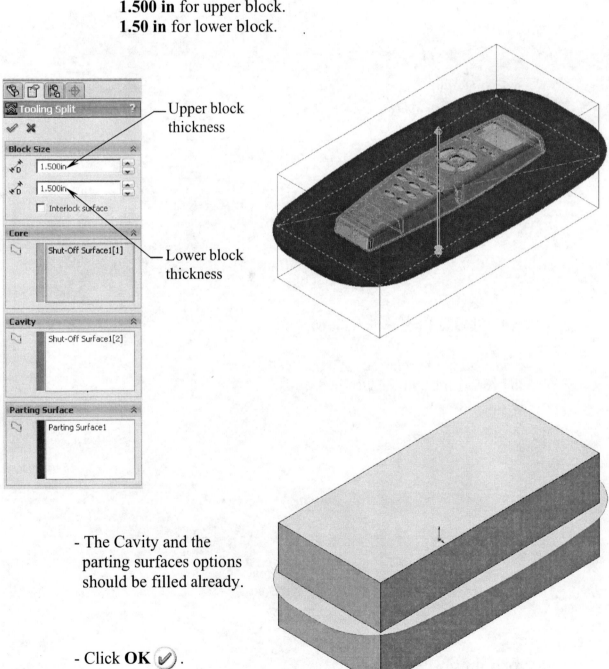 or select:

Insert / Molds / Tooling Split.

- In the Block Size selection, enter:

1.500 in for upper block.
1.50 in for lower block.

Upper block thickness

Lower block thickness

- The Cavity and the parting surfaces options should be filled already.

- Click **OK**.

7. Hiding the Solid Bodies:

- From the Feature Manager Tree, expand the Surface Bodies folder.

- Hold the CONTROL key and select all **3 surfaces** in the folder.

- Right click over one of the 3 surfaces and select **Hide Bodies**.

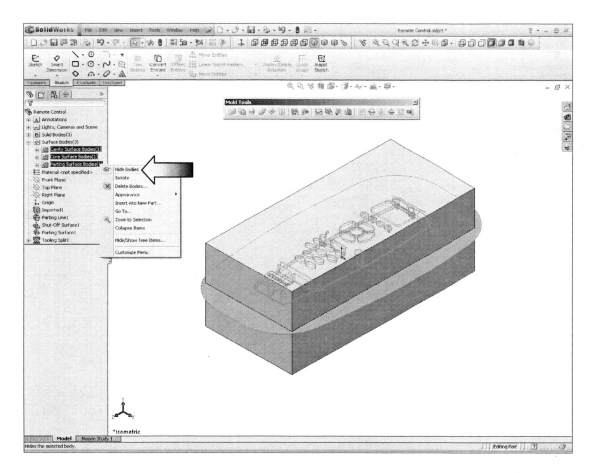

- The 3 surfaces that were created in the previous steps are temporarily removed from the graphics.

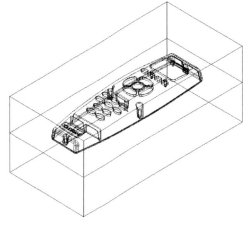

- Change to the Wireframe mode to see the inside details of the blocks.

8. Saving the parts:

- Expand the **Solid Bodies folder**, right mouse click on **Tooling Split [1],** and select **Insert into New Part**.

- Enter: **Remote_Control_Core**, for file name.

- Click **Save**.

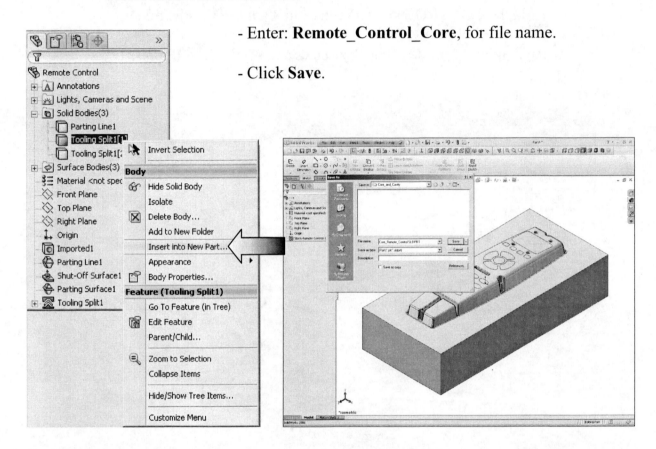

- Click **Yes** to confirm the References.

- Click **Save** to save the original part.

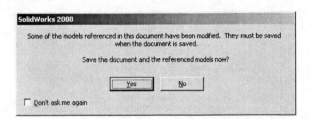

- Repeat the same step to save the Tooling-
Split[2], use **Remote_Control_Cavity**, for the name of the 2nd block.

9. Separating the 2 blocks:

- Select **Insert / Feature / Move-Copy**.

- Select the upper block in the graphics.

- Click the vertical Green arrow to define the direction.

- Under the Translate section, enter **6.00in** and press ENTER.

- Click **OK**.

- The upper block moved 6 inches upwards, from its original position.

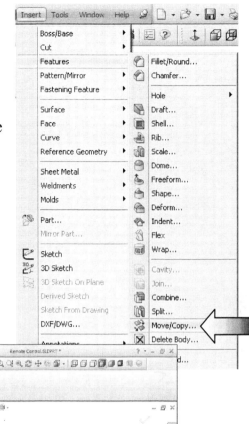

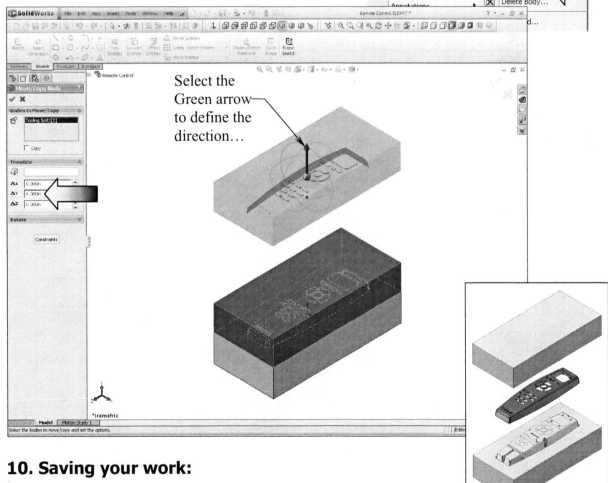

Select the Green arrow to define the direction…

10. Saving your work:

- Save a copy of your work as **Remote Control Tooling**.

11. Optional:

- Start a new Assembly document and assemble the 3 components.

- Create an Assembly Exploded View as a separate configuration.

- Add Injector hole.

- Ejector holes.

- Alignment Pins

- Make copies of the components and create an exploded view as shown.

Questions for Review

Core & Cavity

1. Using the finished model, the mold tools can be used to analyze and correct its deficiencies such as undercuts, draft angles, shut-off surfaces, etc.
   a. True
   b. False

2. The Parting Lines are used to create the Parting Surfaces and to separate the surfaces.
   a. True
   b. False

3. A shut-off surface closes up a through hole by creating a surface patch along the edges that form a continuous loop.
   a. True
   b. False

4. The Parting Surfaces extrude from the parting lines and are used to separate the mold cavity from the core.
   a. True
   b. False

5. To create a tooling split, what surface bodies are needed for this operation?
   a. The Core
   b. The Cavity
   c. The Parting Surface
   d. All of the above

6. The Interlock surfaces help prevent the core and cavity blocks from shifting and are located along the perimeter of the parting surfaces.
   a. True
   b. False

7. The solid bodies can be hidden or shown just like any other features in SolidWorks.
   a. True
   b. False

7. TRUE

6. TRUE   5. D

4. TRUE   3. TRUE

2. TRUE   1. TRUE

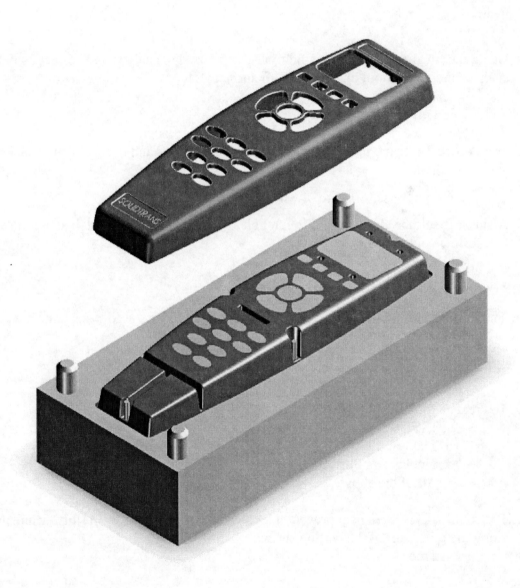

CHAPTER 16

Top-Down Assembly

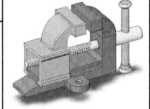

Top-Down Assembly

- This lesson will guide us through some techniques of creating new parts in the context of an assembly, or Top Down mode.

- By using the existing geometry of other parts such as their locations, features and sizes, to construct new components, is referred to as In-Context-Assembly. This option greatly helps capturing your design intents and reduces the time it takes to do a design change. The parts update within themselves based on the way they were created.

- While working in the top down assembly mode, every time a face or a plane is selected as a sketch plane to create a feature of the new part, the system automatically creates an INPLACE mate to reference the new part.

- The Inplace mates can be suppressed so that components can be moved or repositioned and the Inplace mates can also be deleted so that new mates can be added to establish new relationships with other components.

- When a part is being edited, the Edit Component icon 🗇 is selected and the part's color changes to Blue or Magenta, depends on the color settings in the system options.

- Upon the successful completion of this lesson, you will have a better understanding of the 2 assembly methods in SolidWorks: the traditional Bottom Up assembly (where parts are created separately, then inserted into an assembly document and get mated together), and the dynamic Top Down assembly (where parts can be created together, in the context of an assembly).

Miniature Vise
Top-Down Assembly

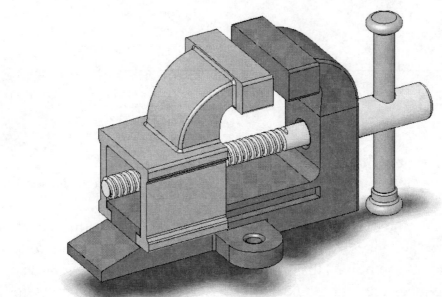

| Dimensioning Standards: **ANSI** |
| Units: **INCHES** – 3 Decimals |

Tools Needed:

Insert Sketch	Rectangle	Circle
Dimension	Add Geometric Relations	Sketch Mirror
Offset Entities	Planes	Fillet/Round
Base/Boss Extrude	Loft	Edit Component

1. Starting with a new assembly:

- Select **File / New / Assembly**.

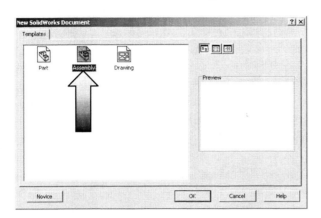

- Click Cancel ✖ to exit the **Begin Assembly** mode.

- **Save** the new assembly document as **Mini Vise.sldasm**

2. Creating the Base part:

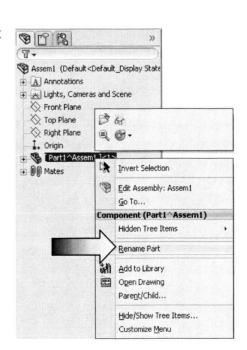

- Select **Insert / Component / New Part**.

- Select the FRONT plane from the
FeatureManager tree to reference the
new part (Inplace1).

- The system creates a new part using its default
name **[Part1^Assembly]<1>.**

- To rename the part, right click on its default
name and select **Rename Part**.

- Enter: **Base** as the new name for the 1st part.

- The new part has the
default Blue color.

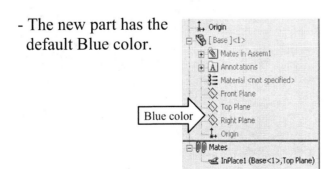

- A new sketch has been created automatically from the previous step.

- Sketch the profile as shown below, keep the Origin on the lower right hand side.

- Add the Dimensions 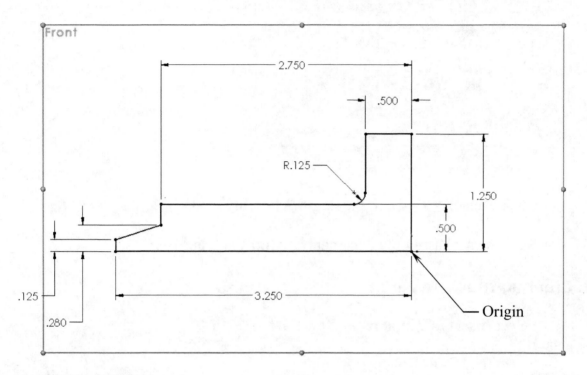 or Relations needed to fully define the sketch.

3. Extruding the Base:

- Click or select **Insert / Boss-Base / Extrude**.

- Direction 1:   **Mid-Plane**

- Extrude Depth: **.750 in.**

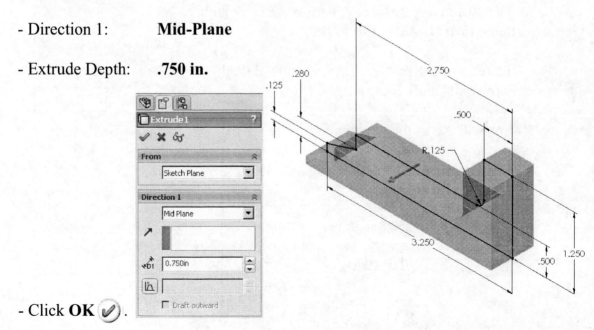

- Click **OK** .

4. Adding the side flanges:

- Select the bottom face of the base and open a new sketch .

- Sketch the profile below; use the Mirror ⚠ option to keep the sketch entities symmetrical with the Centerline.

- Add dimensions 🔷 as shown.

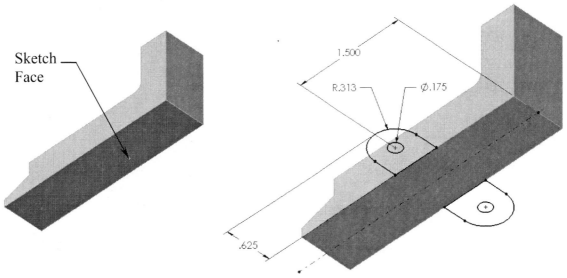

Sketch Face

1.500

R.313   Ø.175

.625

5. Extruding the Flanges:

- Click 🗔 or select **Insert / Boss-Base / Extrude**.

- Direction 1:   **Blind** (Reverse)

- Extrude Depth: **.200 in.**

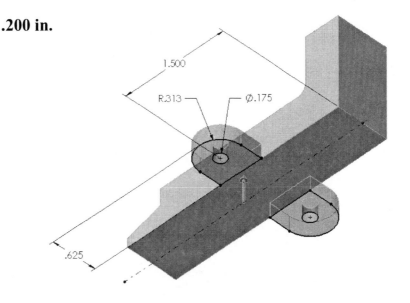

1.500

R.313   Ø.175

.625

- Click **OK** ✔ .

6. Adding the side cuts:

- Select the face as indicated, and click 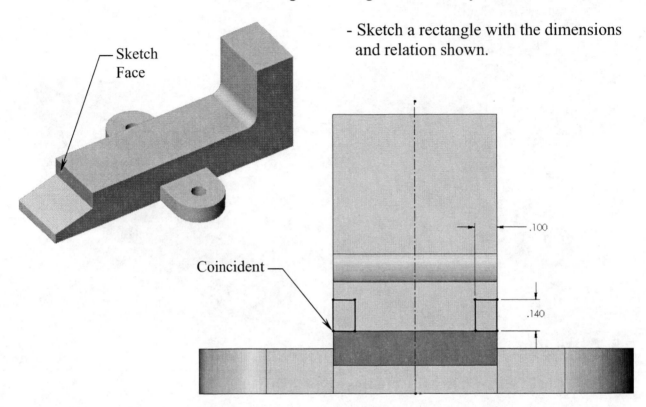 or select **Insert / Sketch**.

- Sketch a Centerline [ ] starting at the Origin and click Dynamic Mirror [ ] .

- Sketch a rectangle with the dimensions and relation shown.

Sketch Face

Coincident

.100

.140

7. Extruding the side cuts:

- Click [ ] or select **Insert / Cut / Extrude**.

- Direction 1: **Up-To-Surface**

- Select the face as indicated.

Select Face

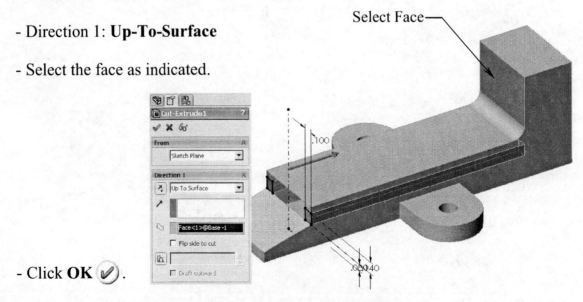

From
Sketch Plane

Direction 1
Up To Surface

Face<1>@Base-1

Flip side to cut

Draft outward

.100

.0040

- Click **OK** ✓.

8. Creating a new work plane:

- Select the face as shown and click 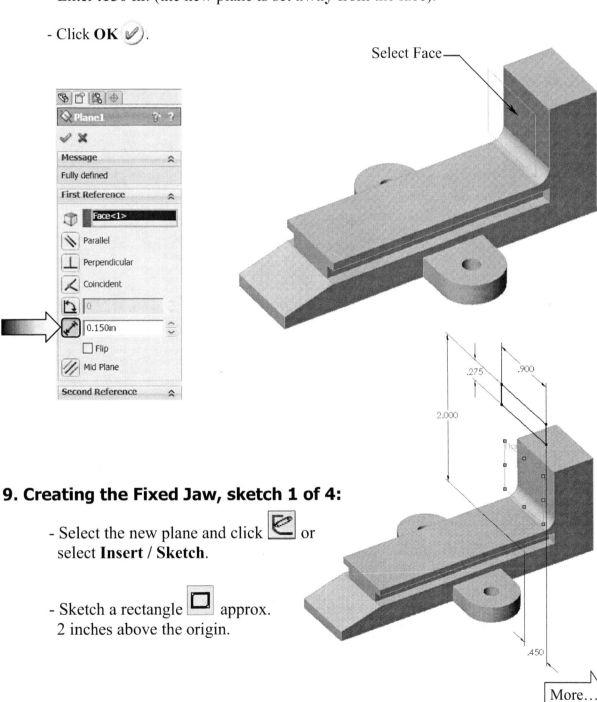 or select **Insert / Reference Geometry / Plane**.

- Click **Offset Distance** option

- Enter **.150 in**. (the new plane is set **away** from the face).

- Click **OK**.

9. Creating the Fixed Jaw, sketch 1 of 4:

- Select the new plane and click or select **Insert / Sketch**.

- Sketch a rectangle approx. 2 inches above the origin.

More...

- Add dimensions 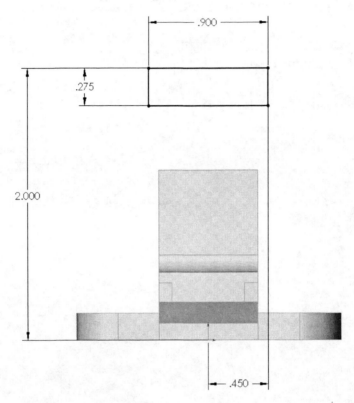 to fully position the sketch.

- Exit the sketch [icon] or select **Insert / Sketch**.

10. Creating the 2ⁿᵈ profile, sketch 2 of 4:

- Select the face as indicated and click [icon] or select **Insert / Sketch**.

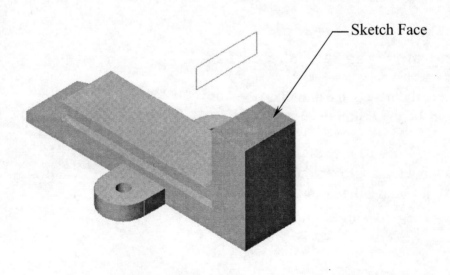

Sketch Face

- Hold down the CONTROL key and select the 4 edges as shown (or simply select the rectangular surface).

- Click **Convert Entities** 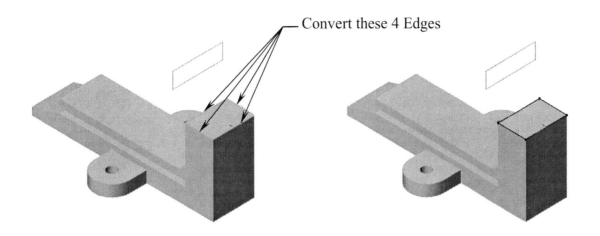 on the Sketch-Tools toolbar.

Convert these 4 Edges

- The 4 selected edges are converted into a new 2D rectangle.

- Exit the sketch or select **Insert / Sketch**.

11. Creating the 1st Guide Curve, sketch 3 of 4:

- Select the FRONT plane and click or select **Insert / Sketch**.

- Sketch a Centerpoint-Arc approximately as shown**

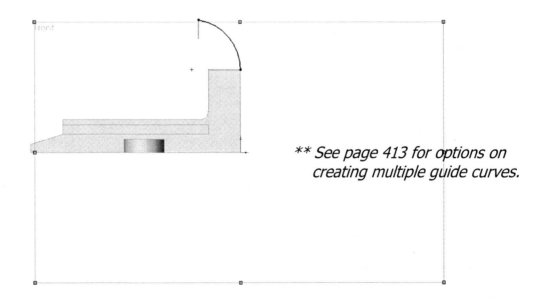

** See page 413 for options on creating multiple guide curves.

- Add the Relations as shown below.

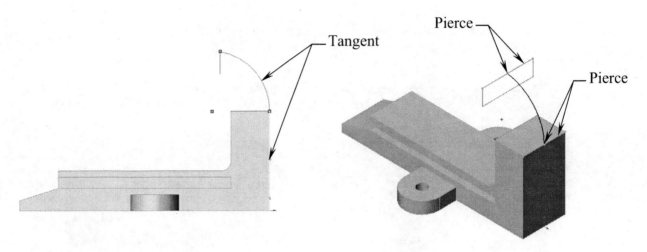

- Exit the sketch or select **Insert / Sketch**.

12. Creating the 2nd Guide Curve, sketch 4 of 4:

- Select the FRONT plane and click or select **Insert / Sketch**.

- Sketch another Centerpoint-Arc approximately as shown.

- Add the Relations needed to fully define the sketch.

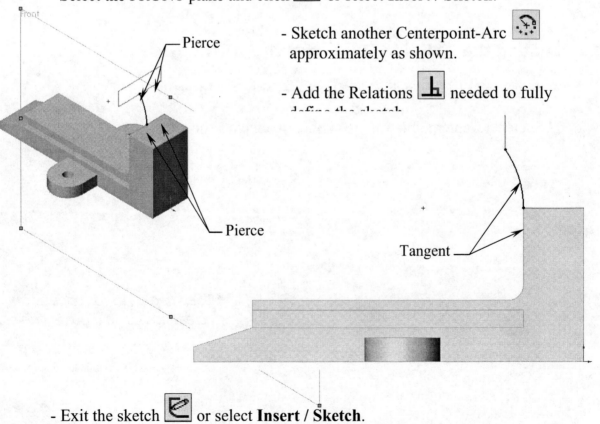

- Exit the sketch or select **Insert / Sketch**.

13. Creating the Fixed Jaw loft:

- Click 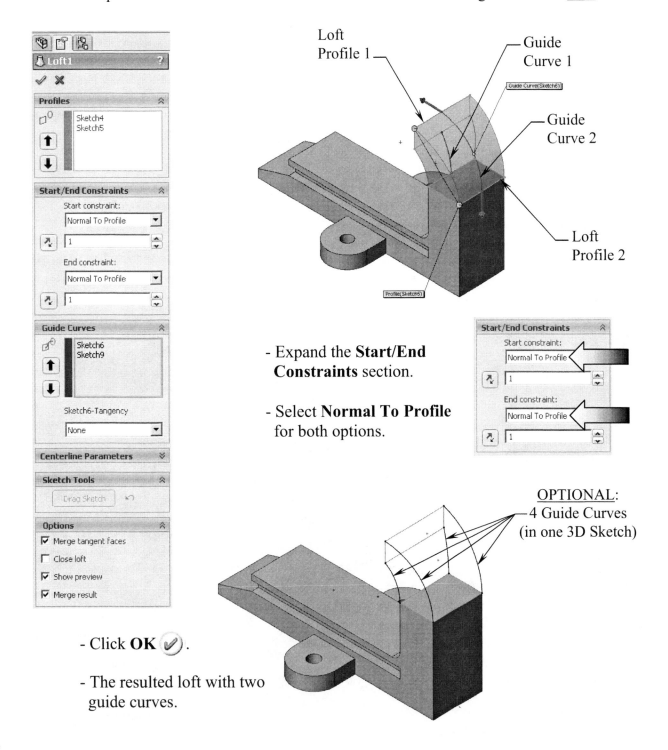 or select **Insert / Boss-Base / Loft**.

- Select the 2 sketch profiles as labeled (Profile 1 and Profile 2) .

- Expand the Guide Curve section and select the 1st and 2nd guide curves .

- Expand the **Start/End Constraints** section.

- Select **Normal To Profile** for both options.

- Click **OK** .

- The resulted loft with two guide curves.

14. Creating the Fixed Jaw Clamp:

- Select the FRONT plane from the FeatureManager tree and click 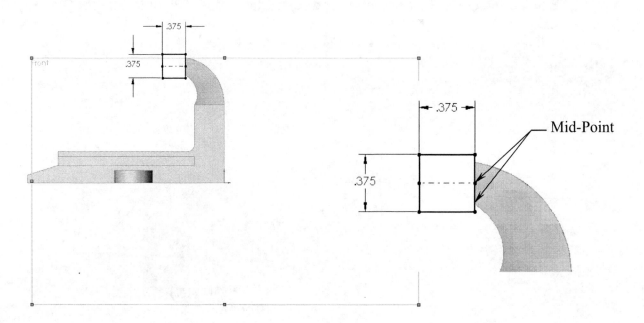 or select **Insert / Sketch**.

- Sketch a Rectangle ☐ and add Dimensions ◇ and Relations ⊥ as indicated.

Mid-Point

15. Extruding the Fixed Jaw Clamp:

- Click ⬚ or select **Insert / Boss-Base / Extrude**.

- Direction 1:   **Mid-Plane**

- Extrude Depth: **1.250 in**.

- Click **OK** ✓.

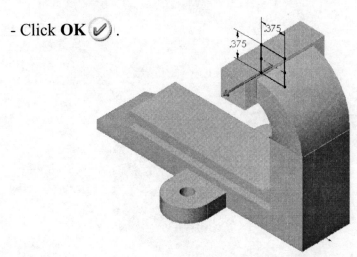

16. Creating the Lead Screw Hole:

- Select the face as indicated

  and open a new sketch 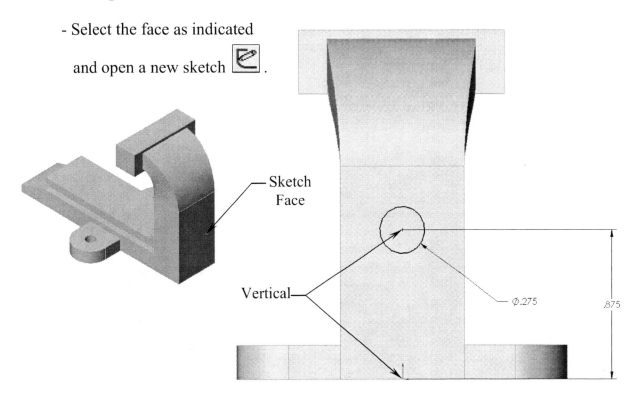.

- Sketch a Circle and add the dimensions and relations as shown.

17. Extruding the Lead Screw Hole:

- Click or select **Insert / Cut / Extrude**.

- Direction 1: **Through All**

- Click **OK**.

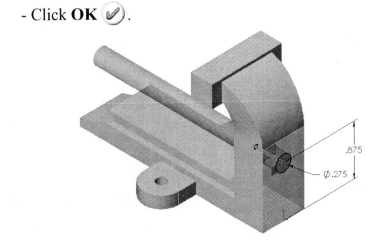

18. Adding Fillets:

- Click Fillet  or select **Insert / Features /Fillets-Rounds**.

- Enter **.032 in**. for Radius .

- Select the edges shown below for Edges to Fillet .

- Click **OK** .

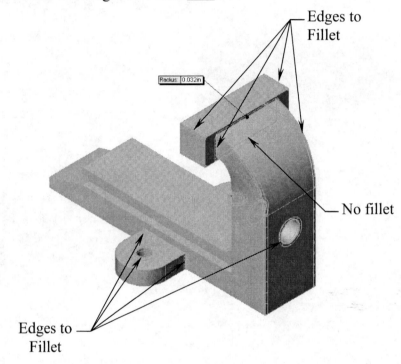

Edges to Fillet

No fillet

Edges to Fillet

- The Base part is shown in Front and Back Isometric views.

19. Saving your work:

- Select **File / Save As / Base / Save**.

- Click 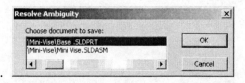 to exit the Edit Component mode.

20. Creating a new component: the Slide Jaw

- Select **Insert** / **Component** / **New Part**.

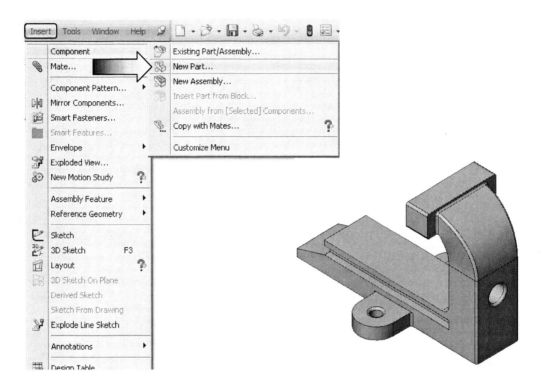

- Select the face indicated as sketch plane for the new component (Inplace2).

- A new part and a new sketch are created in the FeatureManager tree.

- **Rename** the component to **Slide Jaw**.

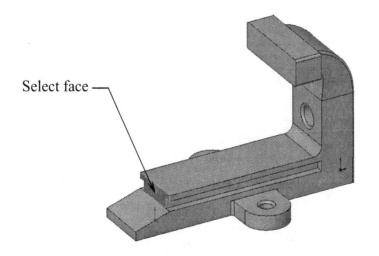

Select face

- A new part is created in the FeatureManager tree and the sketch pencil is activated.

- An INPLACE mate is also created for the new component to reference its location.

21. Using the Offset Entities command:

- Select the 4 edges of the model (as shown) and click **Offset Entities** 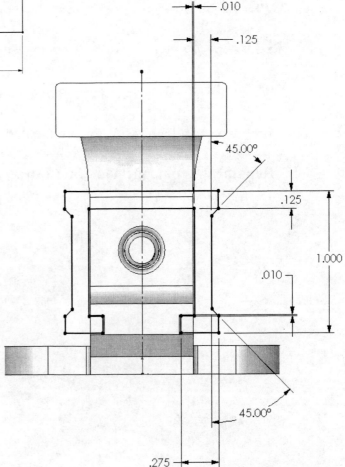 .

- Enter **.010 in**. for offset value.

Edges to Offset*

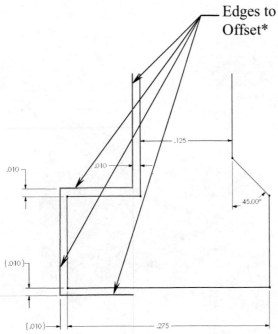

-⎼Ḁ- **Offset Entities**

* Geometry of a model such as edges, faces, and other sketch entities can be offset and converted by a specified distance.
* The offset entities can be set to one direction or bidirectional.
* An On Edge relation is created between each original entity and the corresponding sketch.

- Sketch the rest of the profile and add the dimensions or relations needed to fully define the sketch.

Note:

The mirror option ⚠ can be used to help speeds up the process and keep the profile symmetrical at the same time.

22. Extruding the Slide Jaw:

- Click 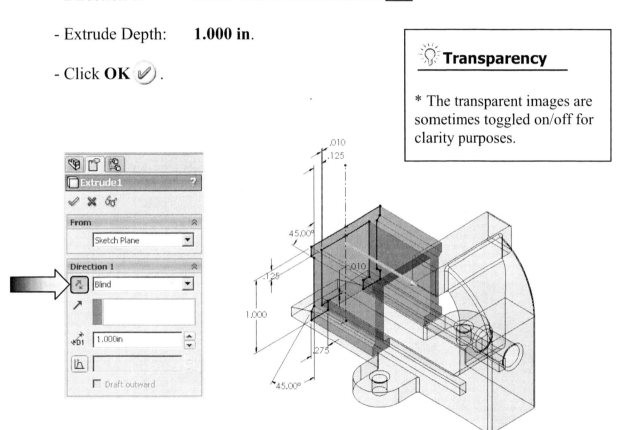 on the Features toolbar or select **Insert / Base / Extrude.**

- Direction 1:   **Blind** and reverse direction

- Extrude Depth: **1.000 in**.

- Click **OK** .

> ### 🔆 Transparency
>
> * The transparent images are sometimes toggled on/off for clarity purposes.

- The Slide Jaw is viewed from the front and back isometric views.

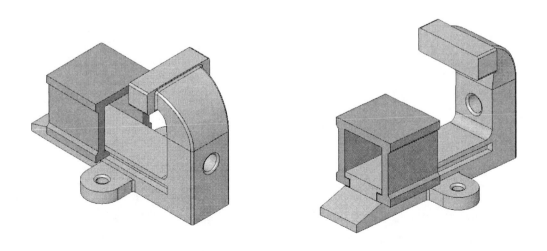

23. Adding the support wall:

- Select the indicated face and open a new sketch 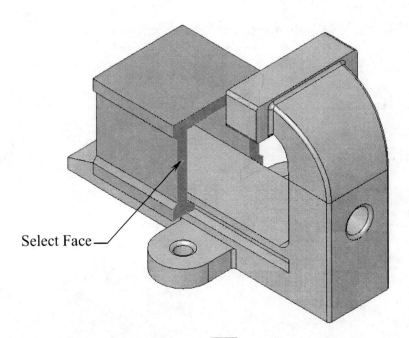 or select **Insert / Sketch.**

Select Face

- Sketch the profile and add dimensions as shown below to fully define the sketch.

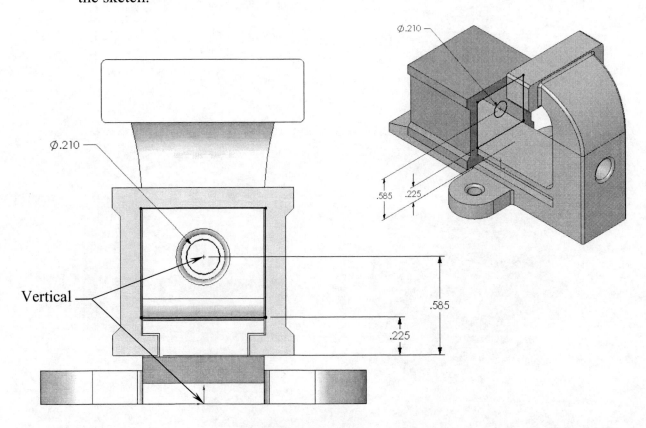

Ø.210

Vertical

.585

.225

.585

.225

24. Extruding the Support Wall:

- Click 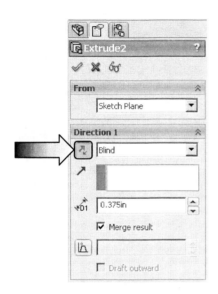 on the Features toolbar or select **Insert / Base / Extrude.**

- Direction 1:   **Blind** and reverse direction ⬈ .

- Extrude Depth: **.375 in**.

- Click **OK** ✅.

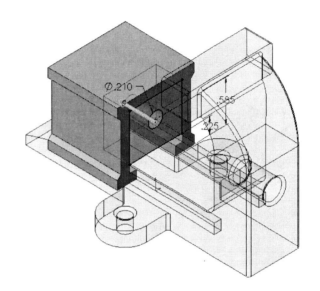

- The Support wall is built with a guide hole.

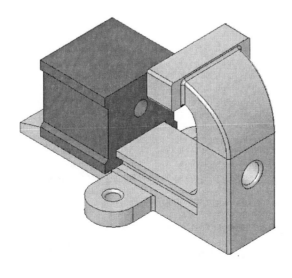

25. Creating a new work plane:

- Select the face as indicated and click 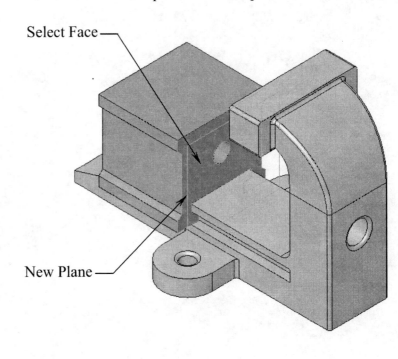 or select **Insert / Reference Geometry / Plane.**

- Enter **.150 in**. in the Offset Distance box and place the new plane on the *outside*.

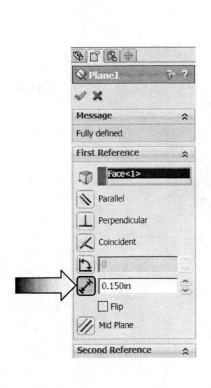

26. Creating the Slide Jaw, 1st sketch:

- Open a new sketch 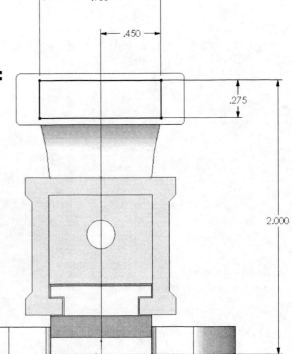 or select **Insert / Sketch.**

- Sketch a rectangle and add the

dimensions shown to fully define the sketch.

- Exit the sketch or select **\Insert / Sketch**.

27. Creating the Slide Jaw, 2nd sketch:

- Select the indicated face and open a new sketch 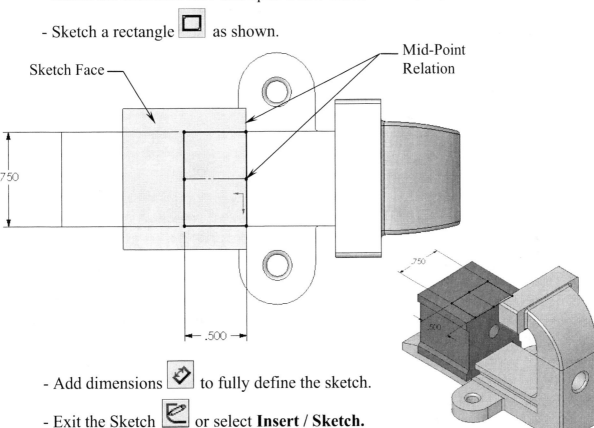 or select **Insert / Sketch.**

- Sketch a rectangle as shown.

Sketch Face ———

Mid-Point Relation

.750

.500

- Add dimensions to fully define the sketch.

- Exit the Sketch or select **Insert / Sketch.**

28. Creating the Guide Curve to connect the two sketches:

- Select the RIGHT plane of the part, from the FeatureManager tree.

- Click 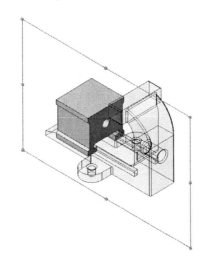 to open a new sketch, or select **Insert / Sketch.**

💡 Guide Curves

* Guide curves are used to control the profile from twisting as the sketch is swept along the path.
* Guide curves are also used in Sweep to shape the 3D Features.
* Each profile is PIERCED or coincident with the guide curve.

- Sketch either a **Centerpoint Arc** or a **3-Point Arc** that connects the two sketches.

- Add the Relations shown below to fully define the sketch.

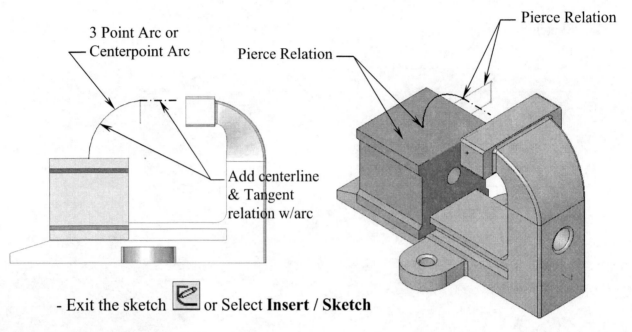

3 Point Arc or
Centerpoint Arc

Pierce Relation

Pierce Relation

Add centerline
& Tangent
relation w/arc

- Exit the sketch or Select **Insert / Sketch**

29. Creating the Slide Jaw Loft:

- Click on the Features toolbar, or select **Insert / Boss / Loft.**

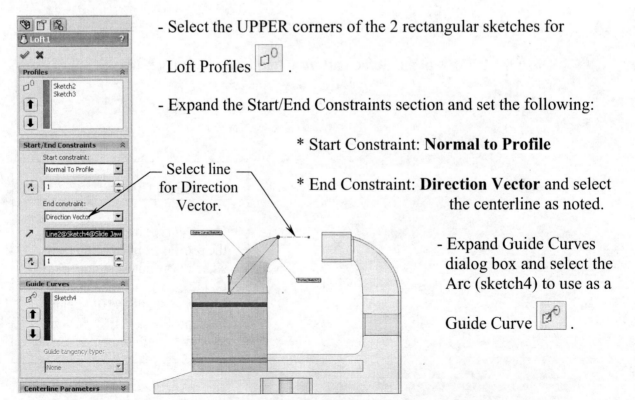

- Select the UPPER corners of the 2 rectangular sketches for

Loft Profiles .

- Expand the Start/End Constraints section and set the following:

* Start Constraint: **Normal to Profile**

Select line
for Direction
Vector.

* End Constraint: **Direction Vector** and select the centerline as noted.

- Expand Guide Curves dialog box and select the Arc (sketch4) to use as a

Guide Curve .

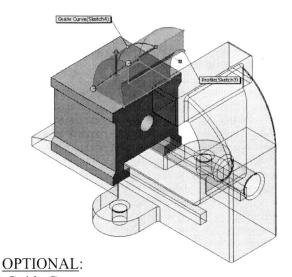

OPTIONAL:
4 Guide Curves
(in one 3D Sketch)

Tangent

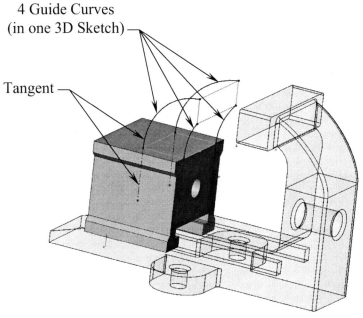

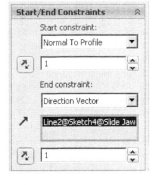

- Click **OK** ✅.

30. Creating the Clamp block:

- Select the part' RIGHT plane from the FeatureManager tree.

- Click 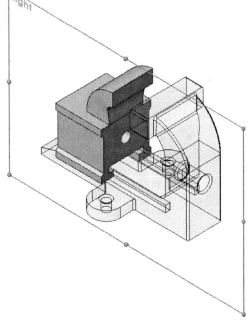 to open a new sketch, or select **Insert / Sketch.**

- Sketch a Rectangle 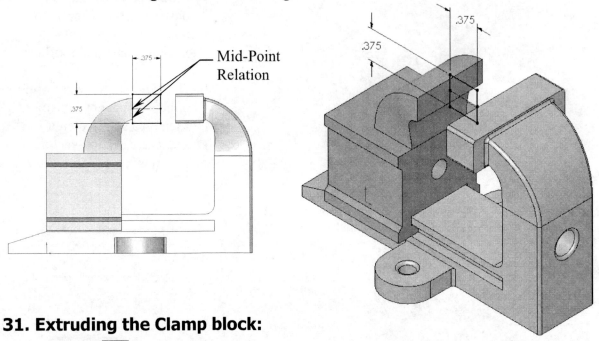 and add Dimensions shown below.

- Add a Centerline in the middle of the rectangle and position it on the Mid-Point of the right-most vertical edge.

Mid-Point
Relation

31. Extruding the Clamp block:

- Click  or select **Insert / Boss-Base Extrude.**

- Direction 1:   **Mid-Plane**

- Extrude Depth: **1.250 in**.

- Merge Result: **Enabled**

- Click **OK** .

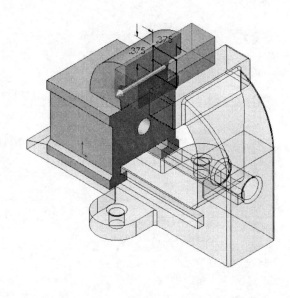

32. Which option is better?

- Instead of using the Mid-Plane extrude option, **Up-To-Surface** can be used to link the length dimensions of the 2 Clamp Blocks together.

- Right-mouse click on the last Extruded feature and select **Edit Feature**.

- Change **Direction 1** from Mid-Plane to **Up-To-Surface** and select the face on the left side.

> ### Up-To-Surface
>
> * Extends the feature from the sketch plane to the selected surface.
> * When the driving surface is changed in length, the referenced extruded feature will also be reflected.

- Change **Direction 2** to **Up-To-Surface** and select the face on the right side as indicated.

- Click **OK** .

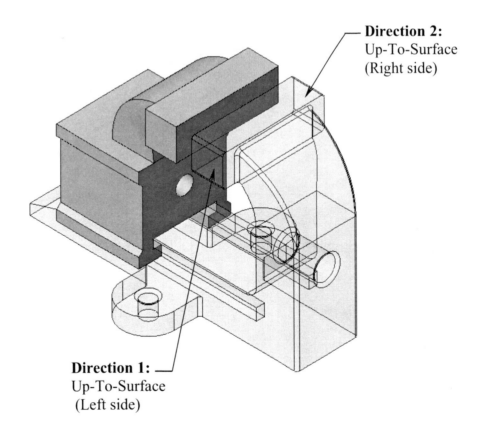

Direction 2:
Up-To-Surface
(Right side)

Direction 1:
Up-To-Surface
(Left side)

33. Adding fillets:

- Click  or select **Insert / Features / Fillet-Round.**

- Enter **.032** for Radius value ⬈ .

- Select the edges as shown ⬚ .

- Click **OK** ✓ .

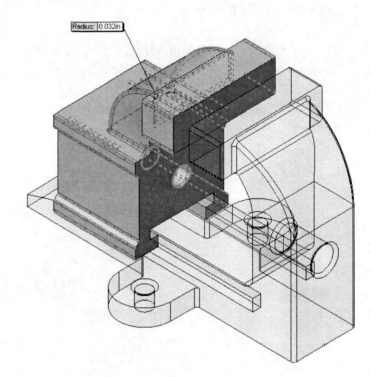

- The fillets are shown in the Front and Back Isometric views for clarity.

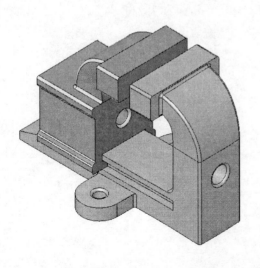

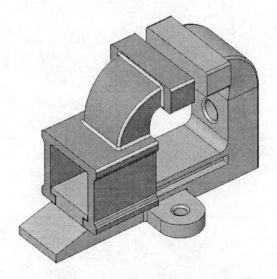

34. Creating the internal threads:

- Starting with the sweep path.

- Select the indicated face and open a new sketch 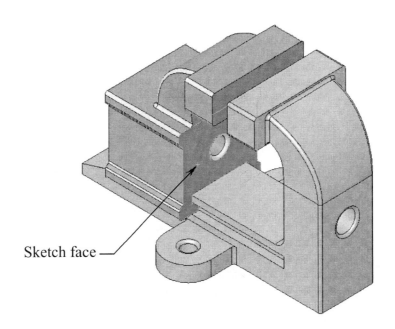 or select **Insert / Sketch.**

Sketch face —

- Sketch a Circle 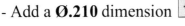 that is Concentric with the hole. Converting the ID of the hole is another good way to make a parametric circle.

- Add a **Ø.210** dimension  to fully define it.

⋰ Wake up Center Point

* Center-points of existing geometry can be "woke-up" for use as snap points in a sketch.

* With a Circle tool selected, position the mouse cursor over the circumference of the hole; the 4 quadrant points appear, and the center-point of the circle is visible for snapping.

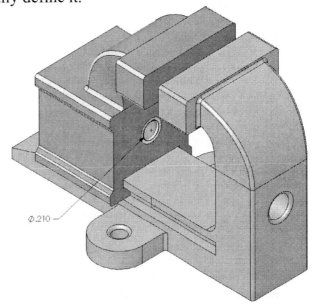

Ø.210 —

- Select **Insert / Curve / Helix-Spiral.**

- Enter the following parameters:

Defined by:	**Pitch and Revolution**
Pitch:	**.080 in**.
Revolution:	**5.000**
Starting Angle:	**90.00 deg**.
Reverse Direction:	**Enabled**
Clockwise:	**Selected**.

- Click **OK** 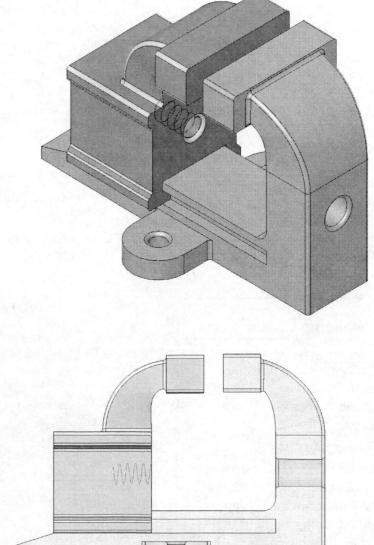.

- Sketching the Sweep Profile:

- Select the part' RIGHT plane from the Feature tree and open a new sketch
  or select **Insert / Sketch.**

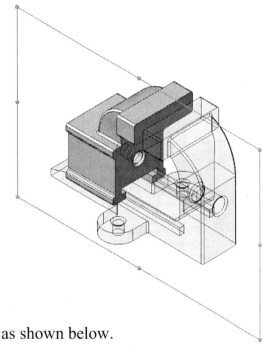

- Sketch the profile as shown below.

- Add Dimensions 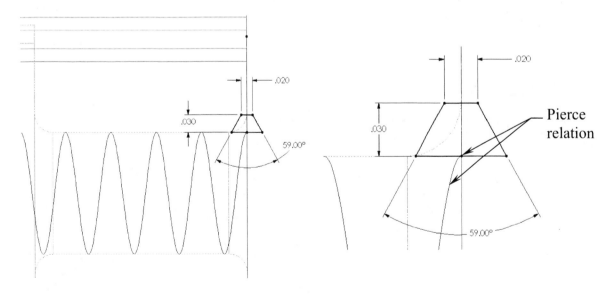 and Relations to fully define the sketch.

- Use Front view with Hidden Lines Visible option .

- Exit the sketch OR Select **Insert / Sketch.**

35. Sweeping the thread Profile along the Helix:

- Select **Insert / Cut / Sweep.**

- Select the thread profile to use as Sweep Profile 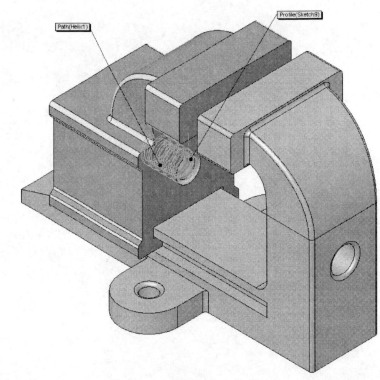 .

- Select the Helix to use as Sweep Path .

- Click **OK** .

36. Creating a Section View:

- Click the **Section View** command or select **View / Display / Section View.** Choose the **Right** plane of the part from the FeatureManager tree to cut with.

- Click **Section View** icon again to turn it off.

- The **Slide Jaw** was built in-context of an assembly or Top-Down mode.

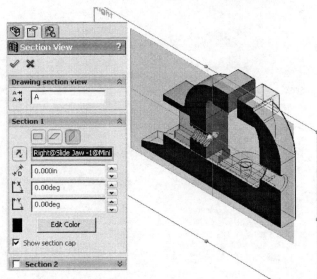

37. Saving your work.

- Save your work once again
  using the same file name:
  Mini-Vise.sldasm

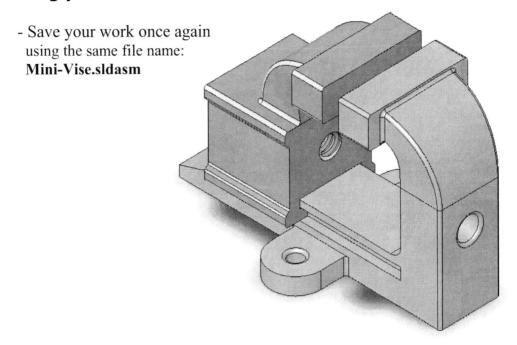

38. Assembly Exploded view (Optional):

- Create the components Lead Screw, Crank Handle, and Crank Knob, using the Top Down Assembly method, and also create an assembly exploded view as shown.

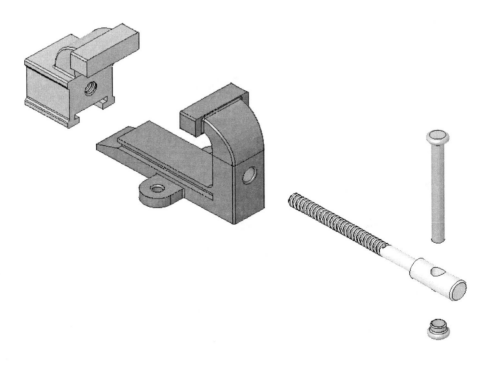

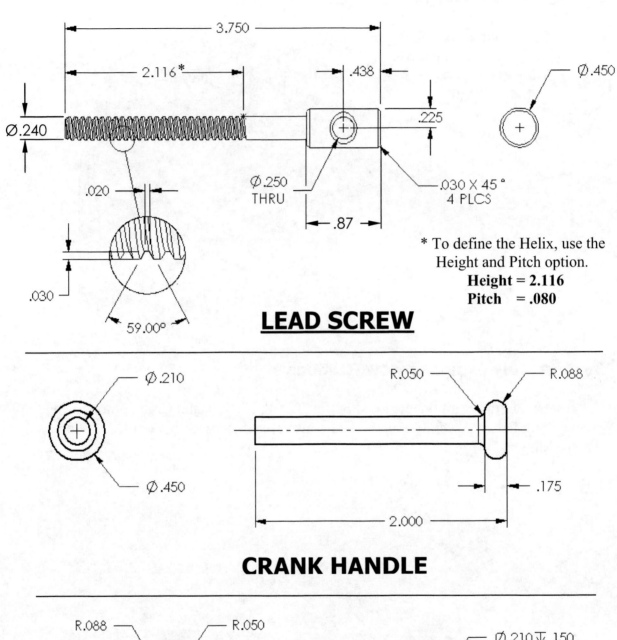

* To define the Helix, use the
Height and Pitch option.
Height = 2.116
Pitch   = .080

LEAD SCREW

CRANK HANDLE

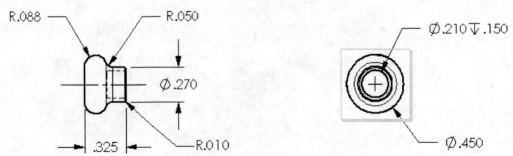

CRANK KNOB

Questions for Review

Top-Down Assembly

1. Component parts can be created in context of an assembly.
    a. True
    b. False

2. Geometry of other components such as model edges, hole diameters, and locations etc., can be used to construct the new part.
    a. True
    b. False

3. Part documents can be inserted into an assembly using:
    a. Insert menu
    b. Windows Explorer
    c. Drag and drop from an open window
    d. All of the above

4. The suffix (f) next to the first part's name in the Feature Manager tree stands for:
    a. Fail
    b. Fixed
    c. Float

5. When inserting new components, Inplace mates are created by the user.
    a. True
    b. False

6. Either in the part or assembly mode, guide curves are used to control the profiles from twisting, as they are swept along the path.
    a. True
    b. False

7. Centerpoint Arcs are drawn from its center, then radius and angle.
    a. True
    b. False

8. The Link Values option allows user to link only two dimensions at a time.
    a. True
    b. False

1. TRUE   2. TRUE
3. D   4. B
5. FALSE   6. TRUE
7. TRUE   8. FALSE

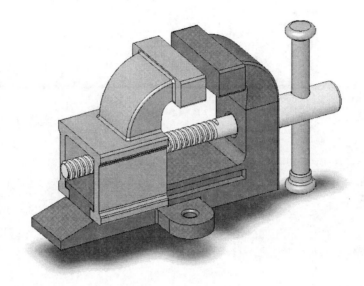

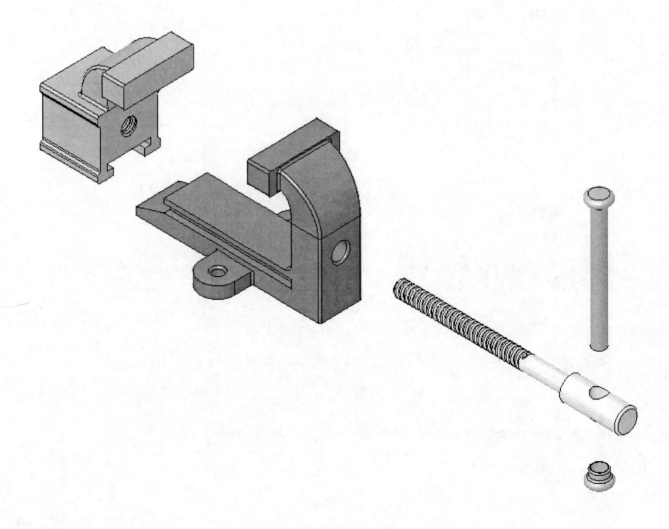

Lips & Grooves for Plastic Parts

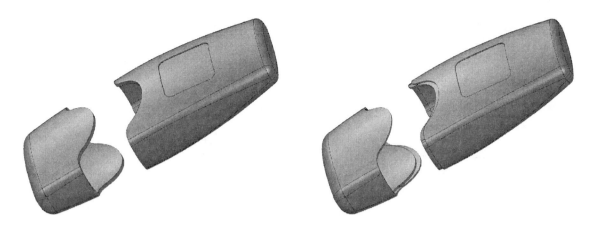

Lip & Groove

- You can create lip and groove fastening features to align, mate, and hold together two plastic parts.
    * The Lip option adds material to the part.
    * The Groove option removes material from the part.

- This session discusses the in-depth details of creating a set of Lip & Groove for the two plastic parts

Fastening features streamline creation of common features for plastic and sheet metal parts. You can create: ⬛ **Lips and Grooves**. Align, mate, and hold together two plastic parts. Lip and groove features support multibodies and assemblies.	
⬛ **Mounting bosses**. Create a variety of mounting bosses. Set the number of fins and choose a hole or a pin.	
⬛ **Snap hooks** and **snap hook grooves**. Customize the snap hook and snap hook groove. You must first create a snap hook before you can create a snap hook groove.	
⬛ **Vents**. Create a variety of vents using a sketch you create. Set the number of ribs and spars. Flow area is calculated automatically. *(Courtesy of the SolidWorks Online Help)*	

Using the Lip & Groove options

1. Opening the existing assembly document named:
Lip&Groove Assembly from the training CD or
from the weblink and **collapse the assembly**.

2. Editing Part: Select the part **Housing** and click **Edit Component**.

- From the **Insert** menu, select **Fastening Feature / Lip /Groove**.

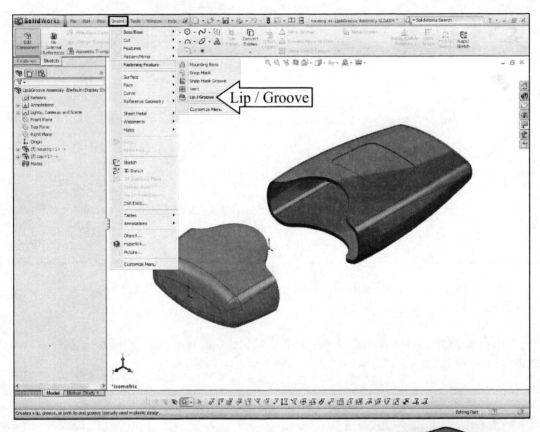

- Select the followings:

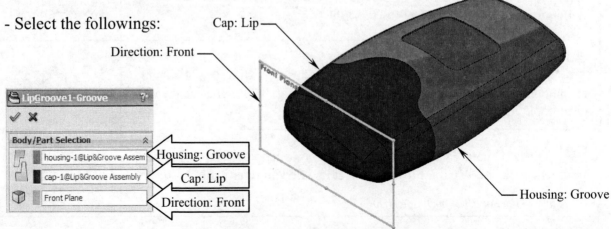

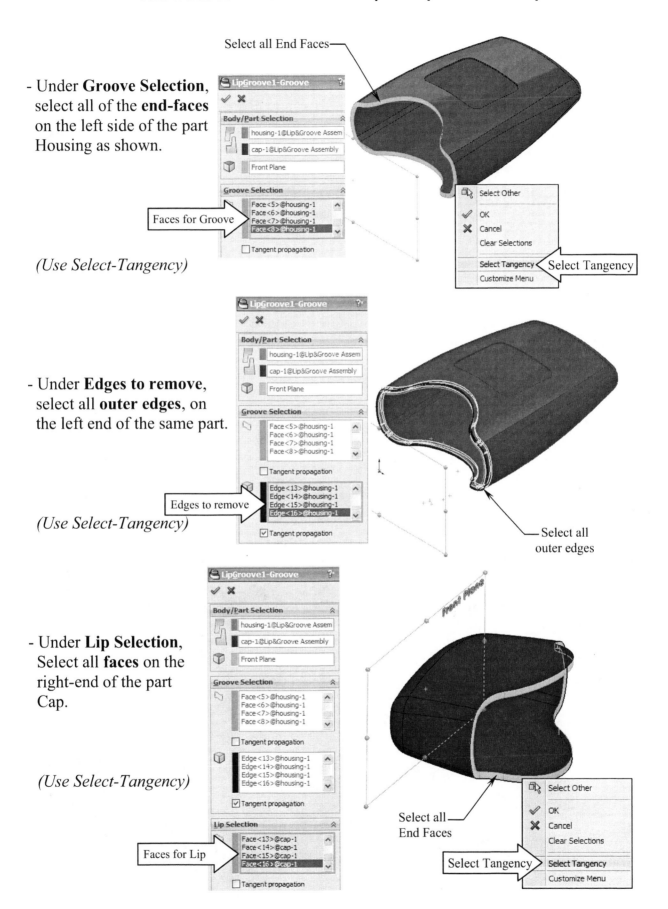

Select all End Faces

- Under **Groove Selection**, select all of the **end-faces** on the left side of the part Housing as shown.

(Use Select-Tangency)

Faces for Groove

Select Tangency

- Under **Edges to remove**, select all **outer edges**, on the left end of the same part.

(Use Select-Tangency)

Edges to remove

Select all outer edges

- Under **Lip Selection**, Select all **faces** on the right-end of the part Cap.

(Use Select-Tangency)

Faces for Lip

Select all End Faces

Select Tangency

- Under **Edges To Add Material**, select all **outer edges**, on the right end of the same part.

(Use Select-Tangency)

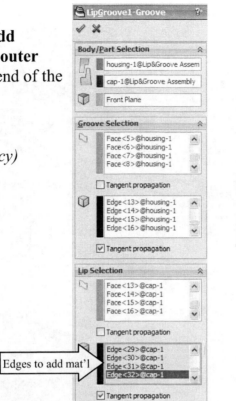

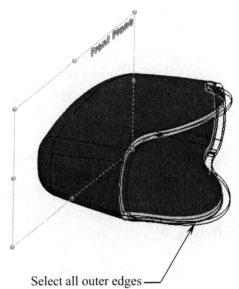

Select all outer edges —

Edges to add mat'l

- Under **Parameters**, set the

followings:

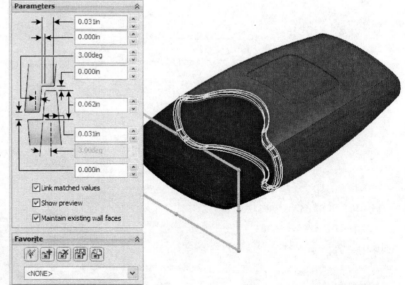

* Groove Width: **.031**

* Spacing : **0.000**

* Groove Draft: **3.00deg.**

* Upper Gap: **0.000**

* Lip Height: **.062**

* Lip Width: **.031**

* Lower Gap: **0.000**

- Click **OK** .

Mounting Bosses for Plastic Parts

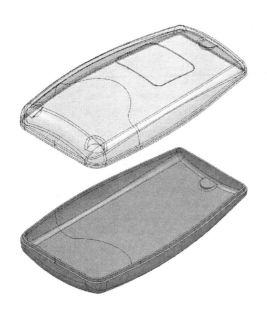
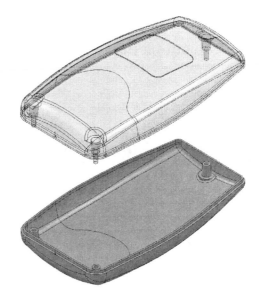

Mounting Bosses

You can create common mounting features for plastic parts like Mounting Bosses, Snap-Hooks, Snap Hook Grooves, Vents and Lips/Grooves.

The mounting bosses come with a variety of options to help streamline the creation of common Fastening features.

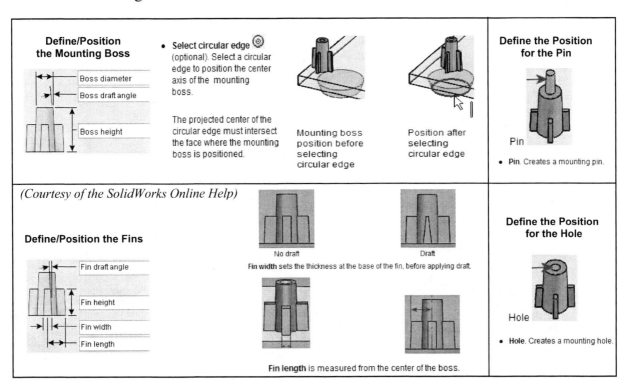

Using the Mounting Boss options

1. Opening the existing assembly document named:
Mounting Boss Assembly from the Training CD folder.
(Collapse the Assembly).

2. Editing Part: Select the part **Lower Half** and click **Edit Component**.

- From the **Insert** menu, select **Fastening Feature / Mounting Boss**.

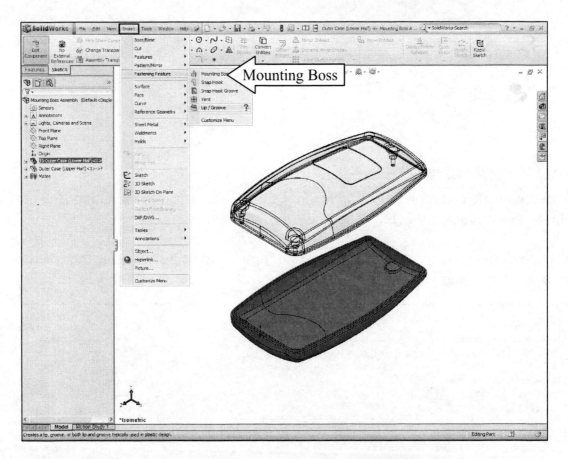

3. Setting the Parameters:

- For **Position Face**
of the Mounting Boss,
select the **face** as
indicated.

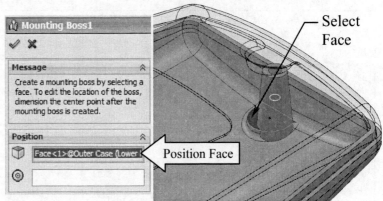

- For **Position Edge** to line up
  the Mounting Boss, select the
  circular edge as shown.

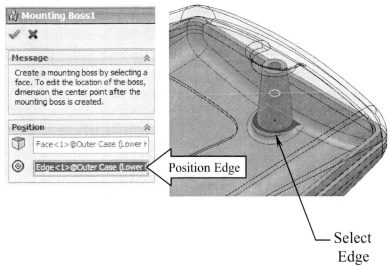

Position Edge

Select
Edge

- Under the **Boss** section, enter:

  * Diameter: **.165in**.

  * Draft: **5.00deg**.

  * Height: **.200in**.

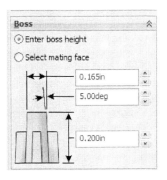

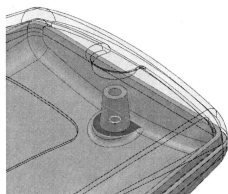

- Under the **Fins** section, enter the
  following:

  * Orientation: **Select Face**

  * Draft Angle: **1.00deg**.

  * Fin' Height: **.125in**.

  * Fin' Width: **.032in**.

  * Fin' Length: **.105in**.

  * Number of Fins: **4**

Select Face
for

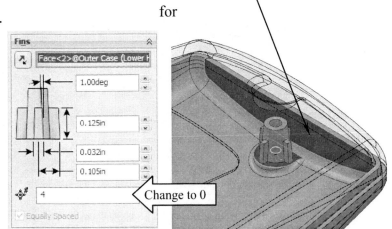

Change to 0

*Note: Set the number of Fins to **0** when finished, no fins are needed for this part.*

- Under **Mounting Hole/Pin** section, select the **Hole** option and enter the followings:

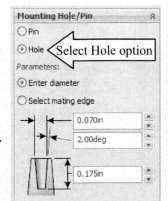

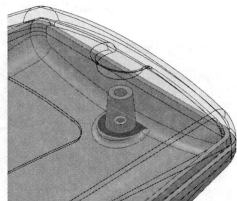

    * Hole Dia.:   **.070in**.

    * Draft: **2.00deg**.

    * Hole depth: **.175in**.

- Click **OK** when finished.

4. Adding 2 more mounting bosses:

Mounting — Boss 1

- Repeat the steps above and create two other Mounting Bosses as shown.

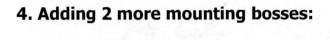

- Exit the **Edit Component** when finished.

5. Toggling between the Explode and the Collapse views:

Mounting Boss 2 & 3 —

- Right click on the name of the assembly and select **Explode**.

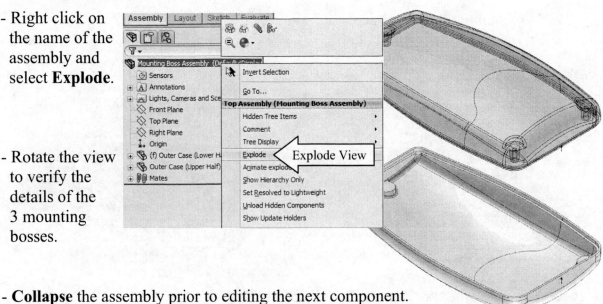

- Rotate the view to verify the details of the 3 mounting bosses.

- **Collapse** the assembly prior to editing the next component.

6. Creating the Mating Bosses:

- Select the part **Outer-Case (Upper Half)**

  and click Edit Component

- Select **Insert/Fastening Feature/ Mounting Boss**.

- For **Position Face**, select the Face as indicated.

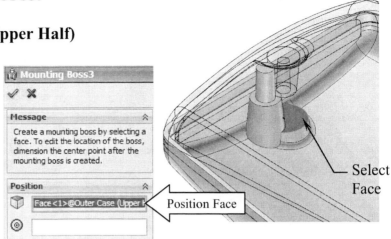

- For **Position Edge**, select the **Edge** as noted, to align the center of the mounting boss to the center of the circular edge.

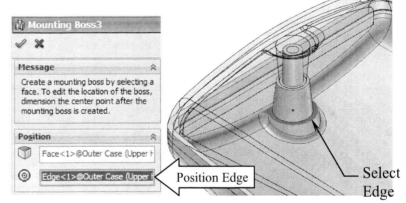

- Under the **Boss** section, select the **Mating Face** option and select the **Face** as shown (use Select Other).

- Enter the followings:

* Diameter: **.165in**.

* Draft: **6.00deg**.

* Height: **2.00in**.

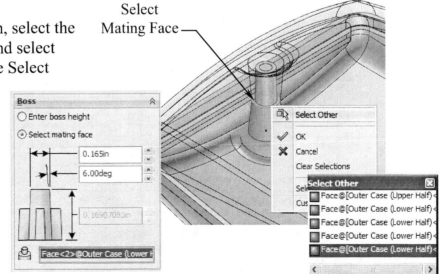

- Under the **Mounting Hole/Pin** section, select the **Pin** option and enter the followings:

  * Hole Dia.: **.060in**.

  * Draft: **2.00deg**.

  * Hole depth: **.165in**.

- Click **OK** when finished.

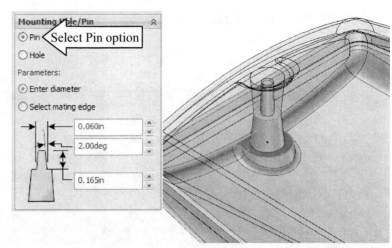

- Click **OK** to accept the External References message between the parts and the assembly.

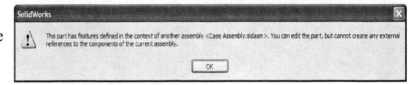

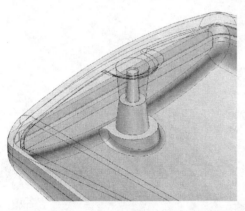

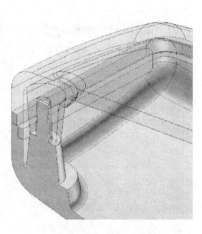

7. Creating a Section View:

- Use the Right plane and create a section view as shown above.

8. Repeating:

- Create two additional Mounting-Bosses using the same settings as the first one.

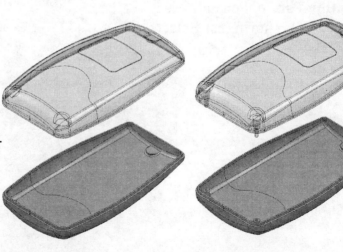

9. Save your work.

CHAPTER 17

External References

External References & Repair Errors

An *external reference* is created when one document is dependent on another document for its solution. If the referenced document changes, the dependent document changes also.

In an assembly, you can create an *in-context* feature on one component that references the geometry of another component. This in-context feature has an external reference to the other component. If you change the geometry on the referenced component, the associated in-context feature changes accordingly.

The External Symbols:

- > .... External Reference   ? .... Out Of Context

(+) .... Over Defined   * .... Reference Locked

X .... Reference Broken

a. External Reference ->:
The part itself or some of its entities depend on the geometry of other parts for its solutions.

b. Out Of Context ?:
The part or its features are not solved, not up-to-date nor disconnected from its assembly.

c. Over Defined (+):
The Dimensions or Relations of the sketch are conflicting; redundant dimensions or wrong relations were used.

d. Reference Locked *:
When the external references of a part are locked, the existing references no longer update and the part will not accept any new references from that point.

e. Reference Broken X:
The references between the part and the others are broken (relations or dimensions created between parts). Changes done to the part will not affect the others.

External References & Repair Errors

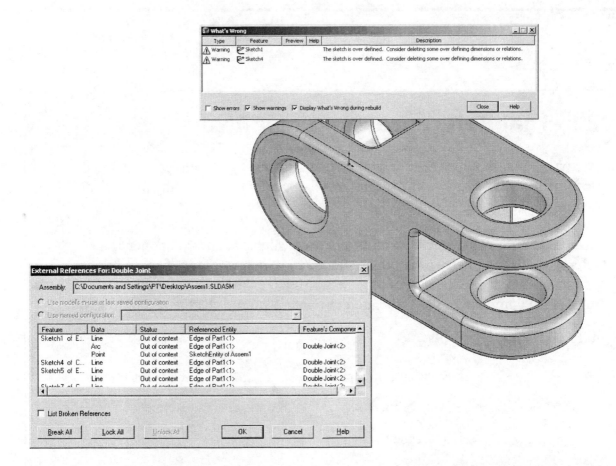

Dimensioning Standards: **ANSI**
Units: **INCHES** – 3 Decimals

External Reference Symbols:

->	External Reference	?	Out of Context
(+)	Over Defined	*	External Reference Locked
X	External Reference Broken		Display/Delete Relations

Understanding & Removing External References

1. Opening an existing part: Double Joint

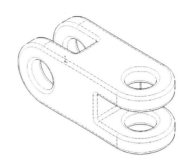

- <u>Go to:</u>

    Training CD or Weblink
    Class Files folder
    Double Joint

- Click **Open**.

- The "What's Wrong" dialog pops
  up displaying the current errors.

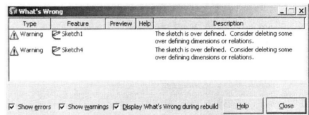

2. Viewing the External References:

- Right click on the part's name and select **List External Refs**.

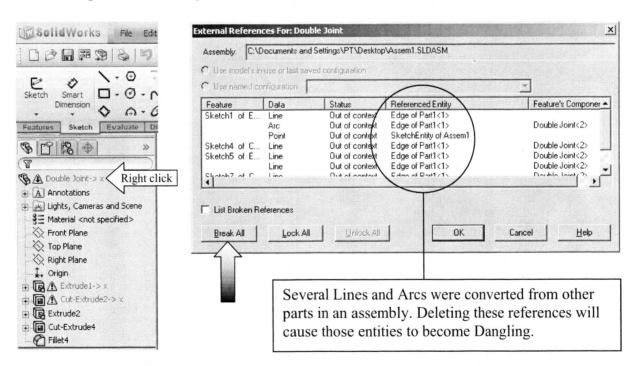

Several Lines and Arcs were converted from other
parts in an assembly. Deleting these references will
cause those entities to become Dangling.

3. Breaking References:

- Click Break all to remove
  the external references.

- Click OK to confirm [OK].

4. Understanding the External Symbols:

-> .... External Reference
? .... Out Of Context
(+) .... Over Defined
∗ .... Reference Locked
X .... Reference Broken

> ☀ **Error Colors**
>
> - **Olive Green:** Dangling
>
> - **Red:** Over Defined
>
> - **Yellow:** Conflicting

(From the Feature-Manager tree, expand the first two features, to see their sketches).

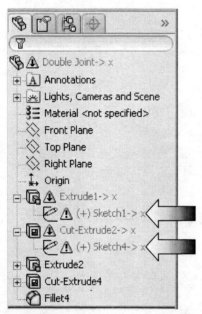

a. External Reference ->:
The part itself or some of its entities are depending on the geometry of other parts for its solutions.

b. Out Of Context ?:
The part or its features are not solved, not up-to-date nor disconnected from its assembly.

c. Over Defined (+):
The Dimensions or Relations of the sketch are conflicting; redundant dimensions or wrong relations were used.

d. Reference Locked ∗:
When the external references on a part are locked, the existing references no longer update - and - the part will not accept any new references from that point.

e. Reference Broken X:
The references between the part and the others are broken. Changes done to the part will not affect the others.

5. Viewing the existing Relations:

- Right-click on the 1st sketch and select **Edit-Sketch** .

- Click or select **Tools / Relations / Display/Delete.**

- The Ø.325 is shown in Olive Green color. This indicates that either a relation is wrong or the sketch is over dimensioned.

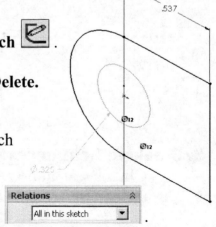

- Change the Relations Filter to **All In This Sketch** 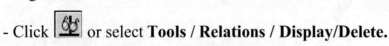 .

6. Repairing the 1st sketch:

- Delete the CORADIAL relation (the Circle is Coradial with an entity that is no longer exists).

- Delete the all External Relations (->X).

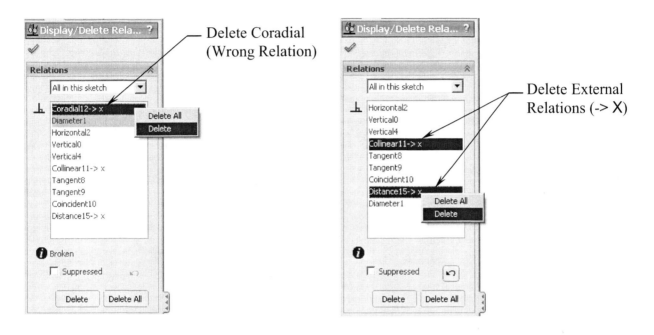

Delete Coradial (Wrong Relation)

Delete External Relations (-> X)

- Add new Dimensions to fully define the sketch.

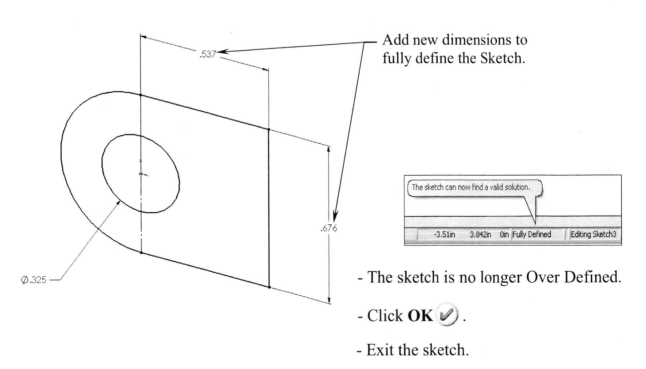

Add new dimensions to fully define the Sketch.

The sketch can now find a valid solution.

- The sketch is no longer Over Defined.

- Click **OK** ✓ .

- Exit the sketch.

7. Repairing the 2nd sketch:

- Right-Click on the 2nd sketch and select **Edit-Sketch** .

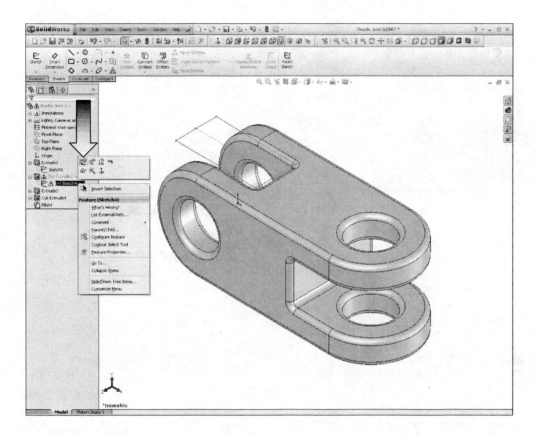

- Delete the External Dimensions and Relations that were created in context of other parts.

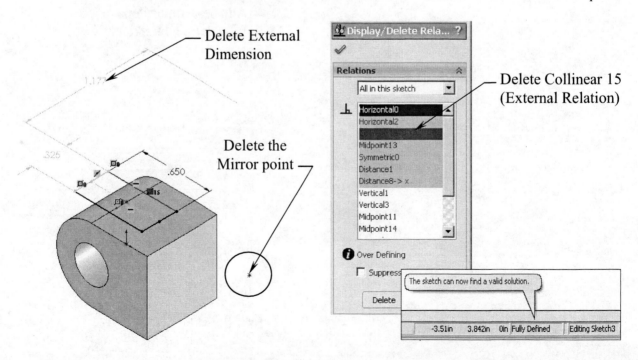

Delete External
Dimension

Delete Collinear 15
(External Relation)

Delete the
Mirror point

8. Rebuilding the model:

- Press Rebuild 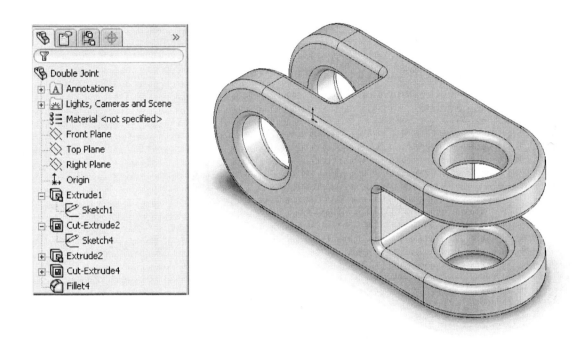 to re-generate the model.

- Verify that the part has no rebuild errors and there should not be any external reference symbols in the Feature Manager tree.

9. Saving your work:

- Select **File / Save As / Breaking External References / Save**.

Questions for Review

External References

1. The symbol -> next to a file name means:
      a. Dangling dimension
      b. External reference
      c. Not solved

2. The symbol ? next to a file name means:
      a. The part cannot be found
      b. Wrong mates
      c. Wrong relations
      d. Out of context

3. The symbol **X** next to a file or a feature name means:
      a. The part or feature is wrong
      b. The part or feature is deleted
      c. The external references are broken

4. The symbol * next to a file name means:
      a. External references are locked
      b. Select all references
      c. Deselect all references

5. The symbol *X next to a feature name means:
      a. The feature is fully defined
      b. The feature is over defined
      c. The feature is under defined
      d. None of the above.

6. The Olive-Green color in a sketch means:
      a. The sketch entity is selected
      b. The sketch entity is being copied.
      c. The sketch has dangling entities, relations or dimensions.

7. The dangling dimensions can be "re-attached" simply by dragging its handle point to a sketch line or a model edge.
      a. True
      b. False

7. TRUE

5. D

3. C

1. B

6. C

4. A

2. D

Repair Errors & External References

1. Opening an existing part: Molded Part

- <u>Go to:</u>

  Training CD or Weblink
  Class Files Folder
  Molded Part

- Click **Open**.

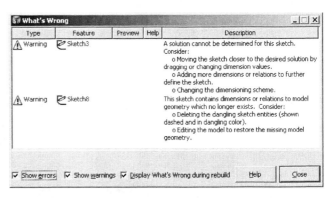

- The "What's Wrong" dialog pop up displaying the current errors.

- Click **Close**. We will be working with 1 error at a time.

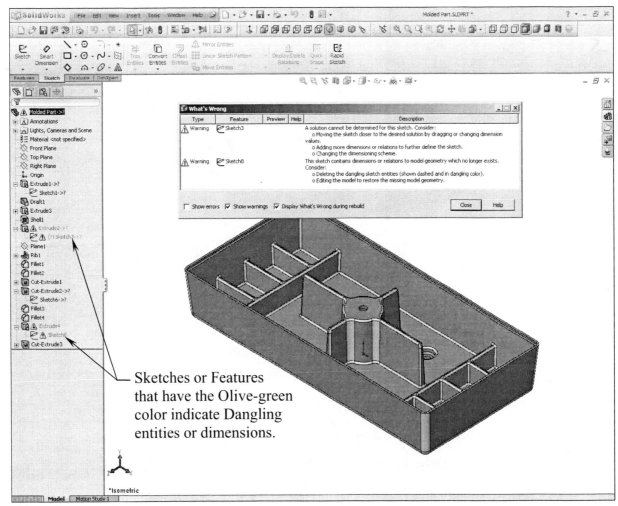

Sketches or Features that have the Olive-green color indicate Dangling entities or dimensions.

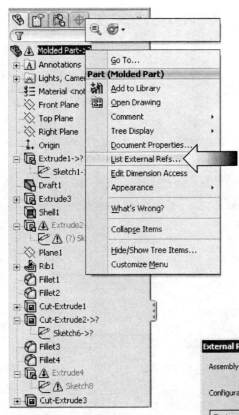

2. Breaking all External References:

- Right click on the part's name and select:

List External Refs.

- All of the **Out of Context** entities are displayed in the dialog box, along with the names of the component parts in which they are related.

- Click **Break All** (Arrow).

Note: The external references cannot be restored after they have been deleted.

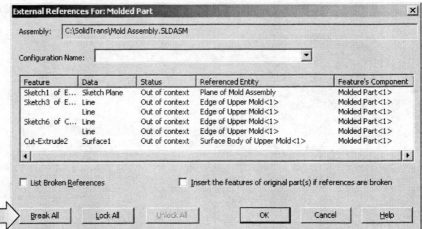

- Click OK to confirm the delete of all External-References.

💡 **TIPS:** *4 basic steps* should be done, in most cases, to repair or replace External References:

1. Break all External references (Right click on the part's name and select List External Refs.)

2. Replace the sketch Plane or Face (if missing).

3. Delete or replace any Relation with an External Reference symbol next to it (Display/Delete Relations).

4. Repair or replace the extrude type.

3. Replacing the Sketch Plane:

- Expand the **Extrude1** feature to see the **Sketch1** below it.

- Right click on **Sketch1** and select **Edit Sketch Plane** .

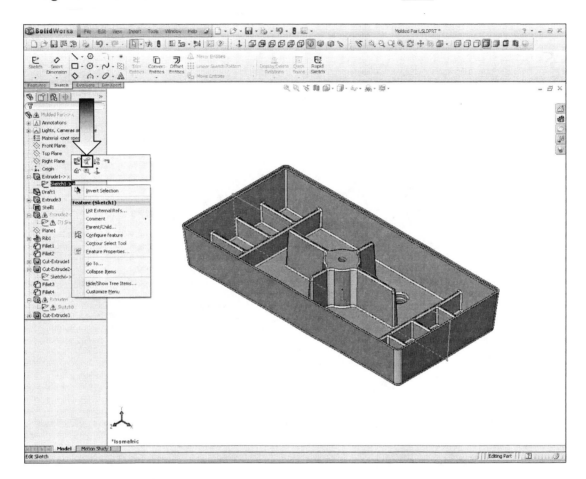

- The Sketch Plane is missing, its dialog box is empty.

- Select the Front plane from the Feature tree to replace with the missing one.

- After replacing the plane, click **OK** .

- The system displays the warning on other errors along with the solutions for repairing.

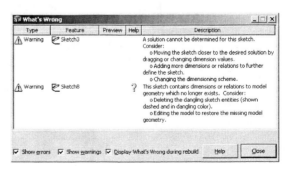

- Click **Close** .

4. Repairing the Sketch relations and Dimensions:

- Right click on **Sketch3** and select **Edit Sketch** 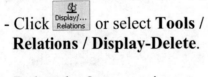 (arrow).

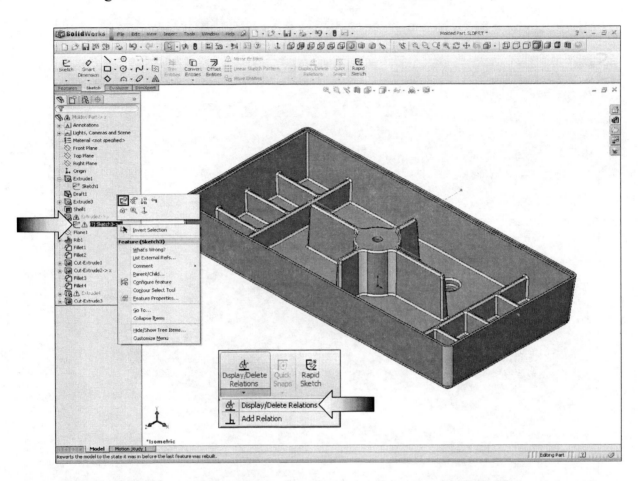

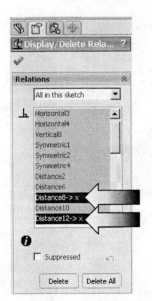

- Click 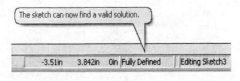 or select **Tools / Relations / Display-Delete**.

- Delete the 2 geometric relations that have the external symbols next their names (arrows).

- The sketch becomes fully-defined.

- Click **OK** (✓).

- **EXIT THE SKETCH** 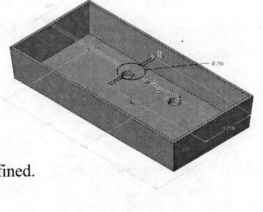.

5. Repairing the next sketch errors:

- Right click on **Sketch6** (under Cut-Extrude2) and

  select **Edit Sketch** 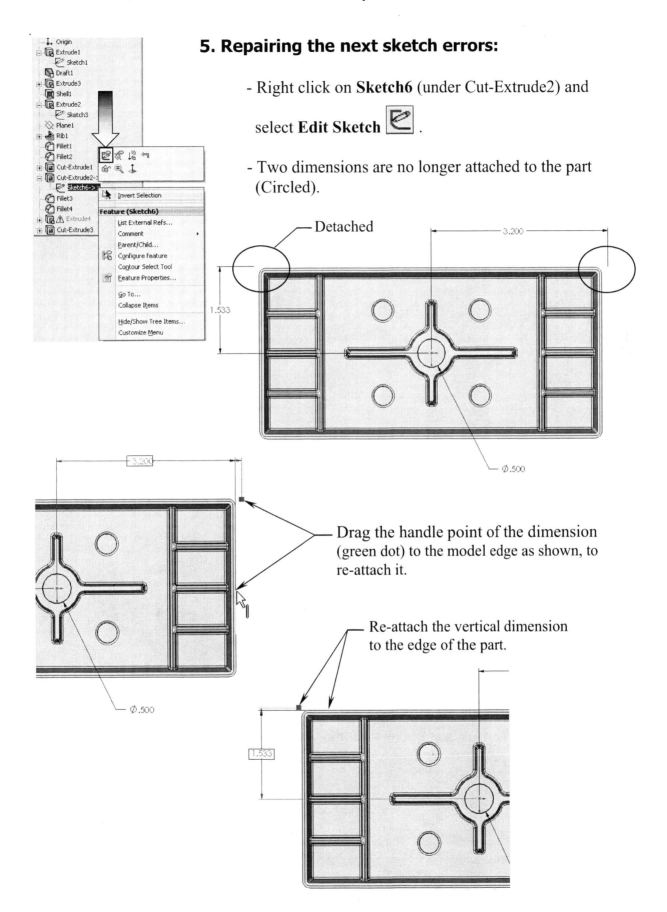 .

- Two dimensions are no longer attached to the part (Circled).

Detached

3.200

1.533

Ø.500

3.200

Drag the handle point of the dimension (green dot) to the model edge as shown, to re-attach it.

Ø.500

Re-attach the vertical dimension to the edge of the part.

1.533

- The sketch becomes fully-defined; the two dimensions are attached to locate the center of the circle.

- **EXIT THE SKETCH** .

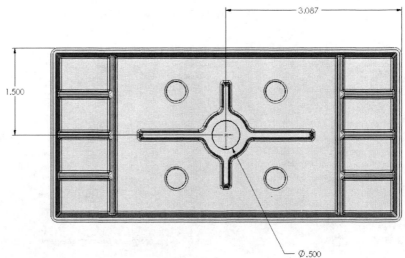

6. Repairing the extrude type:

- This time the error symbol is on the extrusion; a reference is missing.

- Right click on **Cut-Extrude2** and select **Edit Feature**.

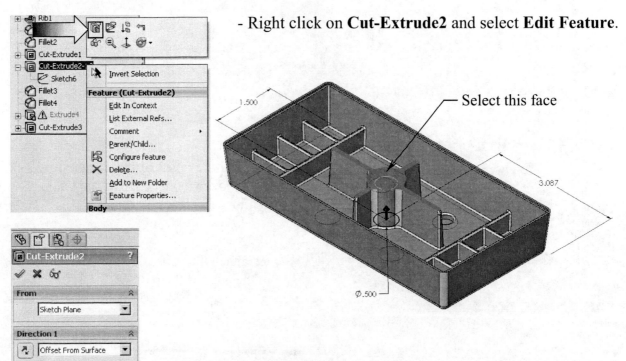

Select this face

- When the surface that was used as the end condition for the extrude is no longer recognized, a new surface has to be selected to replace it.

- Select the face as indicated.

- Leave extrude depth as **.100**in.

- Click **OK** .

7. Repairing the errors in the last sketch:

- Right click on the **Sketch8** and select **Edit Sketch**.

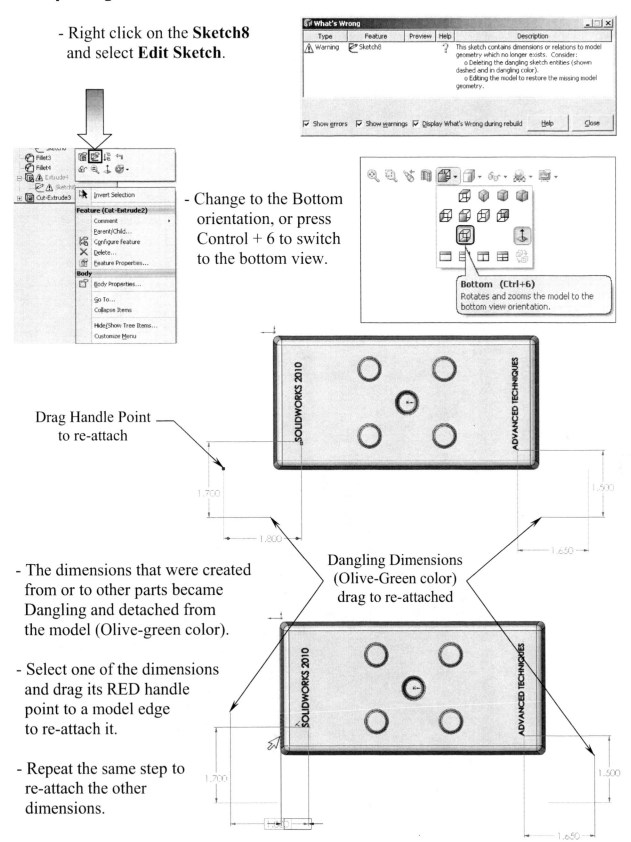

- Change to the Bottom orientation, or press Control + 6 to switch to the bottom view.

Drag Handle Point to re-attach

- The dimensions that were created from or to other parts became Dangling and detached from the model (Olive-green color).

- Select one of the dimensions and drag its RED handle point to a model edge to re-attach it.

- Repeat the same step to re-attach the other dimensions.

Dangling Dimensions (Olive-Green color) drag to re-attached

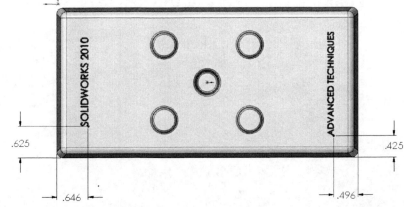

- The sketch becomes fully defined after all dimensions are re-attached.

- The text color was set to Blue (not under defined).

- **EXIT THE SKETCH** 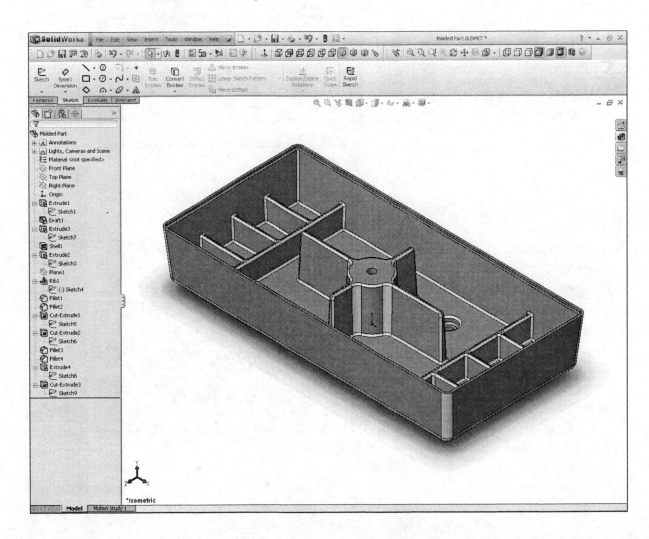 .

- The reference symbols and the error colors on the FeatureManager tree should now be all removed.

8. Saving your work:

- Select **File / Save As / Repair Errors / Save**.

L4 – Final Exam:

1. Open the existing part document:

Go to:

Training CD or from the Weblink
Tooling Design folder
L4 Final Exam.sldprt

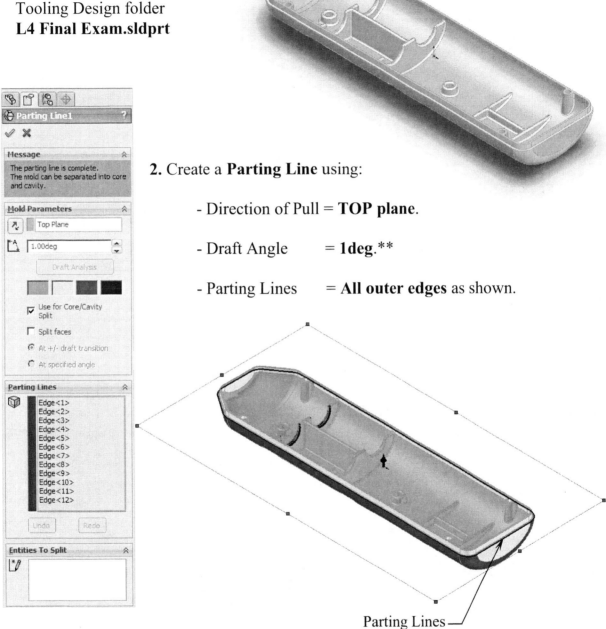

2. Create a **Parting Line** using:

- Direction of Pull = **TOP plane**.

- Draft Angle   = **1deg.****

- Parting Lines   = **All outer edges** as shown.

Parting Lines ⎯

** _Important_ - Roll back below the Loft feature and:

a/ Add 1º drafts to all Yellow faces, including the 4 holes. This change will create some errors in the part.

b/ Repair the errors. _Re-order_ or _re-create_ the fillets after adding the drafts if needed.

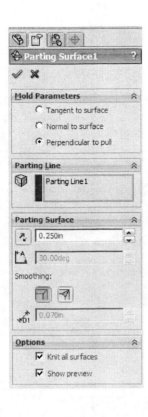

3. Create a **Parting Surface** using:

- **Perpendicular to Pull**.

- **Parting Line1**.

- Parting Surface Length = **.250in**.

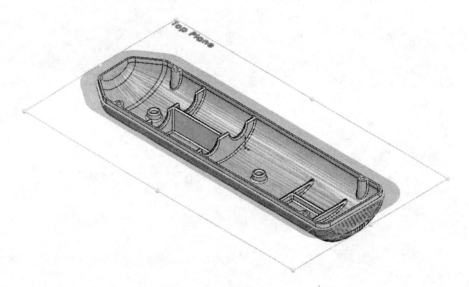

4. Create a new **Offset Distance plane** using:

- The **TOP** reference plane and **.375in**. distance.

- The new plane is placed **above** the Top plane.
(This new plane will also be use to create the Interlock Surfaces).

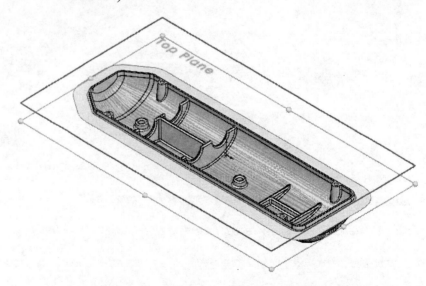

5. Sketch a Rectangle on the new plane (Plane1) and add **Dimensions*** as shown.

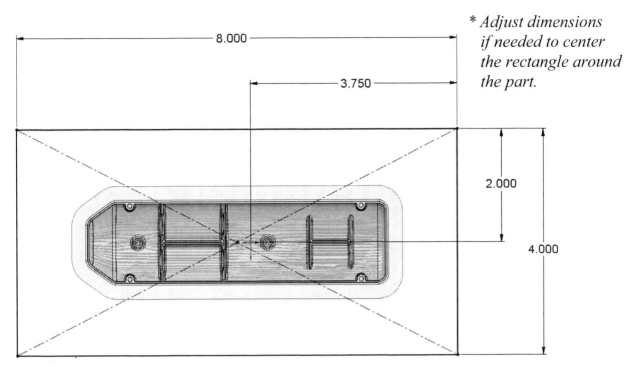

* *Adjust dimensions if needed to center the rectangle around the part.*

8.000
3.750
2.000
4.000

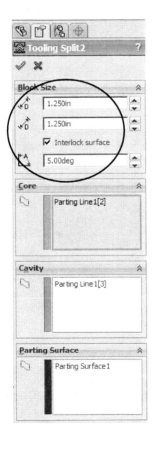

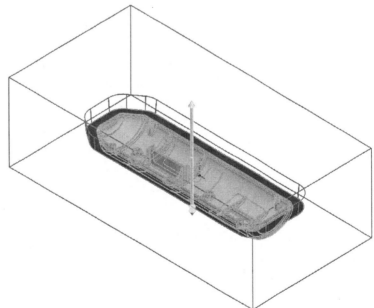

6. Exit the Sketch and create a **Tooling split** using:
- **1.250in.** (upper block)
- **1.250in.** (lower block)
- Use **Interlock Surface** with **5° Draft**.

7. Re-order or re-create the fillets if necessary.

** <u>OPTIONAL</u>: Make the upper and lower solid bodies transparent for clarity.

8. Save your work as L4-Final.

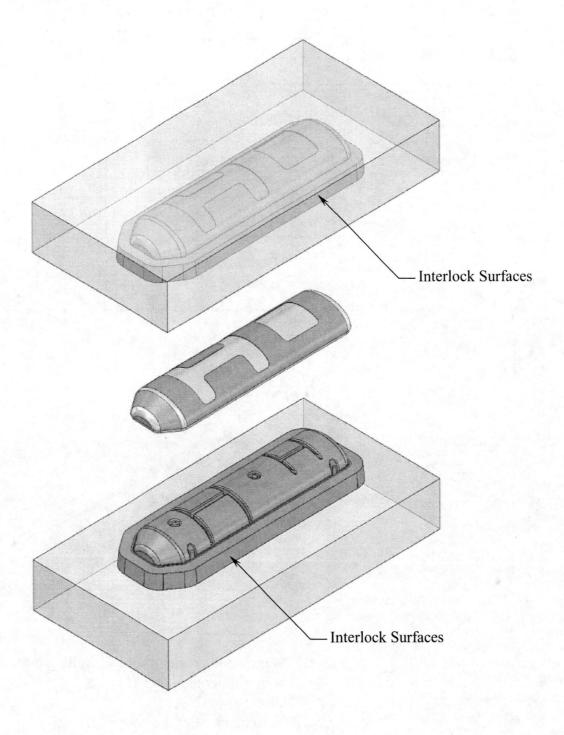

Interlock Surfaces

Interlock Surfaces

SolidWorks 2010

Certified SolidWorks Professional (CSWP)

Certification Practice for the Core Examination

Courtesy of Paul Tran, Sr. Certified SolidWorks Instructor

Certified-SolidWorks-Professional program (CSWP)
Certification Practice for the Core-Exam

Challenge I: Part Modeling & Modifications

Complete this challenge within 90 minutes

- Create this part in SolidWorks.   - Unit: **Inches, 3 decimals**   - Origin: **Arbitrary**

- Drafting Standards: **ANSI**   - Material: **Cast Alloy Steel**   - Density: **0.264 lb/in^3**

1. Creating the 1st revolve body:

- Sketch the profile as shown on the Front plane.

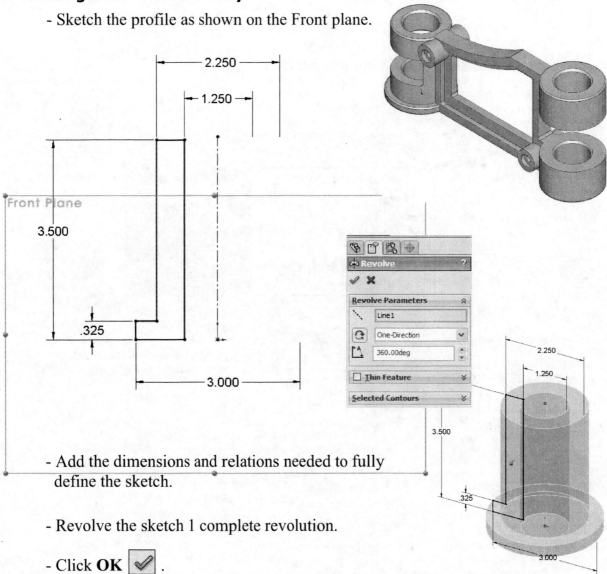

- Add the dimensions and relations needed to fully define the sketch.

- Revolve the sketch 1 complete revolution.

- Click **OK** .

2. Creating the 2nd revolve body:

- Open a new sketch on the Front plane once again.

- Sketch 2 circles on the far right as shown.

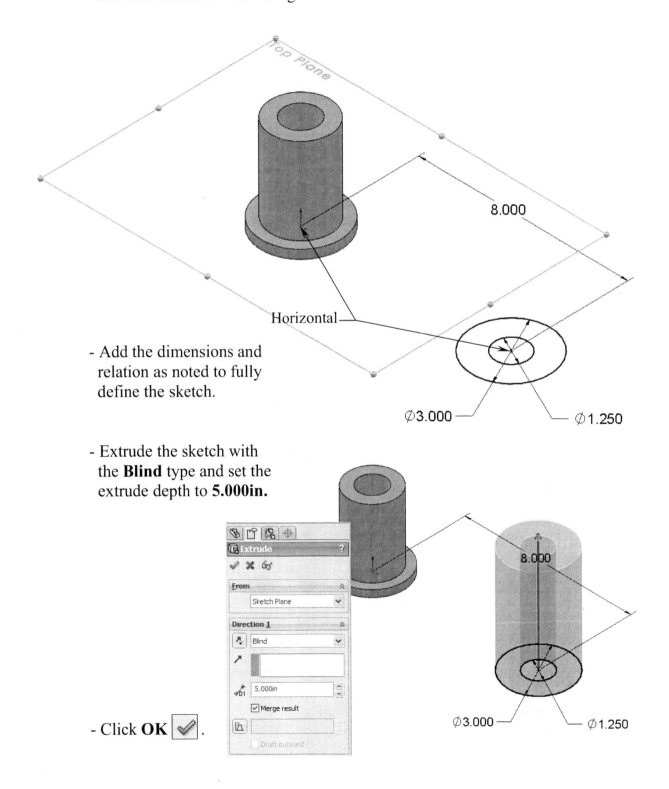

- Add the dimensions and relation as noted to fully define the sketch.

- Extrude the sketch with the **Blind** type and set the extrude depth to **5.000in.**

- Click **OK** .

3. Linking the dimension values:

- To save time on features editing later on, we will link some of the dimensions together.

- From the FeatureManager tree, right click on Annotations and enable both options:

    * **Display Annotations**

    * **Show Feature Dimensions**

- At this moment, we will link the two ID dimensions (Ø1.250), by giving them the exact same name.

- Hold the Control key and select both ID dimensions (circled), right click on one of them and select: **Link Values** (arrow).

- Enter **ID Holes** for Name and click OK.

- The linked dimensions now have a red link symbol next to their values.

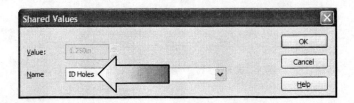

4. Creating the transition wall:

- Select the Front plane and open a new sketch.

- Sketch the profile as shown.

- Add the dimensions and the relations as indicated.

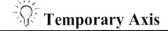
Temporary Axis

Enable the Temporary Axis from the View pull down menu.

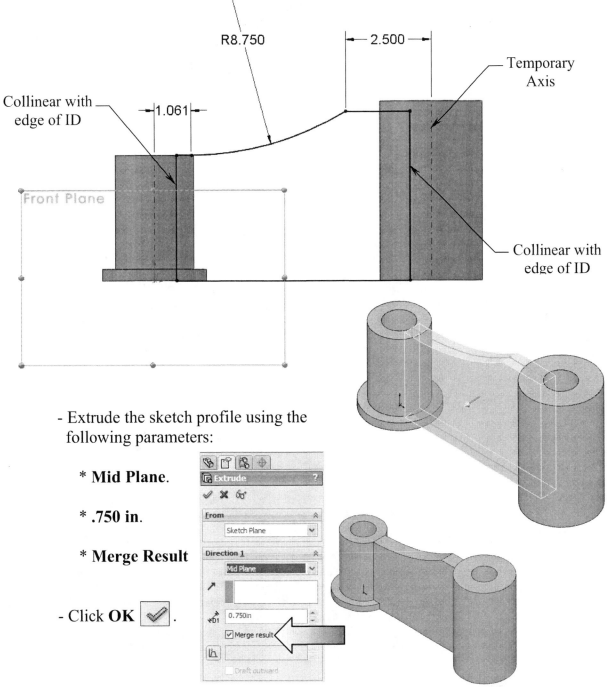

R8.750

2.500

Temporary Axis

Collinear with edge of ID

1.061

Front Plane

Collinear with edge of ID

- Extrude the sketch profile using the following parameters:

    * **Mid Plane**.

    * **.750 in**.

    * **Merge Result**

- Click **OK**.

5. Creating a recess feature:

- Select the face as indicated and open a new sketch.

- Select the arc and the 2 lines and click **Offset Entities**.

- Enter **.375"** for offset distance and click OK.

- Add 2 more line as shown and trim them to their nearest intersections.

- Add a sketch fillet of R.125 to 5 places.

- Enable the Temporary Axis and add the dimensions as shown to fully define this sketch.

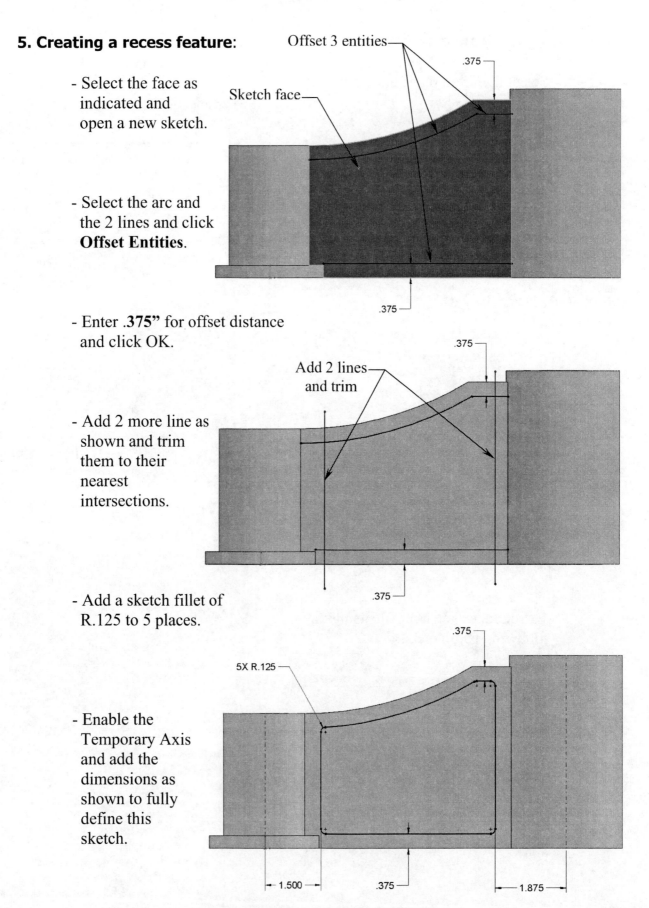

- Click **Extruded Cut** and use the following parameters:

    * **Blind**

    * **.215 in**.

- Click **OK** ✓.

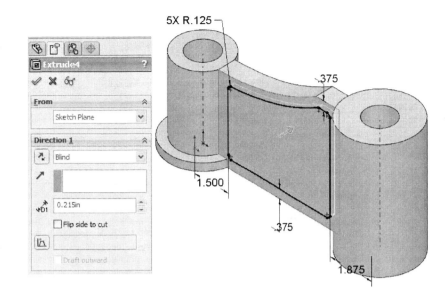

6. Mirroring the recess feature:

- Select the Front plane for use as the Mirror plane, and click the **Mirror** Command from the Features toolbar.

- Click the recess feature either from the graphics area or from the FeatureManager tree.

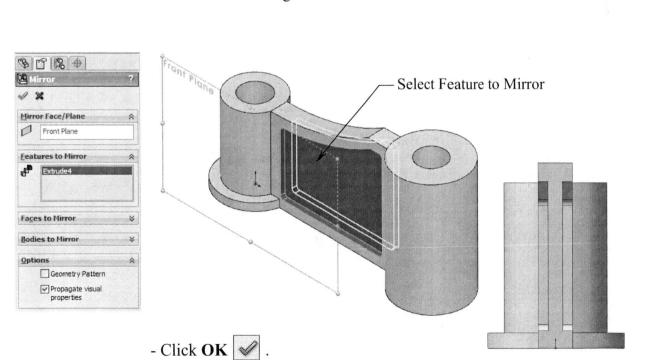

Select Feature to Mirror

- Click **OK** ✓.

(Section View)

7. Adding Fillets:

- Click the **Fillet** command and enter **.062** for radius value.

- Select the **6 edges** as shown.

- Click **OK** ✓.

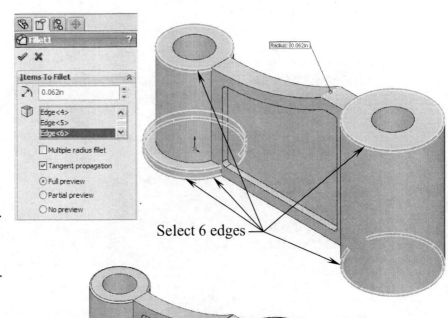

Select 6 edges

8. Changing dimension values:

- The grading scores is based upon the mass of the part after certain changes. At this point, we will change several dimensions and see what the final mass may be.

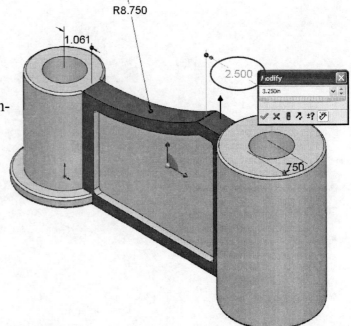

- Double click on the Transition-Wall to see its dimensions.

- Locate the **2.500"** dimension and change it to **3.250"**.

- Change the dimension
  8.000" to **8.750"**

- Click Rebuild or **Control + Q**.

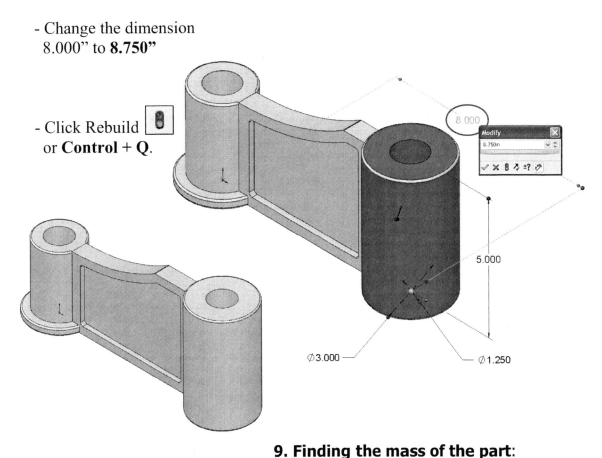

5.000

⌀3.000   ⌀1.250

9. Finding the mass of the part:

- Select **Tools / Mass Properties**.

- Enter the Mass here: _____ pounds.

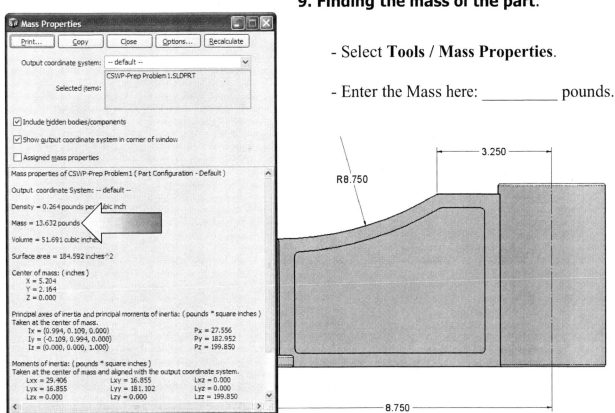

Mass Properties

Print...   Copy   Close   Options...   Recalculate

Output coordinate system: -- default --

Selected items: CSWP-Prep Problem 1.SLDPRT

☑ Include hidden bodies/components

☑ Show output coordinate system in corner of window

☐ Assigned mass properties

Mass properties of CSWP-Prep Problem1 (Part Configuration - Default)

Output coordinate System: -- default --

Density = 0.264 pounds per cubic inch

Mass = 13.632 pounds

Volume = 51.691 cubic inches

Surface area = 184.592 inches^2

Center of mass: (inches)
   X = 5.204
   Y = 2.164
   Z = 0.000

Principal axes of inertia and principal moments of inertia: (pounds * square inches)
Taken at the center of mass.
   Ix = (0.994, 0.109, 0.000)   Px = 27.556
   Iy = (-0.109, 0.994, 0.000)   Py = 182.952
   Iz = (0.000, 0.000, 1.000)   Pz = 199.850

Moments of inertia: (pounds * square inches)
Taken at the center of mass and aligned with the output coordinate system.
   Lxx = 29.406   Lxy = 16.855   Lxz = 0.000
   Lyx = 16.855   Lyy = 181.102   Lyz = 0.000
   Lzx = 0.000   Lzy = 0.000   Lzz = 199.850

R8.750

3.250

8.750

10. Adding the cut features:

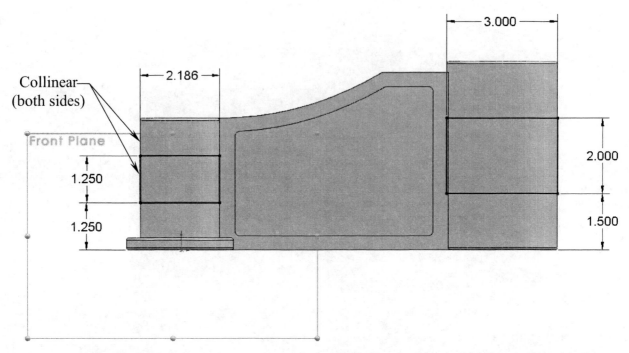

Collinear (both sides)

Front Plane

3.000

2.186

1.250

1.250

2.000

1.500

- Sketch the 2 rectangles as shown, and add dimensions/relations to fully define the sketch.

- Click **Extruded Cut**.

- Under Direction1, select: **Through All**.

- For Direction2 also select: **Through All**.

- Click **OK**.

- Rotate the part to verify the cut feature.

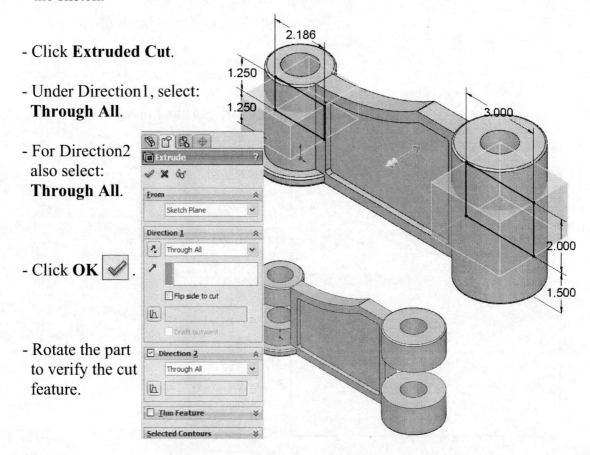

11. Adding fillets and chamfers:

- Click the Fillet command.

- Enter **.093"** for radius value.

- Select the **4 Edges** as noted.

- Click **OK**.

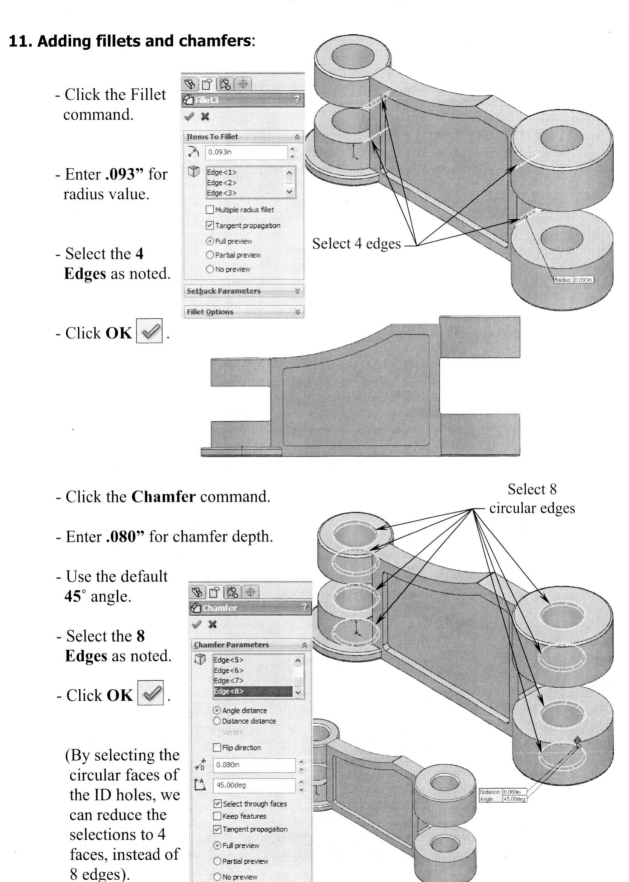

Select 4 edges

- Click the **Chamfer** command.

- Enter **.080"** for chamfer depth.

- Use the default **45°** angle.

- Select the **8 Edges** as noted.

- Click **OK**.

(By selecting the circular faces of the ID holes, we can reduce the selections to 4 faces, instead of 8 edges).

Select 8 circular edges

12. Adding a recess feature:

- Select the face as indicated and open a new sketch.

- Create an Offset of **.250"** from the **2 edges** as noted.

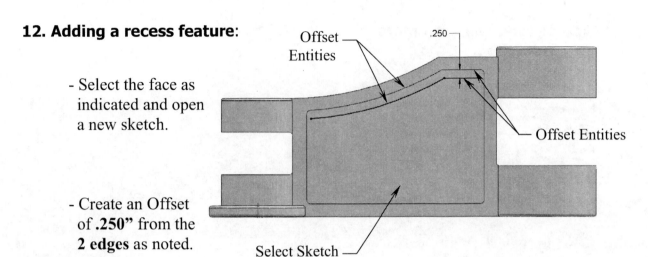

Offset Entities

Offset Entities

.250

Select Sketch Face

- Add **3 lines** approximately as shown.

- Add the dimensions as indicated in the image below.

- Trim the lines to their closest intersections.

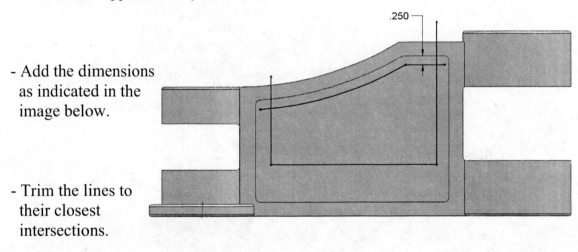

.250

- Add the **sketch fillets** of **R.093"** to 5 places.

- Make sure the sketch is fully defined.

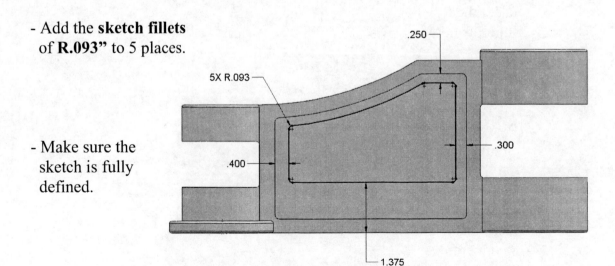

.250

5X R.093

.300

.400

1.375

- Click **Extruded Cut**.

- Under Direction1, select:
  Through All.

- For Direction2
  also select:
  Through All.

- Click **OK** .

- Rotate the part
  to verify the cut
  feature.

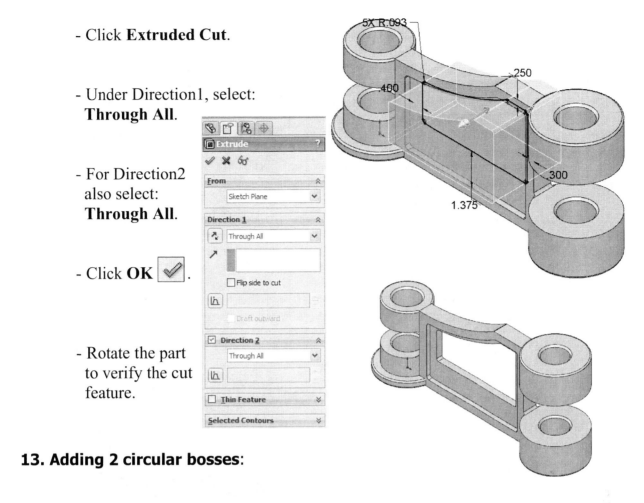

13. Adding 2 circular bosses:

- Select the Front plane from the FeatureManager tree and open a new sketch.

- Sketch 2 circles and add the dimensions as shown to fully define them.

- Link the diameter dimensions using the Link Values option. Rename them to:
  Cir_Bosses.

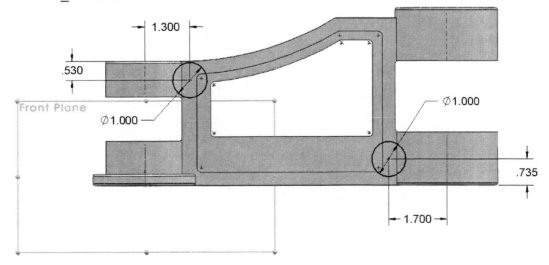

- Click **Extruded Boss/Base**.

- Under Direction1, select: **Mid Plane**.

- For extrude depth enter: **2.000in**.

- Click **OK** .

- Change to the Top view (Control + 5) to verify the boss feature.

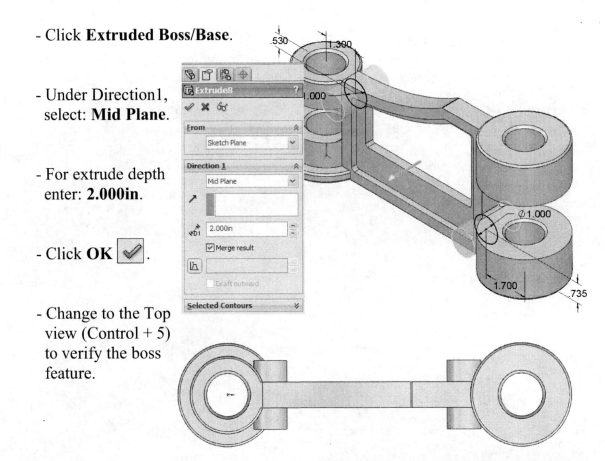

14. Finding the mass of the part:

- Click **Tools / Mass Properties**.

- Locate the mass (arrow) and enter it

here _____ lbs.

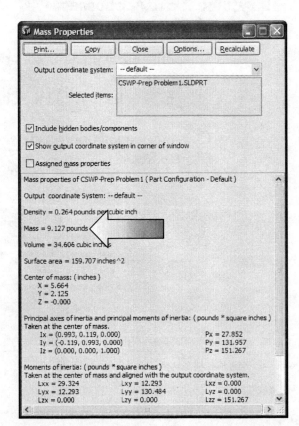

Note: _The mass included in this dialog is_
for example only, they're not the actual
weight of the part.

15. Modifying the feature dimensions:

- Locate the diameter
  dimensions for the
  2 ID holes (circled)
  and change them
  from: Ø1.250
  to **1.500"**.

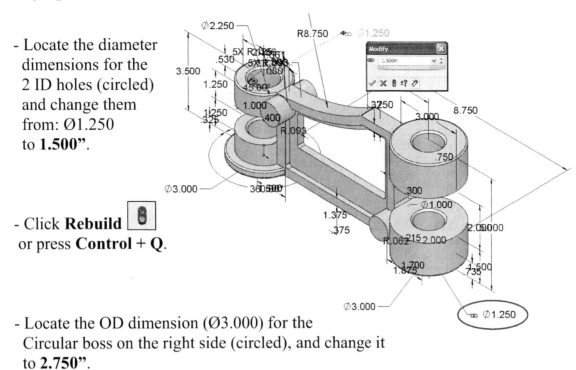

- Click **Rebuild**
  or press **Control + Q**.

- Locate the OD dimension (Ø3.000) for the
  Circular boss on the right side (circled), and change it
  to **2.750"**.

- Click **Rebuild**
  or press **Control + Q.**

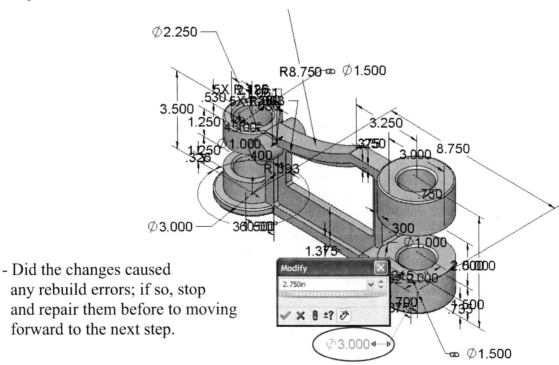

- Did the changes caused
  any rebuild errors; if so, stop
  and repair them before to moving
  forward to the next step.

- Locate the OD dimension for the circular boss on the left (circled) and change it from Ø2.250 to **2.500"**.

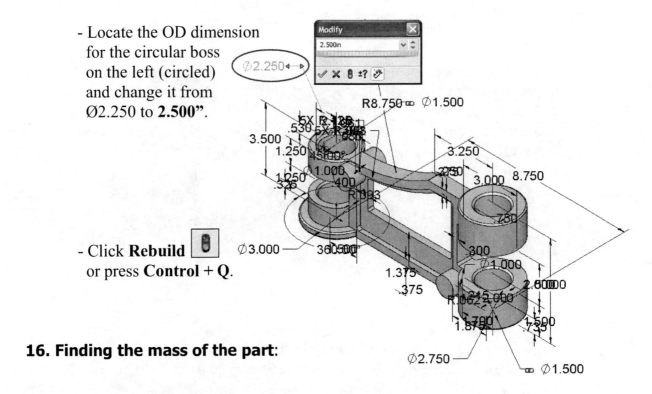

- Click **Rebuild** or press **Control + Q**.

16. Finding the mass of the part:

- Click **Tools / Mass Properties**.

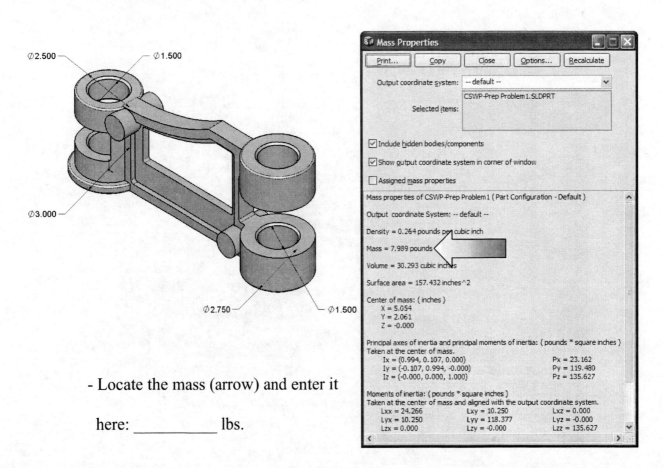

- Locate the mass (arrow) and enter it

here: _____ lbs.

17. Creating the Counter-Bores:

- Click the **Hole-Wizard** command from the Features toolbar.

- Select the following:

 * Hole Type:
  Counterbore

 * Standard:
  Ansi Inch

 * Type:
  Binding Head Screw

 * Size:
  1/4

 * Fit:
  Normal

 * End Condition:
  Through All

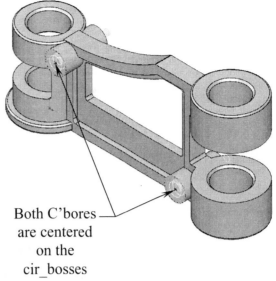

Both C'bores are centered on the cir_bosses

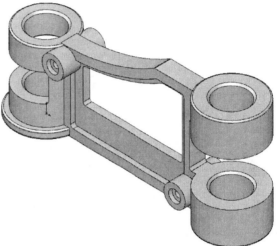

- Change to the **Positions** tab (circled) and place 2 Counter-bores on the same centers as the circular boss features, click OK when finished.

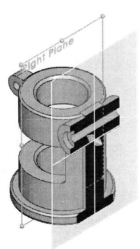

- Create a **Section View** similar to the one shown below to verify the 2 counter bores.

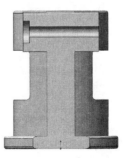

18. Adding a side tab:

- Open a new sketch on the Front plane.

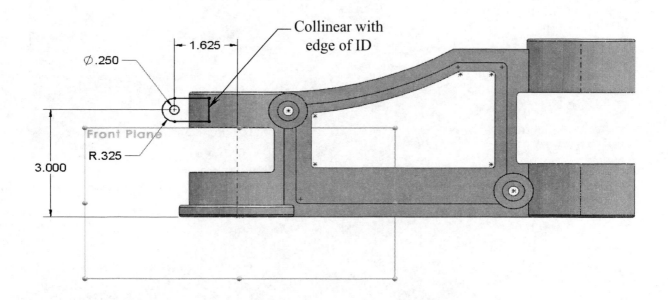

- Sketch the profile of the tab as show.

- Add the dimensions and relations needed to fully define the sketch.

- Click **Extruded Boss/Base**.

- Under Direction1, select: **Mid Plane**.

- For extrude depth enter: **.425 in**.

- Click **OK** ✓ .

- Rotate the part and Verify that the tab is centered on the Front plane.

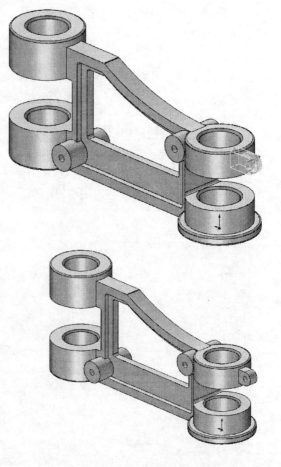

19. Modifying the recess feature:

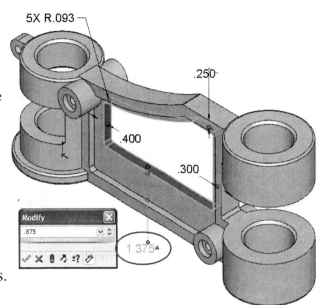

5X R.093

.250

.400

.300

- Locate the spacing dimension of the recess (1.375") and change it to **.875**".

- Click **Rebuild** .

Modify
.875

- Find the final mass of the part and enter it here: _____ lbs.

1.375

20. Saving your work:

- Save your work as **Problem1** and close the document when done.

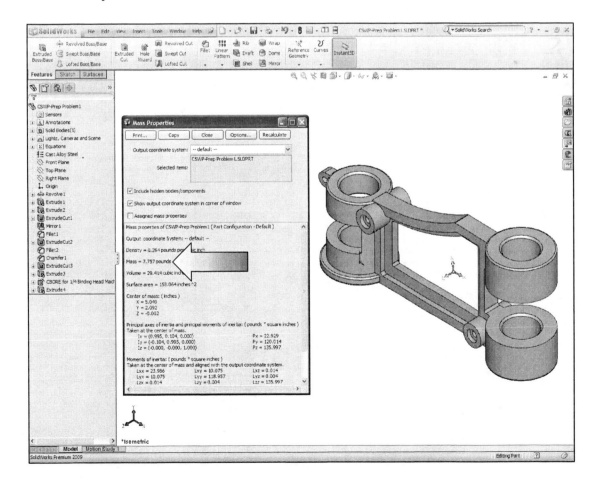

Certified-SolidWorks-Professional program (CSWP)
Certification Practice for the Core-Exam

Challenge II: Part Configurations & Modifications

Complete this challenge within 40 minutes

- Modify this part in SolidWorks.   - Unit: **Millimeter**, **2 decimals**   - Origin: **Arbitrary**

- Drafting Standards: **ANSI**   - Material: **Alloy Steel**   - Density: **0.008 /mm^3**

1. Opening the attached part named:

  Challenge II.

2. Setting the options:

  - Change the material to **Alloy Steel**.

  - Change the system options to match the settings above.

3. Switching Configuration:

  - Activate **Configuration A**.

4. Finding the current Mass:

  - Select **Tools/ Mass Properties**.

  - Enter the mass in grams:

  _____ grams

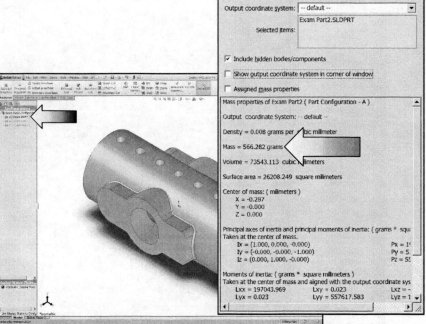

5. Adding a New Configuration:

- Create a <u>new configuration</u> named **D**, and enter the comment: **Added a 10mm hole**.

- Select the face as shown below and open a new sketch.

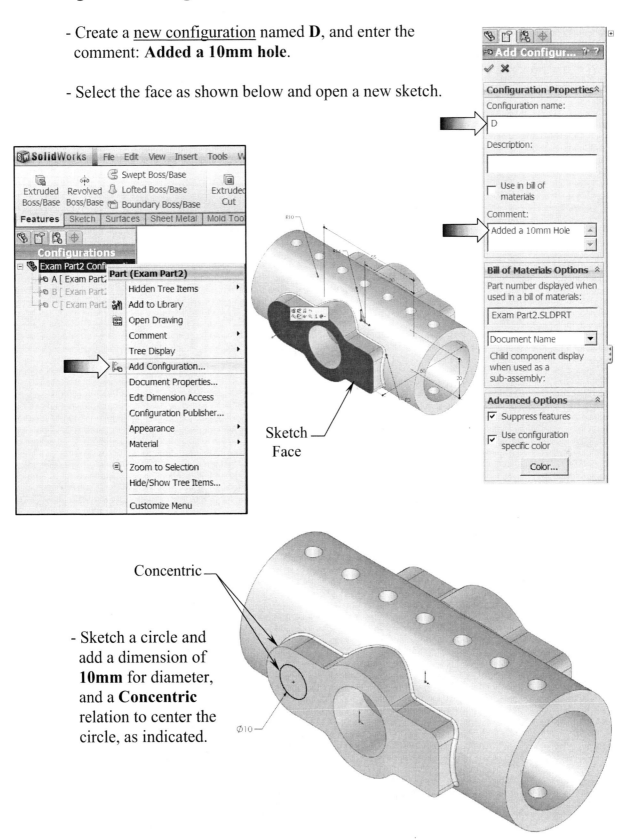

Sketch Face

Concentric

- Sketch a circle and add a dimension of **10mm** for diameter, and a **Concentric** relation to center the circle, as indicated.

Ø10

6. Extruding a cut:

- Click **Extruded Cut**.

- Set Direction1 to:

  Through All

- Click **OK** 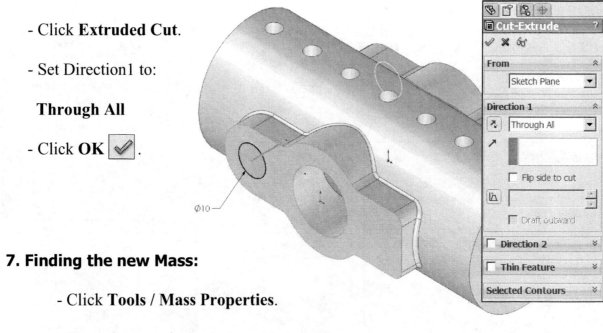.

7. Finding the new Mass:

- Click **Tools / Mass Properties**.

- Enter the mass in grams:

_____ grams.

Note: The mass in the dialog boxes are examples only. The actual mass will be based on the material and its density.

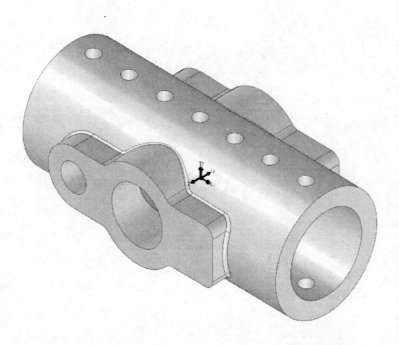

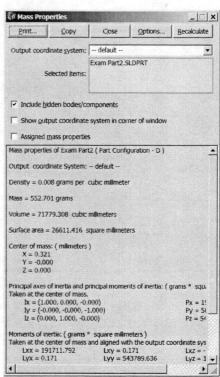

8. Switching configuration:

- Double click on **Configuration B** to make it active.

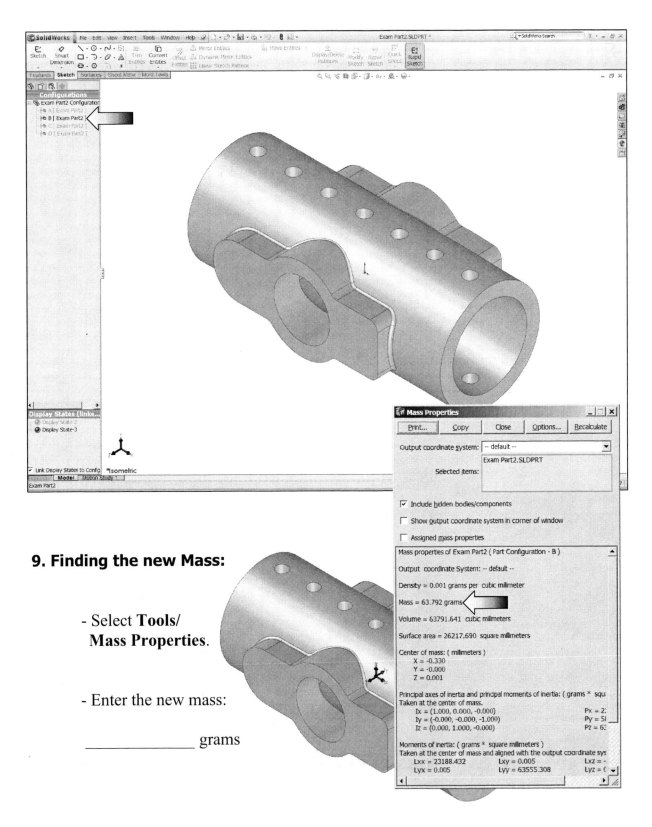

9. Finding the new Mass:

      - Select **Tools/
Mass Properties**.

      - Enter the new mass:

      _____ grams

10. Creating a Design Table:

- Select **Insert/ Tables /Design Tables**.

- Click the **Auto-Create** option and leave all other options defaults.

11. Adding new Configurations:

- Right click on **Row4** and select **Copy**.

- Right click on **Row7** and select **Paste**.

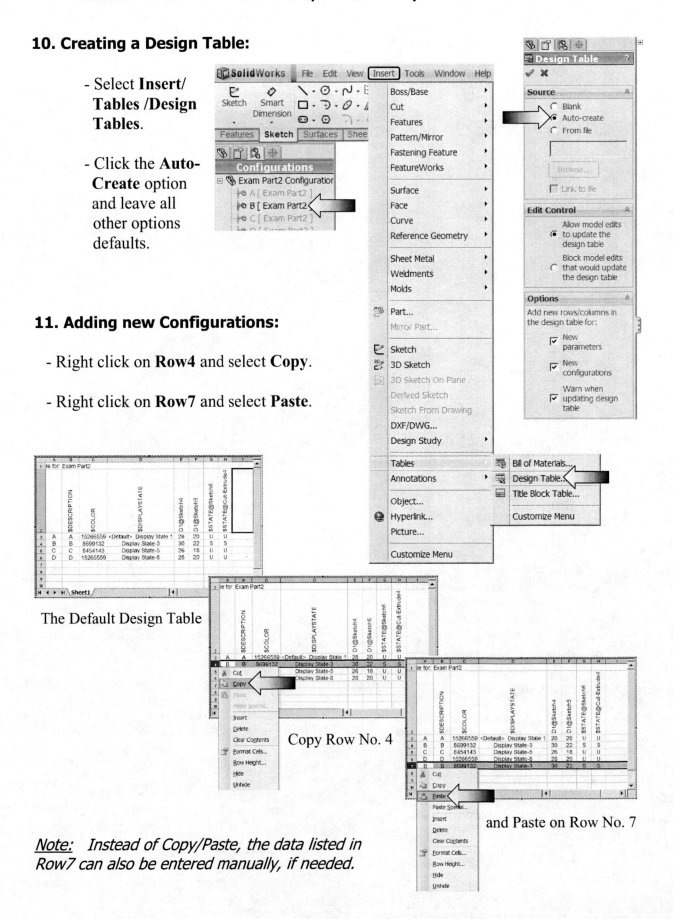

The Default Design Table

Copy Row No. 4

and Paste on Row No. 7

Note: _Instead of Copy/Paste, the data listed in Row7 can also be entered manually, if needed._

12. Modifying the new configurations:

- Change the name of the new config. to **E**.

- Change the ID dimension on the body to **24**.

- Change the hole Diameter to **16**.

- Leave the Suppression States at Suppressed (S).

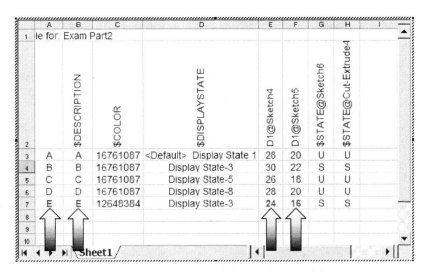

	A	B	C	D	E	F	G	H	I
1	le for: Exam Part2								
2		$DESCRIPTION	$COLOR	$DISPLAYSTATE	D1@Sketch4	D1@Sketch5	$STATE@Sketch6	$STATE@Cut-Extrude4	
3	A	A	16761087	<Default> Display State 1	28	20	U	U	
4	B	B	16761087	Display State-3	30	22	S	S	
5	C	C	16761087	Display State-5	26	18	U	U	
6	D	D	16761087	Display State-8	28	20	U	U	
7	E	E	12648384	Display State-3	24	16	S	S	

- Click anywhere in the background to return to SolidWorks.

- Double click on **Configuration E** to activate it.

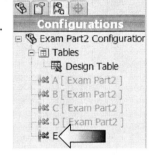

Configurations
- Exam Part2 Configuration
  - Tables
    - Design Table
  - A [Exam Part2]
  - B [Exam Part2]
  - C [Exam Part2]
  - D [Exam Part2]
  - E

13. Finding the final Mass:

- Select **Tools/ Mass Properties**.

- Enter the final mass: _____ grams

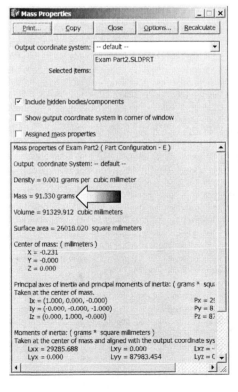

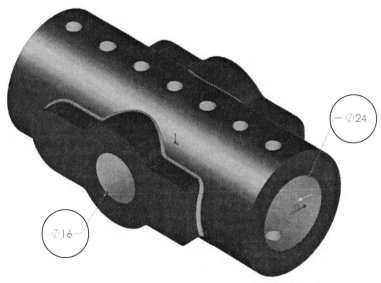

14. Save your work as Challenge 2.

Certified SolidWorks Professional program (CSWP)
Certification Practice for the Core-Exam

Challenge III: Bottom Up Assembly

Complete this challenge within 80 minutes

1. Assemble the components using mates.
2. Create a new coordinate system in the Assem.
3. Units: IPS (Inch/Pound/Second).

4. Detect and repair all interferences.
5. Mate modifications.
6. Decimal: 3 places

1. Opening the 1st part document:

- Open the document named: **Base** from the Challenge 3 folder.

- This part will be used as the Parent component in the assembly.

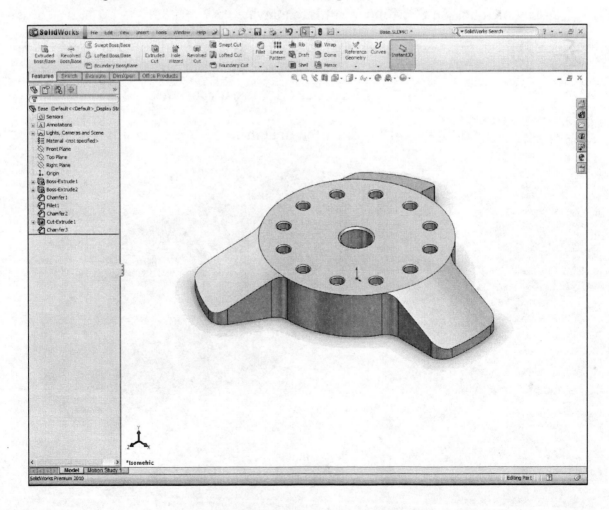

2. Transferring the part to Assembly:

- Select **Make Assembly From Part** from the **File** pull down menu (arrow).

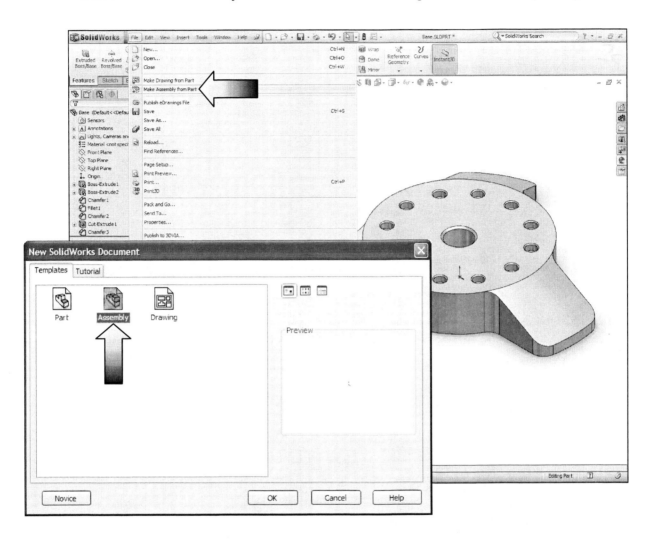

- Select the default **Assembly Template** and click OK.

- Place the component on the assembly's origin as indicated.

- The 1st component should be fixed before other components can be mated to it.

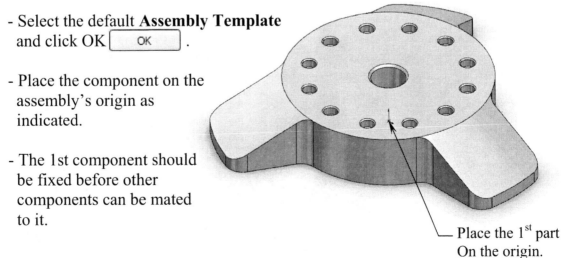

Place the 1st part On the origin.

3. Creating a Coordinate System:

- Click 3D Sketch under the sketch button (arrow).

- Sketch the **3 lines** as shown, along the **X**, **Y** and **Z** axis.

- Add the **4.000"** dimension and make the 3 line **Equal**.

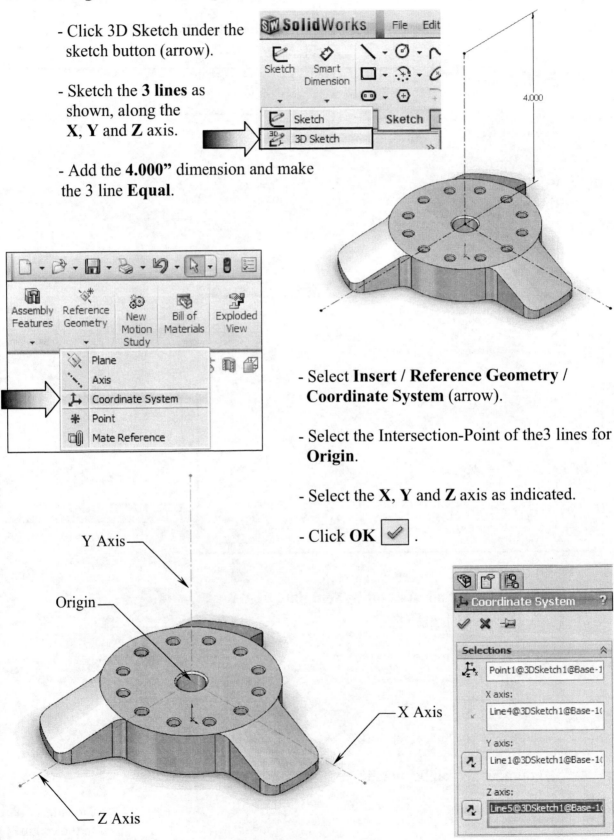

- Select **Insert / Reference Geometry / Coordinate System** (arrow).

- Select the Intersection-Point of the 3 lines for **Origin**.

- Select the **X**, **Y** and **Z** axis as indicated.

- Click **OK**.

Y Axis

Origin

X Axis

Z Axis

4. Inserting the 2ⁿᵈ component:

- From the Assembly toolbar, click the **Insert Component** command.

- Click Browse [Browse...] and open the component named: **Pivot**.

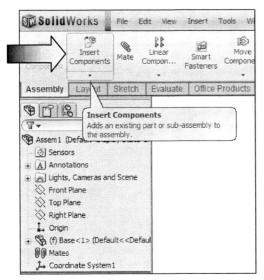

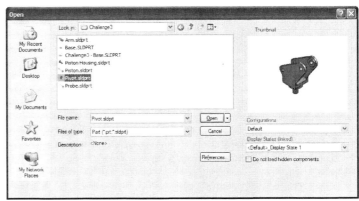

- Place the component approx. as shown below.

5. Adding the 1ˢᵗ mate:

- From the Assembly toolbar, click **Mate**.

- Select the Circular Boss and the Hole as indicated.

- The **Concentric** mate is automatically created by default.

- Click **OK** [✓] .

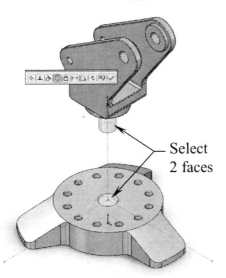

Select 2 faces

NOTE:

Most components will receive only 2 mates, since they were designed to move and rotate after everything is assembled.

Sometimes you may need to create the 3ʳᵈ mate just to align the components. These mates should be suppressed prior to mating other components.

6. Adding the 2nd mate:

- Click **Mate** again if you are not already there.

- Select the bottom face of the Circular Boss and the upper face of the Base.

- The **Coincident** mate is added automatically.

- Click **OK** ✔.

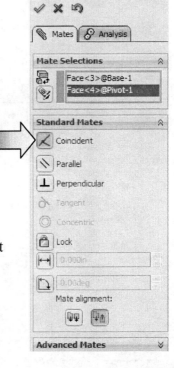

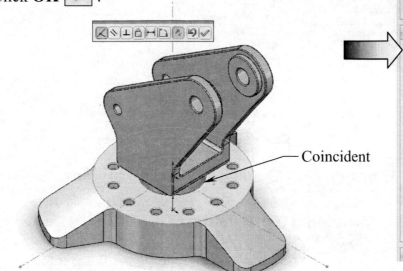

Coincident

7. Adding the 3rd mate:

- Click **Mate** again.

- Select the FRONT of the Base and the FRONT plane of the Pivot.

- Click the **Parallel** mate option.

- Click **OK** ✔.

NOTE:
This parallel mate will align the 2 components for the time being, it will get changed to an Angle mate later on.

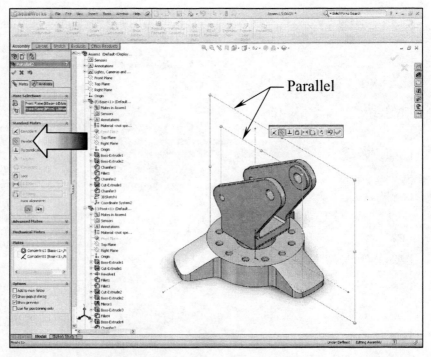

Parallel

8. Finding the Center Of Mass:

- Select **Tools / Mass Properties**.

- Change the default output to:
  Coordinate System1.

- Enter the Center Of Mass (in Inches).

$$X = \underline{\hspace{6cm}}.$$

$$Y = \underline{\hspace{6cm}}$$

$$Z = \underline{\hspace{6cm}}$$

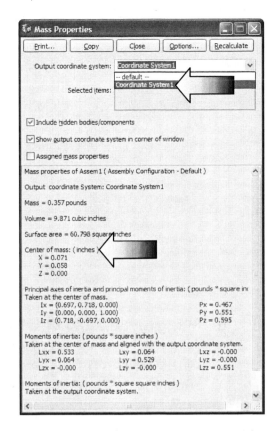

NOTE:
The center of mass shown in the dialog boxes are examples for use with this hand out only.

The actual mass properties of the components and the center of mass of the assembly are dependent upon the materials and the locations specified for each part in the assembly.

9. Creating an Angle mate:

- Expand the **Mate Group** from the bottom of the FeatureManager tree.

- Edit the **Parallel** mate, change it to **Angle** mate and enter **30.00deg**. Click **OK**

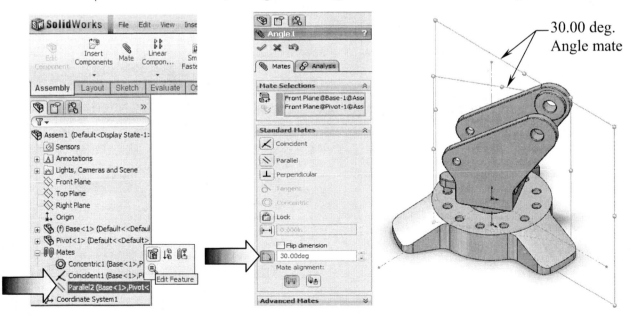

30.00 deg.
Angle mate

10.   Finding the new Center Of Mass:

- Select **Tools / Mass Properties**.

- Use the same output **Coordinate System1**.

- Enter the Center Of Mass (in Inches).

X = _____

Y = _____

Z = _____

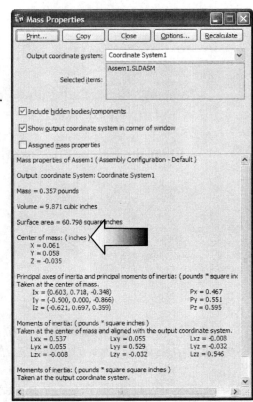

11. Inserting and mating other components:

- Click the **Insert Component** command from the Assembly toolbar.

- **Insert** and **Mate** the following components:

* Arm   * Probe   * Piston   * Piston Housing

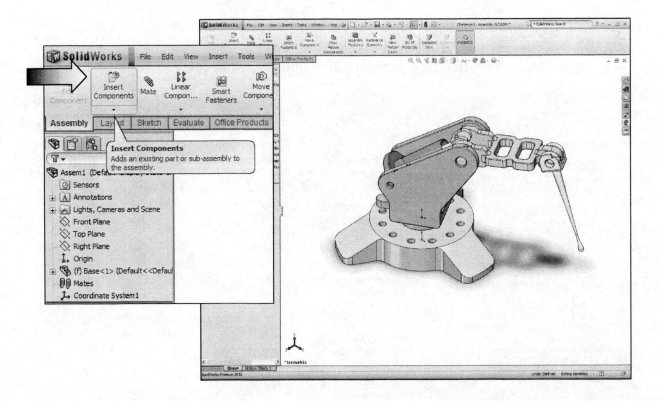

- Use the reference views below to mate the new components.

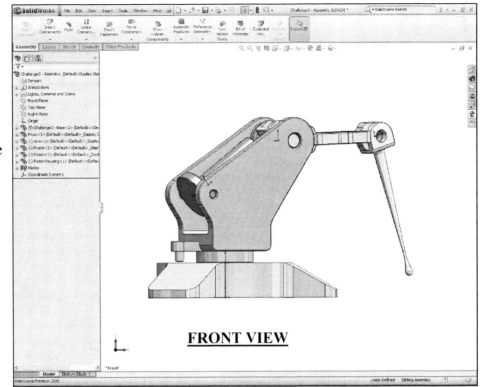

FRONT VIEW

- Use either the Front planes of each component to center the components with Coincident mates

– OR –

use the Width mate option to achieve the same results.

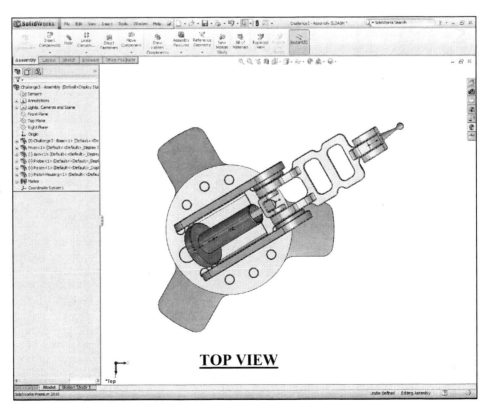

TOP VIEW

- Most component should have at least 1 degree of freedom left.

- You should be able to rotate the assembly back and forth, or up and down at this point.

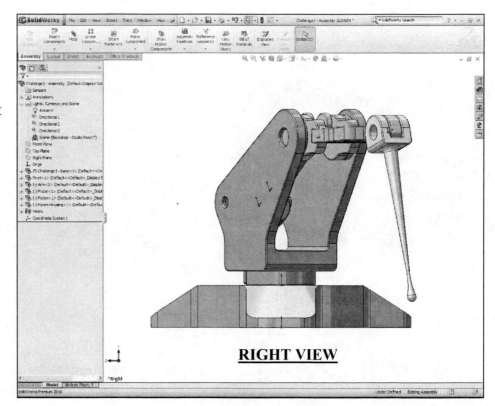

RIGHT VIEW

12. Finding the new Center Of Mass:

- Select **Tools / Mass Properties**.

- Use the same output **Coordinate System1**.

- Enter the Center Of Mass (in Inches).

X = _____

Y = _____

Z = _____

NOTE:
The current angle between the Base and the Pivot is still at 30 degrees.

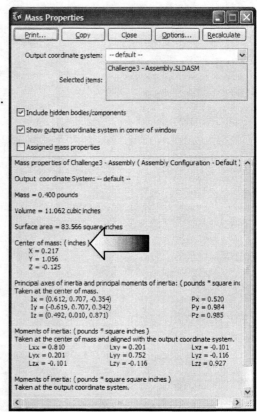

13. Changing the mate angle:

- Edit the **30deg** mate and change it to **180deg**.

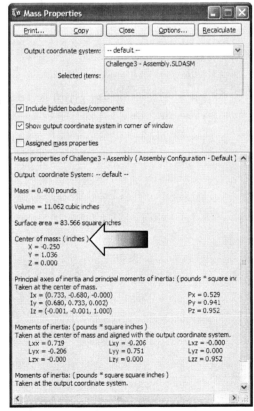

Change the mate angle from 30 deg. to 180deg.

- Click **OK** ✓.

14. Finding the final Center Of Mass:

- Select **Tools / Mass Properties**.

- Use the same output **Coordinate System1**.

- Enter the Center Of Mass (in Inches).

X = _____

Y = _____

Z = _____

15. Save your work as Challenge 3.

NOTE: When you're ready to take the actual examination, log on to: **www.solidworks.com/sw/mcad-certification-programs.htm**, click on the CSWP option and select **purchase exam**. After the registration is completed, you will receive 2 emails from SolidWorks; one of them is the receipt for the purchase of the exam and the other have the instruction on how to download and take the exam.

If you passed, an email will be sent to you from the Grading server notifying you of the results and instructing you on how to print out your certificate. If you failed, there is a 30 day waiting period, you will need to register and pay for the exam and start the process over again.

Student testimonials

Nearly 6000 actual student testimonials (as of March-2010)
Originals are filed at local SolidWorks Resellers and Academic Training Centers.

Student Testimonials

Joseph Hurlbut – NASA Ames Research Center
I cannot put into words sufficient praise for the product, program of instruction and the ability and approach of the Instructor. I've received a lot of training this year and I am happy to report that this course outshined all the others by far.

Carrie Keeney – Novera Optics
I had a great class with Paul. He is very knowledgeable and fun to work with. Thanks.

Kirk Sadler – Massie Research Labs.
The course objectives were clearly met and covered. My questions and concerns were answered and explained very clearly. I was very pleased with this course and the Instructor Paul Tran. This course has and will help me perform my job with more confidence and ease.

Joe Podhasky – Lynx Therapeutics
Paul was an excellent instructor, probably the best Technical Instructor I've ever had. He was very clear, knowledgeable and eager to help others.

Brent Rothert – Chahaya Optronics
A colleague of mine who completed this course earlier recommended it to me. He especially commented that Paul Tran was an excellent instructor and I agreed wholeheartedly. I am very fortunate to have taken this course from Paul.

Todd Rodericks – HealthTech
I have taken many PTC courses and none of them compare to the overall experience I had taking this course. Paul Tran did an exceptional job presenting the material in a clear concise fashion.

George Heropoulos – Leapfrog Toys
Most excellent instructor. Very clear, precise, professional and polite.

Mike Donndelinger – Volex Inc.
Paul is a truly outstanding teacher. This was the best software training I have ever attended by far.

John Edwards – Marqun Corporation
Paul Tran is the best instructor of this kind that I have ever experience in twenty years of engineering practice. He has an exceptional talent for clearly and concisely presenting complicated materials.

Jill Cregan – Starion Instruments Inc.
I have no experience with any CAD programs. However, with the way Paul described and brought me through this course, I had no problems with keeping up. Excellent!

Caesar Marmolejo - Moldex-Metric
Paul Tran certainly has the knowledge and know how of SOLIDWORKS. This instructor is by far the best instructor I have ever encountered for any type of Solidworks training. If I take any other class (advance, advanced drawing, etc.) I would like it to be with him.

Rick Faeth – Cepheid
Although I am not a design engineer, I felt I learned a great deal about SolidWorks and how to create parts, assemblies and drawings. Paul Tran is extremely gifted and patient instructor.

Bob Lucero – Stryker Endoscopy
The instructor presented each topic very well. I was never lost during class, thanks.

Lich Tran – Sverdrup Technology
Very good instructor. He knows the materials in and out and explained it very well. He cares for the student's performance. I really like the one on one support by Paul. I would recommend the teacher and the course to all my friends.

Vincent King – Shur-Lok Corporation
This was my first exposure to this software. Paul was a very patient and competent instructor; I gained a lot of knowledge considering I had no experience before. Thanks

Spencer Knock – Disneyland
I think Paul Tran is an excellent instructor. His years of experience in the field as well as with the software and his knowledge of how parts are actually manufactured are invaluable.

Michael Davison – Tsunami
Paul is such a good instructor that anytime he is offering a course in our area, we always send at least one company representative to receive his training.

David Gandocfo – Self Employed
I have been taking CAD training classes since 1985 but nothing compare to this course. Mr. Tran was the best instructor I have ever had. He was very informative and gave a lot of time to get everyone up to speed. Thanks.

Bob Pearce – TSK America
Paul Tran showed what a skilled and knowledgeable instructor should be like. He is very patient!! The software was easy to use but without Paul's shortcuts and tips and background experience, it may not have been as productive a class as it was for me.

Anthony Gonzalez – CD Alexander
The software is excellent, surpassed my expectations. The instructor was really outstanding, he took his time with students and he was very knowledgeable with all aspects of the software. Paul Tran made the course very productive and worthwhile.

Mark Tussey – Berkley Ind.
Paul was a fantastic instructor!!! He had such an interesting teaching method, easy to follow and understand the training sessions. Highly recommended.

Richard Loquet – Control Components Inc.
I enjoyed the course and appreciate the thoroughness of our instructor. He presented logical problems related to the work environments. My thanks to Paul Tran for a job well done.

Paul Johnson – Impco Technology Inc.
Paul Tran was an excellent Instructor. He explained everything in a clear concise manner and was extremely helpful. I would recommend this course to anyone.

MasterPieces - Designed by Students & CSWPs

SolidWorks 2010 Quick-Guide®

Quick Reference Guide To
SolidWorks® 2010 Command Icons & Toolbars

SolidWorks® Quick-Guide

Quick Reference Guide To SolidWorks® 2010 Command Icons & Toolbars

The STANDARD Toolbar

- Creates a new document.
- Opens an existing document.
- Saves an active document.
- Make Drawing from Part/Assembly
- Make Assembly from Part/Assembly
- Prints the active document.
- Displays full pages as they are printed.
- Cuts the selection & puts it on the clipboard.
- Copies the selection & puts it on the clipboard.
- Inserts the clipboard contents.
- Deletes the selection.
- Reverses the last action.
- Redo the last action that was undone.
- Rebuilds the part / assembly / drawing.
- Saves all documents.
- Changes the color of the current selection(s).
- Edits material.
- Closes an existing document
- Shows or hides the Selection Filter toolbar.
- Shows or hides the Web toolbar.
- Displays Help topics for SolidWorks.
- Displays full pages as they will be printed.

The STANDARD Toolbar (Cont.)

- Loads or unloads the 3D instant website add-in
- Select tool.
- Reloads the current document from disk.
- Places an online order for a rapid prototype part.
- Checks read-only files for write access.
- Show/Edit the properties of the current selection.
- Changes options settings for SolidWorks.
- Tiles windows vertically, as non-overlapping.
- Tiles windows horizontally, as non-overlapping.
- Opens another window for the active document.

The SKETCH TOOLS Toolbar

- Sketches a rectangle from the center.
- Sketches a centerpoint arc slot.
- Sketches a 3-point arc slot.
- Sketches a straight slot.
- Sketches a centerpoint straight slot.
- Stretches sketch entities and annotations.
- Inserts an Equation Driven Curve.
- Sketches a 3-point arc.
- Inserts a picture into the sketch background.
- Creates sketched ellipses.

The SKETCH TOOLS Toolbar

Selects items for commands to act on.

Sets up Grid parameters.

Creates a sketch on a selected plane or face.

Creates a 3D sketch.

Scales/Translates/Rotates the current sketch.

Moves or copies sketch entities and annotations.

Scales sketch entities and annotations.

Sketches an angle rectangle from the center.

Sketches a parallelogram.

Sketches a line.

Creates a center point arc: center, start, end.

Creates an arc tangent to a line.

Sketches splines on a surface or face.

Sketches a circle.

Sketches a circle by its perimeter.

Sketches a partial ellipse.

Makes a path of sketch entities.

Mirrors entities dynamically about a

Insert a plane into the 3D sketch.

Rotates sketch entities and

Copies sketch entities and

Sketches on a plane in a 3D sketch.

Moves sketch entities without solving dimensions or relations.

The SKETCH TOOLS Toolbar (Cont.)

Partial ellipses.

Adds a Parabola.

Creates sketched splines.

Sketches a polygon.

Sketches a rectangle.

Sketches a parallelogram.

Creates points.

Creates sketched centerlines.

Adds text to sketch.

Converts selected model edges or sketch entities to sketch segments.

Creates a sketch along the intersection of multiple bodies.

Converts face curves on the selected face into 3D sketch entities.

Mirrors selected segments about a centerline.

Fillets the corner of two lines.

Creates a chamfer between two sketch entities.

Creates a sketch curve by offsetting model edges or sketch entities at a specified distance.

Fits a spline to selected entities.

Trims a sketch segment.

Extends a sketch segment.

Splits a sketch segment.

Construction Geometry.

Creates linear steps and repeat of sketch entities.

Creates circular steps and repeat of sketch entities.

The SHEET METAL

Inserts a FlattenBends & a ProcessBends feature, A sheet metal feature will be added.

Shows flat pattern for this sheet metal part.

Shows part without inserting any bends.

Inserts a rip feature to a sheet metal part.

Inserts a Sheet Metal Base Flange or a Tab feature.

Inserts a Sheet Metal Miter Flange feature.

Folds selected bends.

Unfolds selected bends.

Inserts bends using a sketch line.

Inserts a flange by pulling an edge.

Inserts a sheet metal corner feature.

Inserts a Hem feature by selecting edges.

Breaks a corner by filleting/chamfering it.

Inserts a Jog feature using a sketch line.

Inserts a lofted bend feature using 2 sketches.

Creates inverse dent on a sheet metal part.

Trims out material from a corner, in a sheet metal

Inserts a fillet weld bead.

Converts a solid/surface into a sheet metal part.

Adds a Cross Break feature into a selected face.

The SURFACES Toolbar

Deletes a face or a set of faces.

Creates mid surfaces between offset face pairs.

Patches surface holes and external edges.

The SURFACES Toolbar (cont.)

Creates an extruded surface.

Creates a revolved surface.

Creates a swept surface.

Creates a lofted surface.

Creates an offset surface.

Radiates a surface originating from a curve, parallel to a plane.

Knits surfaces together.

Creates a planar surface from a sketch or A set of edges.

Creates a surface by importing data from a file.

Extends a surface.

Trims a surface.

Generating MidSurface(s).

Deletes Face(s).

Replaces Face with Surface.

Patches surface holes and external edges by extending the surfaces.

Creates parting surfaces between core & cavity surfaces.

Inserts ruled surfaces from edges.

The WELDMENTS Toolbar

Creates a weldment feature.

Creates a structure member feature.

Adds a gusset feature between 2 planar adjoining faces.

Creates an end cap feature.

Adds a fillet weld bead feature.

Trims or extends structure members.

The DIMENSIONS/RELATIONS Toolbar

Inserts dimension between two lines.

Creates a horizontal dimension between selected entities.

Creates a vertical dimension between selected entities.

Creates a reference dimension between selected entities.

Creates a set of ordinate dimensions.

Creates a set of Horizontal ordinate dimensions.

Creates a set of Vertical ordinate dimensions.

Creates a chamfer dimension.

Adds a geometric relation.

Automatically Adds Dimensions to the current sketch.

Displays and deletes geometric relations.

Fully defines a sketch.

Scans a sketch for elements of equal length or radius.

Automatically recognize tolerance features.

Creates linked, unlinked, or collection pattern feature.

Paints faces of toleranced features in different colors.

Adds DimXpert location dimension.

Adds DimXpert datum.

Copies existing tolerance scheme to current configuration.

Adds DimXpert size dimension.

Adds DimXpert geometric tolerance.

Deletes all tolerance data base.

Adds new Tol Analyst.

The STANDARD VIEWS

Front view.

Back view.

Left view.

Right view.

Top view.

Bottom view.

Isometric view.

Trimetric view.

Dimetric view.

Normal to view.

Links all views in the viewport together.

Displays viewport with front & right views

Displays a 4 view viewport with 1st or 3rd Angle of projection.

Displays viewport with front & top

Displays viewport with a single

The Block Toolbar

Makes a new block.

Edits the selected block.

Inserts a new block to a sketch or drawing.

Adds/Removes sketch entities to/from blocks.

Updates parent sketches effected by this block.

Saves the block to a file.

Explodes the selected block.

Inserts a belt.

Did you know??
* Ctrl+Q will force a rebuild on all features of a part.
* Ctrl+B will rebuild the feature being worked on and its dependants.

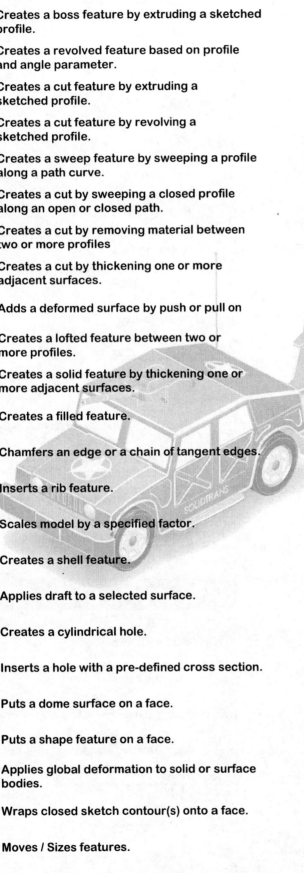

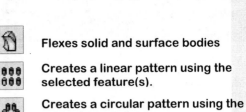

The FEATURES Toolbar

Creates a boss feature by extruding a sketched profile.

Creates a revolved feature based on profile and angle parameter.

Creates a cut feature by extruding a sketched profile.

Creates a cut feature by revolving a sketched profile.

Creates a sweep feature by sweeping a profile along a path curve.

Creates a cut by sweeping a closed profile along an open or closed path.

Creates a cut by removing material between two or more profiles

Creates a cut by thickening one or more adjacent surfaces.

Adds a deformed surface by push or pull on

Creates a lofted feature between two or more profiles.

Creates a solid feature by thickening one or more adjacent surfaces.

Creates a filled feature.

Chamfers an edge or a chain of tangent edges.

Inserts a rib feature.

Scales model by a specified factor.

Creates a shell feature.

Applies draft to a selected surface.

Creates a cylindrical hole.

Inserts a hole with a pre-defined cross section.

Puts a dome surface on a face.

Puts a shape feature on a face.

Applies global deformation to solid or surface bodies.

Wraps closed sketch contour(s) onto a face.

Moves / Sizes features.

Suppresses the selected feature or component.

Unsuppresses the selected feature or component.

Flexes solid and surface bodies

Creates a linear pattern using the selected feature(s).

Creates a circular pattern using the selected feature(s).

Mirrors a feature about a plane.

Creates a Curve Driven Pattern.

Creates a Sketch Driven pattern.

Creates a Table Driven Pattern.

Inserts a split Feature.

Combines two or more solid bodies.

Joins bodies from one or more parts into a single part in the context of an assembly.

Deletes a solid or a surface.

Inserts solid(s) or surface(s) into an existing open document.

Inserts a part from file into the active part document.

Moves/Copies solid and surface bodies or moves graphics bodies.

Merges short edges on faces

Pushes solid / surface model by another solid / surface model

Moves face(s) of a solid

Area fills faces or bodies into one or more contours.

Inserts holes into a series of parts.

Returns suppressed items with dependents to the model.

Cuts a solid model with a surface.

Adds material between profiles in two directions to create a solid feature.

Cuts a solid model by removing material between profiles in two directions.

Did you know??

* Right-mouse drag a component in an assembly rotates it.
* Left- mouse drag a component in an assembly moves it.

The **MOLD TOOLS** Toolbar

 Extracts core(s) from existing tooling split

 Constructs a surface patch

 Moves face(s) of a solid

 Finds & creates mold shut-off surfaces

 Inserts cavity into a base part.

 Scales a model by a specified factor.

 Applies draft to a selected surface.

 Inserts a split line feature.

 Creates an offset surface.

 Creates parting lines to separate core & cavity surfaces

 Creates a planar surface from a sketch or A set of edges.

 Knits surfaces together.

 Analyzes draft angles of faces, based on a mold pull direction.

 Inserts ruled surfaces from edges.

 Creates parting surfaces between core & cavity surfaces

 Creates multiple bodies from a single body.

 Inserts a tooling split feature.

 Identifies faces that form undercuts.

 Creates parting surfaces between the core & cavity.

 Inserts surface body folders for mold operation.

The **SELECTION** FILTERS

 Turns selection filters on and off.

 Clears all filters.

 Selects all filters.

 Inverts current selection.

The **SELECTION** FILTERS cont.

 Allows selection of edges only.

 Allows selection of faces only.

 Adds filter for Surface Bodies.

 Adds filter for Solid Bodies.

 Adds filter for Axes.

 Adds filter for Planes.

 Adds filter for Sketch Points.

 Adds filter for Sketch Segments.

 Adds filter for Midpoints.

 Adds filter for Center Marks.

 Adds filter for Centerline.

 Adds filter for Dimensions and Hole Callouts.

 Adds filter for Surface Finish Symbols.

 Adds filter for Geometric Tolerances.

 Adds filter for Notes / Balloons.

 Adds filter for Weld Symbols.

 Adds filter for Datum Targets.

 Adds filter for Cosmetic Threads.

 Adds filter for blocks.

 Adds filter for Dowel pin symbols.

 Adds filter for connection points.

 Allows selection filter for vertices only.

 Allows selection of weld symbols only.

 Allows selection of blocks only.

 Adds filter for routing points.

The **FLYOUT** Toolbar

 2D to 3D.

 Align.

 Annotation.

 Assemblies.

 Curves.

 Dimensions / Relation.

 Drawings.

 Features.

 Fonts.

 Line Formats.

 Macros.

 Molds.

 Reference Geometry.

 Quick snap filters.

 Selection Filters.

 Sheet Metal.

 Simulation.

 Sketch.

 SolidWorks Office.

 Splines.

 Standard.

 Standard Views.

 Surfaces.

 Tools.

 View.

 Web.

 Weldments.

 Block commands.

 Explode sketch commands.

 Table commands.

 Fastening feature commands.

 Creates a rounded internal or external fillet.

 Linear Patterns Features, Faces and Bodies.

 Creates various corner treatments.

 Displays Deletes geometric relations.

 Creates dimensions for one or more entities.

 Adds an existing part or assembly.

 Linear Patterns components in assembly.

 Moves components in assembly.

 Adds section view with a section line.

 Creates various assembly features.

 Toggles various view settings.

The **SCREEN CAPTURE** Toolbar

 Copies the current graphics window to the clipboard.

 Records the current graphics window to an AVI file.

 Stops recording the current graphics window to an AVI file.

The **Explode Line Sketch** Toolbar

 Adds a route line that connect entities.

 Adds a jog to the route lines.

The LINE FORMAT Toolbar

 Changes layer properties.

 Changes line color.

 Changes line thickness.

 Changes line style.

 Hides a visible edge.

 Shows a hidden edge.

 Changes line display mode.

The 2D-To-3D Toolbar

 Makes a Front sketch from the selected entities.

 Makes a Top sketch from the selected entities.

 Makes a Right sketch from the selected entities.

 Makes a Left sketch from the selected entities.

 Makes a Bottom sketch from the selected entities.

 Makes a Back sketch from the selected entities.

 Makes an Auxiliary sketch from the selected entities.

 Creates a new sketch from the selected entities.

 Repairs the selected sketch.

 Aligns a sketch to the selected point.

 Creates an extrusion from the selected sketch segments, starting at the selected sketch point.

 Creates a cut from the selected sketch segments, optionally starting at the selected sketch point.

The ALIGN Toolbar

 Aligns the left side of the selected annotations with the leftmost annotation.

 Aligns the right side of the selected annotations with the rightmost annotation.

Aligns the top side of the selected annotations with the topmost annotation.

Aligns the bottom side of the selected annotations with the lowermost annotation.

 Evenly spaces the selected annotations horizontally.

 Evenly spaces the selected annotations vertically.

 Centrally aligns the selected annotations horizontally.

 Centrally aligns the selected annotations vertically.

 Compacts the selected annotations horizontally.

 Compacts the selected annotations vertically.

 Aligns the center of the selected annotations between

 Creates a group from the selected items

 Deletes the grouping between these items

 Aligns & groups selected dimensions along a line or an arc

 Aligns & groups dimensions at a uniform distances

The SIMULATION Toolbar

 Stops Record or Playback.

 Records Simulation.

 Replays Simulation.

 Resets Components.

 Adds Linear Motor.

 Adds Rotary Motor.

 Adds Spring.

 Adds Gravity.

The MACRO Toolbar

 Runs a Macro.

 Stops Macro recorder.

 Records (or pauses recording of) actions to create a Macro.

 Launches the Macro Editor and begins editing a new macro.

 Opens a Macro file for editing.

 Creates a custom macro.

The **TABLE** Toolbar

 Adds a hole table of selected holes from a specified origin datum.

 Adds a Bill of Materials.

 Adds a revision table.

 Displays a Design table in a drawing.

 Adds a weldments cuts list table.

 Adds a Excel based of Bill of Materials

 Adds a general table to a drawing sheet.

The **REFERENCE GEOMETRY**

 Adds a reference plane

 Creates an axis.

 Creates a coordinate system.

 Adds a reference point

 Specifies entities to use as references using SmartMates.

The **SPLINE TOOLS** Toolbar

 Adds a point to a spline.

 Displays points where the concavity of selected spline changes.

 Displays minimum radius of selected spline.

 Displays curvature combs of selected spline.

 Reduces numbers of points in a selected spline.

 Adds a tangency control.

 Adds a curvature control.

 Adds a spline based on selected sketch entities & edges.

 Displays all handles of selected splines.

 Displays the spline control polygon.

The **ANNOTATIONS** Toolbar

 Inserts a note.

 Inserts a surface finish symbol.

 Inserts a new geometric tolerancing symbol.

 Attaches a balloon to the selected edge or face.

 Adds balloons for all components in selected view.

 Inserts a stacked balloon.

 Attaches a datum feature symbol to a selected edge / detail.

 Inserts a weld symbol on the selected edge / face / vertex.

 Inserts a datum target symbol and / or point attached to a selected edge / line.

 Selects and inserts block.

 Inserts annotations & reference geometry from the part / assembly into the selected.

 Adds center marks to circles on model.

 Inserts a Centerline.

 Inserts a hole callout.

 Adds a cosmetic thread to the selected cylindrical feature.

 Inserts a Multi-Jog leader.

 Selects a circular edge or and arc for Dowel pin symbol insertion.

 Toggles the visibility of annotations & dimensions.

 Inserts latest version symbol.

 Adds a cross hatch patterns or solid fill.

 Adds a weld symbol on a selected entity.

 Adds a weld bead caterpillar on an edge.

The "Feathers"

 Lightweight component.

 Out-of-Date component.

Hidden Lightweight component.

 Hidden, Out-of-Date and Lightweight.

The DRAWINGS Toolbar

Updates the selected view to the model's current stage.

Creates a detail view.

Creates a section view.

Inserts an aligned section using the selected line or section line.

Unfolds a new view from an existing view.

Generates a standard 3-view drawing (1st or 3rd angle).

Inserts an auxiliary view of an inclined surface.

Adds an Orthogonal or Named view based on an existing part or assembly.

Adds a Relative view by two orthogonal faces or planes.

Adds a Predefined orthogonal projected or Named view with a model.

Adds an empty view.

Adds vertical break lines to selected view.

Crops a view.

Creates a Broken-out section.

Inserts an Alternate Position view.

The QUICK SNAP Toolbar

Snap to points.

Snap to center points.

Snap to midpoints.

Snap to quadrant points.

Snap to intersection of 2 curves.

Snap to nearest curve.

Snap tangent to curve.

Snap perpendicular to curve.

Snap parallel to line.

Snap horizontally / vertically.

Snap horizontally / vertically to points.

Snap to discrete line lengths.

Snap to grid points.

Snap to angle.

The LAYOUT Toolbar

Creates the assembly layout sketch.

Sketches a line.

Sketches a rectangle.

Sketches a circle.

Sketches a 3 point arc.

Rounds a corner.

Trims or extends a sketch.

Adds sketch entities by offsetting faces, Edges curves.

Mirrors selected entities about a centerline.

Adds a relation.

Creates a dimension.

Displays / Deletes geometric relations.

Makes a new block.

Edits the selected block.

Inserts a new block to the sketch or drawing.

Adds / Removes sketch entities to / from a block.

Saves the block to a file.

Explodes the selected block.

Creates a new part from a layout sketch block.

Positions 2 components relative to one another.

Moves a component within the degrees of freedom defined by its mates.

The CURVES Toolbar

Projects sketch onto selected surface.

Inserts a split line feature.

Creates a composite curve from selected edges, curves and sketches.

Creates a curve through free points.

Creates a 3D curve through reference points.

Helical curve defined by a base sketch and shape parameters.

The VIEW Toolbar

Displays a view in the selected orientation.

Reverts to previous view.

Zooms out to see entire model.

Zooms in by dragging a bounding box.

Zooms in or out by dragging up or down.

Zooms to fit all selected entities.

Dynamic view rotation.

Scrolls view by dragging.

Displays image in wireframe mode.

Displays hidden edges in gray.

Displays image with hidden lines removed.

Controls the visibility of planes.

Controls the visibility of axis.

Controls the visibility of parting lines.

Controls the visibility of temporary axis.

Controls the visibility of origins.

Controls the visibility of coordinate systems.

Controls the visibility of reference curves.

Controls the visibility of sketches.

Controls the visibility of 3D sketch planes.

Controls the visibility of 3D sketch

Controls the visibility of all annotations.

Controls the visibility of reference points.

Controls the visibility of routing points.

Controls the visibility of lights.

Controls the visibility of cameras.

Controls the visibility of sketch relations.

Redraws the current window.

Rolls the model view.

Turns the orientation of the model view.

Dynamically manipulate the model view in 3D to make selection.

Changes the display style for the active view.

Displays a shade view of the model with its edges.

Displays a shade view of the model.

Toggles between draft quality & high quality HLV.

Cycles through or applies a specific scene.

Views the models through one of the model's cameras.

Displays a part or assembly w/different colors according to the local radius of curvature.

Displays zebra stripes.

Displays a model with hardware accelerated shades.

Edits the real view appearance of entities in the model.

Applies a texture to entities in a model.

Changes the visibility of items in the graphics area.

Controls visibility of the sketch grid.

The **TOOLS** Toolbar

 Calculates the distance between selected items.

 Adds or edits equation.

 Calculates the mass properties of the model.

 Checks the model for geometry errors.

 Inserts or edits a Design Table.

 Evaluates section properties for faces and sketches that lie in parallel planes.

 Reports Statistics for this Part/Assembly.

 Deviation Analysis.

 Runs the **COSMOSXpress** analysis wizard Powered by COSMOS.

 Checks the spelling.

 Import diagnostics.

 Runs the **DFMXpress** analysis wizard.

 Runs the **DriveWorkXpress** wizard.

 Runs the **COSMOSFloXpress** analysis wizard.

The **ASSEMBLY** Toolbar

 Creates a new part & inserts it into the assembly.

 Adds an existing part or sub-assembly to the assembly.

 Creates a new assembly & inserts it into the assembly.

 Turns on/off large assembly mode for this document.

 Hides / shows model(s) associated with the selected model(s).

Toggles the transparency of components.

Changes the selected components to suppressed or resolved.

Toggles between editing part and assembly.

Inserts a belt.

Inserts a new part into an

 Smart Fasteners.

 Positions two components relative to one.

 External references will not be created.

 Moves a component.

 Rotates an un-mated component around its center point.

 Replaces selected components.

 Replaces mate entities of mates of the selected components on the selected Mategroup.

 Creates a New Exploded view.

 Creates or edits explode line sketch.

 Interference detection.

 Changes assembly transparency.

 Shows or Hides the Simulation toolbar.

 Patterns components in one or two linear directions.

 Patterns components around an axis.

 Toggles the transparency of components Between 0 and 75 percent.

 Toggles between editing a Part and Assembly.

 Adds fasteners to the assembly using **Toolbox**.

 Displays statistics and check the health of The current assembly.

 Patterns components relative to an existing Pattern in a part.

 Shows hidden components.

 Toggles large assembly mode for this document.

 Checks assembly hole alignments.

 Mirrors subassemblies and parts.

To add or remove an icon
to or from the toolbar, first select:

Tools/Customize/Commands

Next select a **Category**, click a button to see its description and then drag / drop the command icon into any toolbar.

Rotate the model

* Horizontally or Vertically: _____ Arrow keys

* Horizontally or Vertically 90°: _____ Shift + Arrow keys

* Clockwise or Counterclockwise: _____ Alt + left or right Arrow

* Pan the model: _____ Ctrl + Arrow keys

* Zoom in: _____ Z (shift + Z or capital Z)

* Zoom out: _____ z (lower case z)

* Zoom to fit: _____ F

* Previous view: _____ Ctrl+Shift+Z

View Orientation

* View Orientation Menu: _____ Space bar

* Front: _____ Ctrl+1

* Back: _____ Ctrl+2

* Left: _____ Ctrl+3

* Right: _____ Ctrl+4

* Top: _____ Ctrl+5

* Bottom: _____ Ctrl+6

* Isometric: _____ Ctrl+7

Selection Filter & Misc.

* Filter Edges: _____ e

* Filter Vertices: _____ v

* Filter Faces: _____ x

* Toggle Selection filter toolbar: _____ F5

* Toggle Selection Filter toolbar (on/off): _____ F6

* New SolidWorks document: _____ F1

* Open Document: _____ Ctrl+O

* Open from Web folder: _____ Ctrl+W

* Save: _____ Ctrl+S

* Print: _____ Ctrl+P

* Magnifying Glass Zoom _____ g

* Switch between the SolidWorks documents _____ Ctrl + Tab

SW 2010 Customized **Hot Keys** (Required System Options Reg. File)

Function Keys

F1	SW-Help
F2	2D Sketch
F3	3D Sketch
F4	Modify
F5	Selection Filters
F6	Move (2D Sketch)
F7	Rotate (2D Sketch)
F8	Measure
F9	Extrude
F10	Revolve
F11	Sweep
F12	Loft

Sketch

C	Circle
P	Polygon
E	Ellipse
O	Offset Entities
Alt + C	Convert Entities
M	Mirror
Alt + M	Dynamic Mirror
Alt + F	Sketch Fillet
T	Trim
Alt + X	Extend
D	Smart Dimension
Alt + R	Add Relation
Alt + P	Plane
Control + F	Fully Define Sketch
Control + Q	Exit Sketch

Part of SolidWorks 2010 – Basic Tools and Advanced Techniques

SolidWorks® Quick-Guide by Paul Tran – Sr. Certified SolidWorks Instructor
© Paul Tran / Issue 9 / Dec-2010 - Printed in The United State of America